Here are your

1998 SCIENCE YEAR
Cross-Reference Tabs

For insertion in your WORLD BOOK

Each year, SCIENCE YEAR, THE WORLD BOOK ANNUAL SCIENCE SUPPLEMENT, adds a valuable dimension to your WORLD BOOK set. The Cross-Reference Tab System is designed especially to help you link SCIENCE YEAR'S major articles to the related WORLD BOOK articles that they update.

How to use these Tabs:

First, remove this page from SCIENCE YEAR.

Begin with the first Tab, **Amber**. Take the A volume of your WORLD BOOK set and find the **Amber** article. Moisten the **Amber** Tab and affix it to that page.

Glue all the other Tabs in the appropriate WORLD BOOK volumes. Your set's R volume does not have an article on **James Randi**. Put the **Randi, James** Tab in its correct alphabetical location in that volume—near the **Rand Corporation** article.

SCIENCE YEAR

1998

The World Book Annual Science Supplement

A review of Science and Technology
During the 1997 School Year

World Book, Inc.

a Scott Fetzer company

Chicago • London • Sydney • Toronto

THE YEAR'S MAJOR SCIENCE STORIES

From the revolutionary cloning of an adult sheep to the discovery of a huge deposit of dinosaur fossils, it was an eventful year in science and technology. On these two pages are the stories the editors chose as the most memorable or important of the year, along with details on where to find information about them in the book.

A prehuman species reconsidered ▶

Researchers in Indonesia reported in December 1996 that skulls found earlier on the island of Java and thought to be of the species *Homo erectus* date from 27,000 to 53,000 years ago—about 250,000 years after the species was believed to have become extinct. The study cast doubt on the theory that *H. erectus* was an ancestor of modern humans. In the Science News Update section, see ANTHROPOLOGY.

◀ Hailing Hale-Bopp

Astronomers and amateur sky-watchers alike proclaimed Comet Hale-Bopp, which adorned the night sky for much of the spring, as one of the major comets of the 1900's. Hale-Bopp was an astronomical rarity, a comet with three tails—though the third was visible only with special instruments. In the Science News Update section, see ASTRONOMY.

Treasure trove of dino fossils

The discovery of a huge collection of dinosaur fossils in China was announced in April 1997 by an international team of paleontologists. The fossils included the first preserved internal organs of dinosaurs ever found. In the Science News Update section, see FOSSIL STUDIES.

World Book, Inc.
525 W. Monroe
Chicago, IL 60661

ISBN: 0-7166-0598-8
ISSN: 0080-7621
Library of Congress Catalog Number: 65-21776
Printed in the United States of America.

Stunning achievement in cloning

Scottish embryologist Ian Wilmut reported in February 1997 that he and his colleagues had created a lamb by cloning an adult sheep from one of its mammary cells—the first such cloning of a mammal. In the Science News Update section, see GENETICS.

A boom in planetary exploration ▶

An unmanned spacecraft called Cassini in mid-1997 was being readied for an autumn launch to Saturn. Cassini, which was to arrive at Saturn in 2004 to study the ringed planet and its moon Titan, was one of several exploratory craft launched or being planned in 1996 and 1997. In the Special Reports section, see PROBING THE PLANETS.

Hope for spinal cord injuries

The first experimental evidence that a severed spinal cord in a mammal can be regenerated and nerve function restored was reported in July 1996 by scientists in Sweden. The research was done with rats, but neuroscientists were hopeful that the results would apply to human spinal cord injuries. In the Science News Update section, see MEDICAL RESEARCH.

Enormous fountain of antimatter

A huge plume of antimatter is spewing from the center of the Milky Way, a team of U.S. astrophysicists reported in April 1997. Antimatter, which is identical to ordinary matter but with the opposite electric charge, had been made experimentally but never detected in large amounts in nature. See ASTRONOMY

◀ World's oldest rock art?

Archaeologists in Australia reported in September 1996 that pictures pecked and carved into sandstone rocks in northwestern Australia are 75,000 to 160,000 years old—far older than cave art that has been found in Europe. In the Science News Update section, see ARCHAEOLOGY.

CONTENTS

Page 120

SPECIAL REPORTS

Special Reports give in-depth treatment to significant and timely subjects in science and technology.

SCIENCE STUDIES

The Population Explosion takes a wide-ranging look at the world's relentlessly increasing population and how it is affecting the planet.

Page 160

SCIENCE NEWS UPDATE

Twenty-eight articles, arranged alphabetically, report on the year's most important developments in all major areas of science and technology, from *Agriculture* to *Space Technology*. In addition, five Close-Up articles focus on especially noteworthy developments:

Page 290

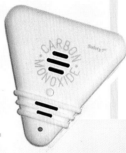

Page 175

SCIENCE YOU CAN USE

Five articles present various topics in science and technology as they apply to the consumer.

WORLD BOOK SUPPLEMENT

Twelve new and revised articles from the 1996 edition of *The World Book Encyclopedia:* **Dinosaur; Brain; Cosmic rays; Oyster; Greenhouse Effect; Penguin; Seal; Water pollution; Jupiter; Tide; Australopithecus,** and **Quark.**

INDEX

A cumulative index of topics covered in the 1997, 1996, and 1995 editions of Science Year.

CROSS-REFERENCE TABS

A tear-out page of cross-reference tabs for insertion in *The World Book Encyclopedia* appears before page 1.

STAFF

EDITORIAL ADVISORY BOARD

CONTRIBUTORS

Asker, James R., B.A.
Washington Bureau Chief,
Aviation Week & Space Technology
magazine.
[*Space Technology; Space
Technology* (Close-Up)]

Black, Harvey, B.A.
Free-Lance Writer.
[Science You Can Use, *Reducing the
Dangers of Hazardous Household
Waste*]

Bolen, Eric G., B.S., M.S., Ph.D.
Professor,
Department of Biological Sciences,
University of North Carolina at
Wilmington.
[*Conservation*]

Brett, Carlton E., M.S., Ph.D.
Professor,
Department of Earth and
Environmental Sciences,
University of Rochester.
[*Fossil Studies*]

Brody, Herb, B.S.
Senior Editor,
Technology Review.
[Special Report, *Digital Flicks*]

Cain, Steven A., B.S.
Communication Specialist,
Purdue University School of
Agriculture.
[*Agriculture*]

Chiras, Dan, B.A., Ph.D.
Adjunct Professor,
Environmental Policy and
Management Program,
University of Denver.
[Science Studies, The *Population
Explosion; Environmental Pollution*]

Cruz-Uribe, Kathryn, B.A., M.A.,
Ph.D.
Associate Professor of Anthropology,
Northern Arizona University.
[*Anthropology*]

Dennett, Joann Temple, B.S., M.S.,
Ph.D.
Free-Lance Writer.
[*Astronomy* (Close-Up)]

George, Karyn Hede, B.A., M.A.,
M.S.,
Free-Lance Science Writer,
[Special Report, *Rogue Proteins*]

Goodman, Richard A., M.D., M.P.H.
Adjunct Professor,
Division of Epidemiology,
Emory University.
[*Public Health*]

Graff, Gordon, B.S., M.S., Ph.D.
Free-Lance Science Writer.
[*Chemistry;* Science You Can Use,
*Carbon Monoxide Detectors: Tracking
"the Silent Killer"*]

Guth, Alan H., B.S., M.S., Ph.D.
Victor F. Weisskopf Professor of
Physics,
Massachusetts Institute of
Technology.
[Special Report, *Beyond the Big
Bang*]

Hart, Benjamin L., D.V.M., Ph.D.
Professor of Physiology and Behavior,
School of Veterinary Medicine,
University of California at Davis.
[Special Report, *Dogs at Work*]

Hart, Bonny, B.S.N.
Free-Lance Writer.
[Science You Can Use, *Is Melatonin a
"Miracle Cure" for Insomnia?*]

Hart, Lynette A., Ph.D.
Associate Professor,
School of Veterinary Medicine,
University of California at Davis.
[Special Report, *Dogs at Work*]

Hay, William W., B.S., M.S., Ph.D.
Professor of Geological Sciences,
University of Colorado at Boulder.
[*Geology*]

Haymer, David S., M.S., Ph.D.
Professor,
Department of Genetics and
Molecular Biology,
University of Hawaii.
[*Genetics*]

Hermann, Richard C., M.S., M.D.
Instructor in Psychiatry,
Harvard Medical School.
[*Psychology*]

Hester, Thomas R., B.A., Ph.D.
Professor of Anthropology and
Director,
Texas Archeological Research
Laboratory,
University of Texas at Austin.
[*Archaeology*]

Johnson, Christina, S., B.A., M.S.
Staff Research Associate,
Scripps Institute of Oceanography.
[*Oceanography*]

Kowal, Deborah, M.A.
Adjunct Assistant Professor,
Emory University School of Public
Health.
[*Public Health*]

Lasser, Robert A., B.A., M.D.
Clinical Associate,
National Institutes of Health.
[*Psychology*]

Limburg, Peter R., B.A., M.A.
Free-Lance Writer.
[Special Report, *Exploring the Ocean
Abyss*]

Lunine, Jonathan I., B.S., M.S.,
Ph.D.
Professor of Planetary Science,
University of Arizona Lunar and
Planetary Laboratory.
[Special Report, *Probing the Planets;
Astronomy*]

Mack, Alison J., A.B., M.A., M.S.
Free-Lance Science and Medical
Writer.
[*Ecology* (Close-Up)]

March, Robert H., A.B., M.S., Ph.D.
Professor of Physics and Liberal
Studies,
University of Wisconsin at Madison.
[*Physics*]

Marschall, Laurence A., B.S., Ph.D.
Professor of Physics,
Gettysburg College.
[*Books About Science*]

Maugh, Thomas H., II, Ph.D.
Science Writer,
Los Angeles Times.
[*Biology*]

Moser-Veillon, Phylis B., B.S., M.S.,
Ph.D.
Professor,
Department of Nutrition and Food
Science,
University of Maryland.
[*Nutrition*]

Mullins, Henry T., B.S., M.S., Ph.D.
Professor of Geology,
Department of Earth Sciences,
Syracuse University.
[*Geology* (Close-Up)]

Peterson, Ray G., B.S., Ph.D.
Research Oceanographer,
Scripps Institute of Oceanography,
University of California at San Diego.
[*Oceanography*]

Riley, Thomas N., Ph.D.
Professor,
School of Pharmacy,
Auburn University.
[*Drugs*]

Sforza, Pasquale M., B.Ae.E., M.S.,
Ph.D.
Professor of Mechanical and
Aerospace Engineering,
Polytechnic University.
[*Energy*]

Sheffield, Richard, B.S.
Senior Technical Writer,
Sterling Software, Inc.
[*Computers and Electronics;* Science
You Can Use, *Digital Video Discs
Usher in a Sight and Sound
Revolution*]

Snow, John T., B.S.E.E., M.S.E.E.,
Ph.D.
Dean,
College of Geosciences,
University of Oklahoma.
[*Atmospheric Sciences*]

Snow, Theodore P., B.A., M.S.,
Ph.D.
Professor of Astrophysics and
Director,
Center for Astrophysics and Space
Astronomy,
University of Colorado at Boulder.
[*Astronomy*]

Stephenson, Joan, B.S., Ph.D.
Associate Editor, Medical News,
Journal of the American Medical
Association.
[Science You Can Use, *Digestive
Aids—Soothing the Beast in the Belly*]

Tamarin, Robert H., B.S., Ph.D.
Dean of Sciences,
University of Massachusetts.
[*Ecology*]

Teich, Albert H., B.S., Ph.D.
Director,
Science and Policy Programs,
American Association for the
Advancement of Science.
[*Science and Society*]

Tressler, Arthur G., A.B.
Free-Lance Science Writer.
[Special Report, *The Galapagos—
Endangered Isles*]

Trubo, Richard, B.A., M.A.
Free-Lance Writer.
[*Medical Research; Medical Research*
(Close-Up)]

Wright, Andrew G., B.A.
Associate Editor,
Engineering News-Record.
[*Engineering*]

Page 115

Page 99

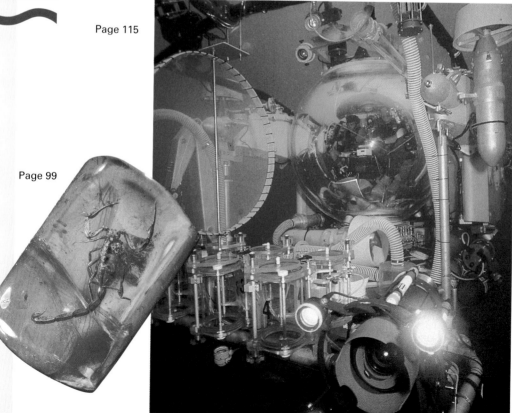

Page 42

In an artist's conception, an unmanned spacecraft called Cassini, approaching Saturn, releases a probe that will plunge toward the planet's moon Titan to study its atmosphere. Cassini was scheduled to be launched in October 1997 and to reach Saturn in 2004 for a four-year study of the ringed planet and mysterious Titan.

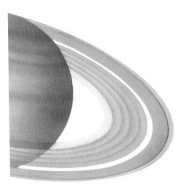

Unmanned spacecraft have revealed a wealth of information about the solar system, and they remain our best option for further exploration of the planets.

Probing the Planets

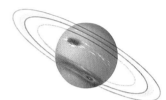

By Jonathan I. Lunine

When American astronaut Neil Armstrong piloted the Apollo 11 lunar module to a soft landing on the surface of the moon in July 1969, he gazed upon a landscape that was, in some respects, already familiar to him. As the spacecraft descended toward the surface, Armstrong scanned the ground below, looking for landmarks he had learned to recognize from photographs. By the time Armstrong walked on the moon, it had been 10 years since Luna 2, an unmanned probe from the Soviet Union, became the first spacecraft to reach the moon. In the decade that followed, more than a dozen other Soviet and United States space vehicles had studied the moon in fine detail. Photographs and data radioed to Earth by these probes were instrumental in the success of the six U.S. manned missions to the lunar surface.

Since then, probes have visited every planet in the solar system except Pluto, and some planets had been visited several times. In November and December 1996, the National Aeronautics and Space Administration (NASA) sent two probes, named Mars Global Surveyor and Mars Pathfinder, on the first survey missions to the red planet since 1975, when the Viking 1 and Viking 2 spacecraft were launched. The new spacecraft were scheduled to reach Mars in the summer of 1997, the Surveyor to observe the planet from orbit and the Pathfinder to explore its surface. Purely by coincidence, these missions were launched on the heels of a 1996 announcement that a meteorite of Martian origin contains the apparent remains of bacterialike microorganisms, raising the possibility that primitive life forms lived on Mars billions of years ago.

Terms and concepts

Carbonates: Carbon-containing compounds, formed by the weathering of rocks, that serve to remove carbon from Earth's atmosphere.

Magnetometer: An instrument that measures the magnetic field emanating from a planet.

Organic molecules: A class of carbon-containing compounds, some of which form the basis of life.

Radio occultation: A method for analyzing a planet's atmosphere by measuring the distortion of radio signals beamed through that atmosphere by a space probe.

Spectrometer: An instrument that measures wavelengths of light from a planet, thereby revealing information about the planet and its atmosphere.

Synthetic aperature radar: An advanced form of radar that enables a space probe to scan a planet's surface in great detail.

The author:
Jonathan I. Lunine is a professor of planetary sciences at the University of Arizona Lunar and Planetary Laboratory in Tucson.

Although their development was already too far along to alter their missions, the Surveyor and Pathfinder may uncover evidence that points toward the existence of life on Mars.

With Mars back on the public's radar screen, some space-exploration enthusiasts advocated sending a manned mission to the red planet. The cost of such a venture, however, would be enormous—up to $400 billion by some estimates. In contrast, probe missions to Mars or other planets can be more than 1,000 times cheaper. Increasingly limited budgets have forced space programs of all nations to abandon the large, complex probe designs of the past in favor of smaller, simpler spacecraft that employ more advanced technologies. Engineers are now building sophisticated probes far more economically than ever before. The Mars Pathfinder Mission, for example, was projected to cost only about one-tenth as much as a Viking mission. Although human beings may set foot on faraway planets and moons at some time in the future, for now probes are by far our best option for exploring the solar system.

Probe designs and functions

On a cosmic scale, the solar system is not vast: The closest star to our sun, Alpha Centauri, is more than 1,000 times more distant from us than is the farthest planet of our solar system, Pluto. But distances within the solar system, though insignificant on the scale of the universe, are enormous on a human scale. Thus, to study the solar system in any detail from Earth is a difficult task. Recent advances in telescope technology have allowed some information about the composition of the atmospheres and surfaces of planets to be discerned with Earth-based telescopes. As advanced as these data and images are, however, the information they reveal is still limited. Sending probes to the various planets not only enables scientists to obtain much better images, it also permits them to directly study physical samples at the same time.

Probes carry many types of instruments. Cameras and other devices that are sensitive to different wavelengths of light, including infrared and ultraviolet, reveal surface features and atmospheric conditions of planets and their moons. Spectrometers divide sunlight that passes through a planet's atmosphere or is reflected from its surface into its component colors, producing patterns that reveal the makeup of soils, clouds, and atmospheric gases. Radiometers measure the intensity of infrared waves, from which scientists can calculate—among other things—the temperature of an object. Magnetometers measure the streams of electrically charged particles and magnetic fields emanating from the planets. All these data are radioed in *digital* form (as a series of 1's and 0's) back to Earth, where they are picked up by sensitive antennas.

Even a probe's radio system can be used to make observations. By bouncing radio signals off of a planet or moon's surface and measuring the time it takes for the signal to be reflected back up to the spacecraft, detailed computer-generated images can be made of a planet's surface features. This technique is known as radar mapping. A planet's atmosphere can be studied using a technique known as radio occultation,

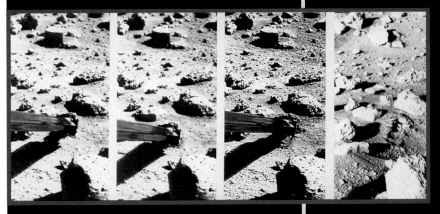

The five types of space probes

There are five basic types of unmanned space probe. A probe's design depends on the nature of the planet or other objects being explored and the kinds of data that scientists on the Earth wish to collect. A probe radios its data to receivers on Earth.

Fly-by

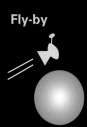

Fly-by probes, such as Voyager 2, often visit more than one planet. They take photographs of the planets and their moons and use sophisticated instruments to measure features such as the planets' density, composition, structure, and temperature.

Orbiter

Orbiters, like the Magellan mission to Venus, are sent to study just one planet or moon in detail. They may use radar to map the surface of a planet whose surface is hidden by clouds. Instruments measure various aspects of the body, such as its gravitational field.

By combining images taken by the Galileo probe during fly-bys in June and September 1996, NASA technicians created this three-dimensional representation of Galileo Regio, a region on Ganymede, one of the moons of Jupiter. The two images were taken at slightly different angles, and a computer was used to interpret the differences in the images as variations in height.

Atmospheric probe

Atmospheric probes, like the one released by the Galileo orbiter in 1995, are packages of instruments designed to take measurements of the deeper regions of a planet's atmosphere.

Lander

Landers, such as Viking 1, analyze soil and air samples in miniature onboard laboratories. They also radio back pictures from the surface of a planet.

Rover

This series of photos shows the operation of the surface sampler arm of the Viking 2 lander on the surface of Mars in 1976. The arm carefully avoids rocky debris to scoop up a sample of Martian soil for analysis. The shallow trench it left behind is visible in the right-hand image.

Rovers, like the Mars Sojourner Rover, have wheels or treads that allow them to travel across the surface of a planet, collecting and analyzing rock and soil samples from different places. The Sojourner Rover can travel more than 0.8 kilometer (0.5 mile) from its landing site.

Landmark space probe missions

Year of Launch	Name	Country	Accomplishments
1959	Luna 2	USSR	First spacecraft to reach the moon; crash-landed on the surface.
1964	Mariner 4	USA	Photographed Mars on July 14, 1965; measured conditions in space.
1966	Luna 9	USSR	First soft landing on the moon on Feb. 3, 1966; sent 27 pictures back to Earth.
	Luna 10	USSR	First spacecraft to orbit the moon; reached orbit April 3, 1966.
1967	Venera 4	USSR	Released a probe into Venus's atmosphere.
	Surveyor 5	USA	Landed on the moon; sent data on lunar soil back to Earth.
1968	Zond 5	USSR	First spacecraft to orbit the moon and return to a soft landing on the Earth.
1970	Venera 7	USSR	First spacecraft to transmit data from Venus's surface; landed Dec. 15, 1970.
	Mariner 9	USA	First spacecraft to orbit Mars; began orbiting Nov. 13, 1971.
1972	Pioneer 10	USA	Flew past Jupiter Dec. 3, 1973, and sent back data; on June 13, 1983, it became the first spacecraft to exit the solar system.
1973	Pioneer-Saturn	USA	Flew by Jupiter in 1974 and Saturn in 1975; sent back data on both planets.
1975	Venera 9	USSR	First probe to send pictures from the surface of Venus; landed Oct. 22, 1975.
	Viking 1	USA	Sent photos and scientific data from Mars; landed July 20, 1976.
	Viking 2	USA	Landed on Mars Sept. 3, 1976; sent back photos and scientific data.
1977	Voyager 2	USA	Flew by Jupiter July 1979; flew by Saturn August 1981; flew by Neptune August 1989; sent back photos.
	Voyager 1	USA	Passed Jupiter March 5, 1979, and flew by Saturn Nov. 12, 1980; sent back photos and made various discoveries about both planets and their moons.
1978	Pioneer Venus 1	USA	Made orbital measurements of Venus's atmosphere and topography; entered orbit Dec. 4, 1978.
	Pioneer Venus 2	USA	Released four probes into Venus's atmosphere to measure its density and composition; reached Venus Dec. 9, 1978.
	Venera 11	USSR	Made chemical analysis of Venus's lower atmosphere; landed Dec. 25, 1978.
	Venera 12	USSR	Made chemical analysis of Venus's lower atmosphere; landed Dec. 21, 1978.
1981	Venera 13	USSR	Sent color photos of Venus's surface and analyzed soil samples; landed March 1, 1982.
1985	Giotto	ESA	Passed Halley's Comet on March 13, 1986; photographed comet's nucleus and sent back scientific data.
1989	Magellan	USA	Used radar to map most of Venus's surface from 1990 to 1994; reached orbit Aug. 10, 1990.
	Galileo	USA	Reached Jupiter orbit December 7, 1995; dropped a probe into Jupiter's atmosphere; sent back photos and scientific data. In 1994, Galileo sent back images of comet Shoemaker-Levy 9 fragments striking Jupiter
1990	Ulysses	ESA/USA	Examined polar regions of the sun in 1994 and 1995.
1996	Mars Surveyor	USA	Scheduled to attain Mars orbit Sept. 12, 1997.
	Mars Pathfinder	USA	Scheduled to land on Mars July 4, 1997; carries Sojourner Rover, a robotic vehicle designed to gather and analyze rock and soil samples.

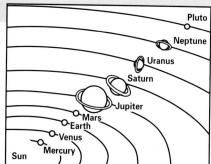

The solar system consists of nine planets. The four closest to the sun are known as the inner planets; the others are the outer planets. As of 1997, Pluto was the only planet that had not been visited by a probe from Earth.

whereby a radio signal, aimed at the Earth, is beamed through the atmosphere of a planet. Scientists on Earth compare the signal with one sent by the probe through space. By analyzing the ways in which the signal has been changed by the atmosphere, they can infer what conditions (such as temperature, clouds, or charged particles) might have caused the changes.

Five basic types of space probes have been sent to examine planets and other bodies in the solar system: fly-by probes, orbiters, atmospheric probes, landers, and rovers. A fly-by probe makes its observations as it passes a celestial body from a distance. Fly-by missions enable a spacecraft to visit more than one object. An orbiter is designed to park itself in a stable orbit around a particular planet or moon for an extended period of time. An orbiter closely circling a body with a substantial atmosphere is gradually slowed by atmospheric friction, which causes it to lose altitude and eventually crash. An atmospheric probe is a package of instruments that descends into the atmosphere of a planet, taking readings on its way down. The probe continues to transmit data until it reaches the surface or is destroyed by heat or atmospheric pressure. A lander is designed to land safely on a planet or moon and analyze soil samples and surface conditions. A rover is a robot vehicle with wheels or treads that roams across the surface. Carried to the surface by a lander, a rover has the advantage of not being confined to one spot.

Investigating the mysteries of Venus

The first spacecraft to travel beyond Earth's moon, the U.S. probe Mariner 2, passed within 34,760 kilometers (21,600 miles) of Venus in December 1962. Mariner 2's microwave radiometer detected a surprising amount of heat, in the form of infrared radiation, seeping up from beneath the layer of clouds that surrounds the planet. This discovery shattered the theory that the climate of Venus was similar to the Earth's. Measurements by subsequent spacecraft showed that the atmosphere of Venus consists mainly of carbon dioxide and that the atmospheric pressure at the surface is 90 times higher than sea-level air pressure on Earth. This enormous blanket of carbon dioxide produces an intense *greenhouse effect:* The atmosphere lets sunlight reach the surface but prevents that energy—converted to infrared radiation by the heated planet—from escaping back into space. Due to the greenhouse effect, the average surface temperature of Venus is 462 °C (864 °F), hot enough to melt lead.

But had it always been like that? The answer to this question had to await the December 1978 arrival of two NASA spacecraft—Pioneer Venus 1, an orbiter, and Pioneer Venus 2, which carried four atmospheric probes. During its descent through Venus's atmosphere, one of the atmospheric probes measured a surprisingly large amount of deuterium—an *isotope* (variant form) of hydrogen—relative to normal hydrogen. This discovery led scientists to theorize that there had once been large amounts of water on Venus.

Several billion years ago, many scientists now believe, an ocean existed on Venus, and the climate was perhaps only somewhat hotter than Earth's is today. The heat, however, was sufficient to cause water from Venus's ocean to evaporate in large quantities. The vapor drifted into the upper atmosphere, where the water molecules were broken apart into hydrogen and oxygen by ultraviolet light from the sun. Only a tiny fraction of ocean water contains deuterium rather than normal hydrogen. The normal hydrogen, however, because it is lighter than deuterium, escaped Venus's atmosphere more easily. As a result, the atmosphere of Venus today is left with a large proportion of deuterium—the ghostly echo of an ocean long gone.

While the ocean evaporated, carbon dioxide from within the planet was building up in the atmosphere. On Earth, carbon dioxide is constantly being removed from the atmosphere by rainfall and plants and by the weathering of rocks to form compounds called carbonates. With none of these processes operating on Venus, the result was an overabundance of carbon dioxide and a runaway greenhouse effect.

Although the Pioneer Venus probes told scientists much about Venus's atmosphere, the surface of the cloud-shrouded planet remained a mystery. It was not until 1984 that the veil began to lift. In that year, twin orbiters launched by the Soviet Union—Venera 15 and Venera 16—successfully mapped about a fourth of Venus's surface using cloud-penetrating radar. The maps revealed a geology unlike anything seen on Earth. Volcanic activity was revealed in several huge regions of fractures on the surface, large volcanoes, and lava flows. But there was virtually no sign of the kinds of long, organized ridges and trenches that on Earth are characteristic of *plate tectonics* (the slow movement of rock plates making up our planet's crust).

More extensive mapping of Venus was carried out by NASA's Magellan spacecraft, which began orbiting Venus in 1990. Armed with *synthetic aperture radar*—an advanced kind of radar that can scan a planet's surface in much greater detail—Magellan mapped virtually the entire surface of Venus. The mountains of Venus shown in Magellan's images have an eerie incompleteness to them; they lack the canyons, gullies, and valleys that water carves into the mountainous regions of the Earth. The absence of such features confirmed that Venus has been without liquid water for most of its geologic history.

Magellan's radar maps also showed that the surface of Venus, compared to other rocky, waterless bodies in the solar system, is pocked by relatively few meteorite craters. Furthermore, the cratering is uniform across the entire surface—no one area has significantly more or fewer craters than any other area. To some geologists, these findings indicate that the surface of Venus is probably relatively young in geologic terms and that the entire present surface of Venus probably formed at about the same time. But what kind of cataclysmic event could have caused the resurfacing of an entire planet remains a mystery. One theory holds that heat builds up within the planet and that every few hundred million years, the entire crust breaks apart, melts, and then re-forms.

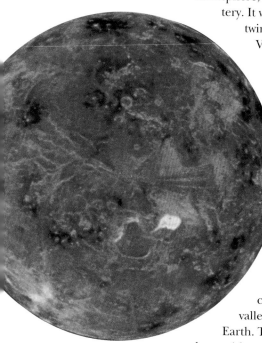

The U.S. probe Magellan used radar beams to map virtually the entire surface of Venus through its dense cloud cover beginning in 1990. This composite image was created by using a computer to combine radar data from many orbital passes.

Mercury and our moon

Inward from Venus lies Mercury, a tiny planet about 1½ times the diameter of our moon. Because of its close proximity to the sun, Mercury is difficult to approach, and only one spacecraft, the U.S. probe Mariner 10, has flown past it. Images returned from Mariner 10 in 1974 revealed a heavily cratered surface, similar to that of our moon. Most surprising was the discovery of a magnetic field, which scientists had believed could be generated only by larger, rapidly spinning planets like Earth and Jupiter. Mercury spins so slowly that it takes about 59 Earth days for a single rotation. The existence of a magnetic field, along with information on the planet's mass, indicated that Mercury is composed largely of iron.

The body nearest to Earth—our own moon—was most closely explored by the Apollo astronauts, who returned hundreds of pounds of lunar samples. But their expeditions were limited in area, and the orbiting command modules never reached the lunar poles. A U.S. probe, Clementine, was launched on a mission to examine the poles of the moon in 1993. In 1996, radio signals from Clementine that were bounced off the poles and received on Earth indicated the presence of frozen lakes. Some scientists believe that comets colliding with the moon could have deposited water ice at the lunar poles, but it remains for future probes to confirm the presence of water on the moon.

Missions to Mars

Of all the wanderers in the night sky, the planet Mars has haunted humanity the most, for centuries stimulating conjecture about extraterrestrial civilizations. Even many scientists speculated that Mars might harbor at least primitive life. But early fly-bys of Mars by NASA's Mariner probes in the 1960's showed a cratered landscape little different from the Earth's moon, and most scientists gave up hope that Mars was anything but a dead world. Those spacecraft, however, photographed only a small portion of the Martian surface. When Mariner 9 reached Mars in 1971 and began to send back photographs of the entire surface, opinions about the planet changed quickly. Evident in the new images were valleys and channels that appeared to have been carved by flowing water, as well as giant canyons and huge volcanoes. These discoveries showed that Mars had once been surging with great geologic upheavals and running water. But was there life on the red planet?

An interplanetary armada of two Viking orbiters and two landers from the United States arrived at Mars in 1976. The landers were equipped with chemical laboratories to detect signs of *metabolic* (living) processes in the soil, and to search for *organic* (carbon-containing) molecules that might be the product of life. No organic compounds were found, but the soil seemed unusually reactive in a way that was initially interpreted as a possible sign of life. Further study of the results, however, showed that the chemistry of the soil itself, which is rich in certain iron oxides, had caused the reactions—the landers had not detected life.

The Viking orbiters, meanwhile, studied Mars from high above. Their images of the Martian surface showed even more dramatically the valley networks, channels, volcanoes, and canyons seen earlier by Mariner 9. The much finer detail of the Viking images enabled scientists to suggest that some geological features on Mars were the remnants of glacial erosion and to identify sediments that may have been left behind by ancient lakes that had long since dried up.

Given the abundant evidence for liquid water on Mars in the past, scientists began to develop theories to explain

The first close-up photographs of Mercury were taken by Mariner 10 in 1974. The probe showed that the planet has a cratered surface resembling that of the moon. Eighteen images from the probe's cameras were combined to create this composite photograph.

why Mars today is a cold, dry planet. Because Mars is considerably farther from the sun than the Earth is, its early wet climate must have been sustained by a much thicker atmosphere. That atmosphere may have been dominated by carbon dioxide, which is still the main component of the now-thin envelope of gases surrounding Mars. Some of the early atmosphere was probably lost as the result of large impacts by asteroids. A larger portion of it may be locked in the crust as carbonates that formed when the planet had abundant water. Like Venus, Mars shows no sign of active plate tectonics, which on Earth returns carbon dioxide to the atmosphere by melting and squeezing carbonates in the crust. On Mars, carbon dioxide, once locked in carbonates, could not be recycled in this way.

To test this theory, NASA in 1992 launched a probe called Mars Observer check for the presence of carbonate minerals on the planet. But the spacecraft was lost when its propulsion system failed in August 1993, just days before reaching Martian orbit, and the search for carbonates on Mars was put on hold. Instead, a series of Mars orbiters, beginning with the one launched in 1996, will conduct the search.

Jupiter and its moons

The first probe to venture to the outer planets was Pioneer 10, which flew past Jupiter in 1973. Jupiter, 318 times the mass of the Earth, is essentially a huge ball of gas, though it has a hot, dense—perhaps solid—core made up of heavy elements. Jupiter's powerful magnetic field traps high concentrations of charged subatomic particles (such as protons and electrons), generating lethal levels of radiation. In 1974, Pioneer 11 encountered Jupiter on its way to Saturn. These missions proved that spacecraft could safely traverse the *asteroid belt* (a band of rocky debris orbiting the sun between Mars and Jupiter) and survive the onslaught of radiation at Jupiter to return data to Earth. Following in their path, the more ad-

An image of the surface of Mars, taken by the Viking 1 lander in 1976, reveals a surprisingly Earthlike landscape, with rocky, reddish soil.

Unveiling the moons of Jupiter

The Voyager probes reached Jupiter and its 16 satellites in 1979. What they found there intrigued scientists so much that in 1989 they sent the Galileo probe specifically to revisit the planet and its moons. The images we have of Io and Europa are the most striking. Although they are of similar size and distance from Jupiter, these moons are as different—quite literally—as fire and ice.

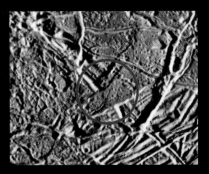

This Galileo probe image of the surface of Europa, another moon of Jupiter, shows evidence that this moon may have an ocean of water beneath its icy crust. The image shows what appears to be a flow of partially melted ice, *circled in red,* that welled up from below the surface, spilling across and erasing part of an older surface ridge, before it froze again.

The violent volcanic activity on Jupiter's moon Io is evident in this spectacular photo captured by the NASA spacecraft Galileo. The blue-colored volcanic plume *(magnified in the inset)* is about 100 kilometers (60 miles) high. Its color may indicate the presence of sulfur dioxide gas and "snow" condensing as the plume expanded and cooled.

vanced Voyager 1 and Voyager 2 probes flew past Jupiter in 1979 on their way to Saturn.

The Voyagers showed that Jupiter has a roiling, turbulent atmosphere, with gigantic storms appearing and then being swallowed up again. They identified hydrogen, helium, and methane in Jupiter's atmosphere and measured their abundance. The probes also found that the planet is circled by a thin ring of dust. The probes also discovered three small moons that were previously unknown—Adrastea, Metis, and Thebe.

But the most startling findings by the Voyager mission at Jupiter centered on the planet's four largest satellites: Io, Europa, Ganymede, and Callisto. The probes showed that the inner two moons, Io and Europa, are composed mostly of rock and are about the size of Earth's moon. The outer two, Ganymede and Callisto, are larger—about 5,000 kilometers (3,000 miles) in diameter—but they are less dense than the inner moons and appear to be composed of roughly equal parts of rock and ice. Although they are similar in size and mass, Ganymede and Callisto seem to have had vastly different geologic histories. Callisto is covered by craters, with nothing to break the monotony of its battered surface. In contrast, Ganymede—the solar system's largest moon—has vast regions where craters have been "erased" by geologic processes and replaced by complex networks of grooves.

Europa's rocky surface, Voyager data reported, is covered by a bright, smooth layer of water ice, which is cracked in places like an eggshell.

Jupiter's other two inner moons, Callisto and Ganymede, also resemble each other in size and mass, but they too exhibit fundamental differences. Callisto's surface, above left, is uniformly covered by impact craters, indicating a lack of geologic activity. The surface of Ganymede, above right, on the other hand, shows large areas where the surface has been renewed, apparently by lava flows resulting from volcanic or tectonic activity.

Encounter with Saturn

In 1980 and 1981, Voyager 1 and 2 visited the planet Saturn. Their findings shed new light on the intricate nature of Saturn's spectacular rings and its atmosphere. The probes also provided extensive data on Saturn's largest moon, Titan.

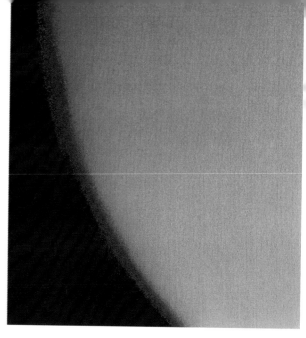

Titan, above, has a thick, orange atmosphere that hid its surface from Voyager 1's cameras. Further data about conditions on Titan's surface could provide clues about how life originates from complex organic molecules. When it arrives at Saturn in 2004, the Cassini probe will map the surface of Titan using cloud-penetrating radar.

The Voyager probes revealed that Saturn's rings are much more numerous and intricate than previously thought. In this computer-enhanced Voyager 2 image, chemical variations in the makeup of the individual rings are highlighted by false-color rendering.

Even more startling was Io, revealed by Voyager's cameras to be covered by active volcanoes that spew tremendous plumes of smoke and lava flows consisting of both molten sulfur and molten rock.

Scientists wondered what the source of energy was that powered all this activity. The answer, they concluded, was gravity. Jupiter's tremendous gravity exerts alternately pulling and squeezing forces on the larger moons as they travel around the planet in their slightly *elliptical* (oval) orbits. Close-in Io is most affected by this gravitational "kneading"—the constant stresses have heated Io to the melting point of rock, sealing its fate as a world of explosive volcanism. Farther out, Europa is also stressed, but only enough internal warming has occurred to melt underground ice to a slush, which then rises to the surface and refreezes. Most intriguing is the possibility that an ocean of liquid water, warmed by gravitational stresses, still exists beneath the icy surface of Europa.

To study Jupiter further, NASA in 1989 launched the Galileo spacecraft on a voyage to the giant planet. Galileo, which consisted of an orbiter and an atmospheric probe, arrived at Jupiter in December 1995. The probe, released from the orbiter several months earlier, plunged into Jupiter's atmosphere, surviving acceleration, pressure, and heating for 57 minutes until it melted and then vaporized. During its descent the probe found no evidence of the water clouds that scientists had expected to find. Concentrations of water vapor in the atmosphere were also lower than expected. One possible explanation for these findings is that the probe fell into an unusually dry, cloudless patch of Jupiter's atmosphere. The probe also reported that wind speeds increased at lower elevations. This indicated that, unlike Earth, where the winds are faster in the upper atmosphere because they are driven by heat from the sun, Jupiter's winds are driven by heat from within the planet.

After the probe mission was completed, the main part of the spacecraft rocketed into orbit around Jupiter to begin a survey of the planet and its moons. Information from Galileo was still being collected in mid-1997 and would be the subject of study for many years. But the spacecraft had already made several significant discoveries about Jupiter's satellites. A close approach to Ganymede revealed evidence that, unlike other moons encountered by probes, it possesses a magnetic field. And a survey of Io, with careful measurement of how the moon's gravity deflected the spacecraft's path, enabled scientists to deduce that this volcanic moon has a distinct, metallic inner core.

Galileo also revealed that the fractured sheath of ice enveloping Europa is divided into an incredibly complex network of cracks. The cracks crisscross one another at many angles, with many cracks obliterated by fresh flows of ice. The newest cracks might be places where liquid water lies only a few kilometers beneath the surface. In April 1997, a scientific panel declared that evidence gathered by the Galileo probe had confirmed this theory. In fact, observations indicate that there is probably more water beneath the surface of Europa than in all the oceans on Earth combined. This subsurface ocean might even support forms of life that rely on heat from within the moon or small amounts of sunlight penetrating the cracks in the surface.

Saturn, Uranus, and Neptune

Voyagers 1 and 2 reached Saturn in 1980 and 1981, respectively. The second-largest planet in the solar system, Saturn has only a third of the mass of Jupiter, though it is still more than 90 times as massive as the Earth. Saturn sports a ring system that has been visible to telescopes on Earth for centuries. Voyager 1's close-up images revealed, however, that the planet's seven major rings are divided into hundreds of thousands of subrings, each divided by a narrow space, like the grooves on a phonograph record. The rocky and icy particles making up the rings are organized in this way by the effects of Saturn's gravity.

Voyager data on Saturn's atmosphere revealed little helium in comparison with Jupiter's atmosphere. Saturn has a colder interior than Jupiter—cold enough so that helium in the atmosphere liquefies. Since helium is denser than hydrogen, it falls through the atmosphere in the form of little droplets until it reaches—and becomes part of—the planet's dense core. The result is that there is now little helium remaining in the higher layers of the atmosphere.

Perhaps the most extraordinary part of the Voyager mission was Voyager 1's exploration of Titan, the largest of Saturn's 18 known moons. Scientists knew that Titan had an atmosphere, but they had not been able to determine its extent or density. Voyager 1's cameras showed that Titan's surface is completely hidden by a thick, orange haze suspended in the atmosphere. The probe revealed that nitrogen is the most abundant gas in the atmosphere. The temperature of Titan is so low—a frigid –178 °C (–289 °F) at its surface—that water is completely frozen out of the atmosphere. At that temperature, however, methane—also plentiful around Titan—can exist as either a liquid or a gas, and it may form clouds in the atmosphere, much as water does on Earth.

The Voyager probes also detected many organic molecules in Titan's atmosphere. These probably form when ultraviolet light from the sun breaks apart methane and nitrogen molecules, some of which then re-combine to form more complex substances, including *hydrocarbons* (molecular chains of carbon and hydrogen) and *nitriles* (molecular chains of carbon, hydrogen, and nitrogen). This photochemical process creates a "smog" that condenses and settles onto the moon's surface. Scientists speculate that pools of liquid organic molecules, or clusters of solid organic molecules, may exist on Titan's surface. Life on Earth may have arisen from reactions in similar collections of organic molecules, and some of the same reactions could be occurring on Titan.

After leaving Saturn, Voyager 1's course took it out of the solar system and into deep space. Voyager 2 continued on to Uranus and Neptune, reaching those planets in 1986 and 1989. Both of these large, gaseous planets are less than a fourth the mass of Saturn, but they still contain

Rendezvous with Neptune

Voyager 2's course took it past Neptune in 1989. The probe showed that Neptune's bright blue atmosphere features clouds and storms whose patterns change continuously. Since little heat from the sun reaches Neptune, its active atmosphere must be powered by a much stronger source of internal heat.

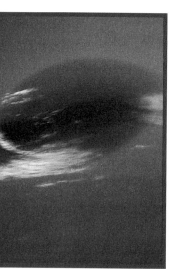

The planet Neptune's Great Dark Spot is featured in this Voyager image from 1989. About the size of the Earth, the Great Dark Spot resembles a giant hurricane. The spiral structure of the spot and the white clouds surrounding it indicate that the storm is rotating counter-clockwise.

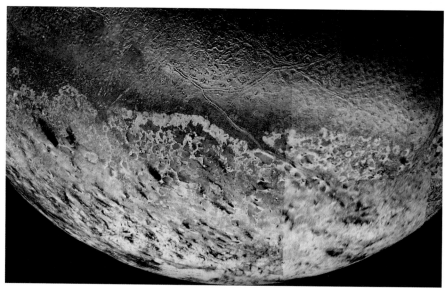

Triton, the largest moon in orbit around Neptune, was visited by Voyager 2 in 1989. This image, a composite of several shots, shows the cap of nitrogen and methane ice at Triton's south pole. The ice reflects so much sunlight that it helps keep the surface temperature of Triton at –233 °C (–388 °F), the coldest surface yet measured by a probe.

thick atmospheres of hydrogen and helium. They are so far from the sun—19 and 30 times the Earth's distance, respectively—that they receive little heat from solar radiation. At Uranus, Voyager 2 discovered a hazy, sluggish atmosphere. At Neptune, it found an atmosphere containing clouds and storms whose patterns change continuously. They concluded that Neptune's atmosphere must be powered by a much stronger source of internal heat, a result confirmed by Voyager 2 measurements.

Voyager 2 also found the magnetic fields of both Uranus and Neptune to be unusual. Unlike the magnetic fields of Earth, Saturn, and Jupiter, which are roughly aligned with the planets' axis of rotation, the fields of Uranus and Neptune are tilted. In Neptune's case, the field is shifted well away from the axis of the planet. The origin of these odd shifts remains poorly understood.

Voyager 2 discovered that Neptune has at least eight moons; only two had been known of previously. Neptune's largest moon, Triton, contained its own surprises. Voyager found that a bright cap of nitrogen and methane ice at the moon's south pole prevents sunlight from heating the surface, keeping temperatures below −233 °C (−388 °F), the coldest surface yet measured by a probe. But despite such low temperatures, there is activity on Triton. Voyager spotted two geysers that were shooting plumes of dark dust to an altitude of 8 kilometers (5 miles). Scientists speculate that the eruptions are powered by underground pockets of nitrogen that are warmed just enough by sunlight to expand and burst through the surface. The plumes were an unexpected final discovery before Voyager 2 followed its sister ship on a perpetual journey beyond the solar system.

Plans for the future

In 1997, with the Mars probes already underway, preparations were being made in the United States, Europe, and elsewhere to launch probe missions to revisit Saturn and to rendezvous with a comet. Several more Mars missions were also on the drawing boards at NASA, as well as in Russia and Japan, for the coming decade. One of their major tasks will be to look for evidence of life on Mars—either presently living microorganisms or remnants of ones from the distant past. Among the spacecraft being planned by NASA was a lander that would bring a sample of Martian soil back to Earth sometime around 2010.

Saturn's moon Titan was also due for a return visit. The possibility that organic molecules exist on the surface of Titan led to speculation that this intriguing moon could serve as a laboratory for examining how life begins. A joint U.S.-European mission named Cassini/Huygens, scheduled for an October 1997 launch, was to explore this possibility further. Plans called for the American-built Cassini orbiter to reach Saturn in 2004. There, if all goes according to plan, it will release a European-built atmospheric probe, Huygens, that will plunge through Titan's atmosphere making chemical measurements all the way down to the moon's mysterious surface. Cassini will then begin a four-year orbital tour of Saturn, making repeated passes by Titan to map its surface with advanced radar. If the mission is successful, Cassini and Huygens could greatly con-

Plans for the future

Plans in the late 1990's called for the launching of a number of new space probes to continue the exploration of the solar system. An emphasis on efficiency and low cost will most likely characterize space exploration well beyond the year 2000.

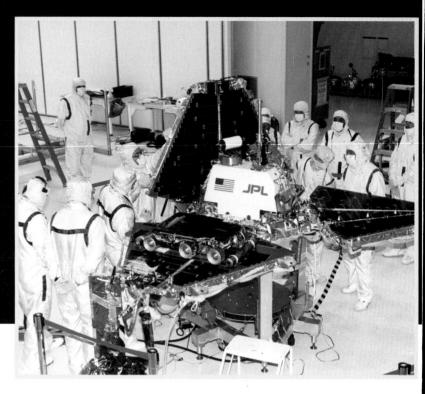

NASA technicians prepare to close up the "petals" of the Mars Pathfinder lander before its December 1996 launch. A wheeled robot, Mars Sojournor Rover, was to be carried to the Martian surface by the Pathfinder. After touchdown, the petals of the lander were to open, enabling the Rover to roll out and begin exploring the surface.

tribute to scientists' understanding of how life emerged on Earth and how it may do so elsewhere.

Future probe missions will also continue to target extraterrestrial objects besides planets and moons. The last major encounter with a comet in deep space took place in 1986, when Halley's Comet was visited by the Giotto probe, sent by the European Space Agency, and two Soviet Vega spacecraft. But far more exploration is needed to tell scientists what comets are made of and whether, as some suspect, the ice they contain has remained largely unaltered since the formation of our solar system. To help answer these questions, the Stardust mission, scheduled by NASA for launch in 1999, is intended to intercept a comet named Wild-2 at a point inside the orbit of Mars in early 2004. Scientists especially want to know whether comets contain organic molecules. Some researchers theorize that Earth and other planets and moons where organic compounds abound obtained those compounds from collisions with comets. The Stardust probe is designed to collect cometary dust and return it to Earth in 2006. More ambitious comet missions were to follow.

There is also interest in sending a mission to Pluto, the last planet in the solar system that remains unexplored by a probe from Earth, and to the Kuiper Belt. The latter is a collection of icy debris, just beyond the orbit of Pluto, that is left over from the formation of the outer planets. A NASA project named Pluto Express was being developed in 1997 to achieve both these goals. Pluto Express would fly past Pluto and then enter the Kuiper Belt to explore what lies at the very edge of the solar system. Scientists now know that at least some of the comets that make their way into the inner solar system originate in the Kuiper Belt. They are

To Pluto and beyond

A proposed mission to Pluto and its moon, Charon, sometime after the year 2000 may also include a trip to the Kuiper Belt, a band of icy debris at the edge of the solar system. Pluto Fast Flyby, shown in an artist's conception, right, was one spacecraft being considered in 1997 for such a mission.

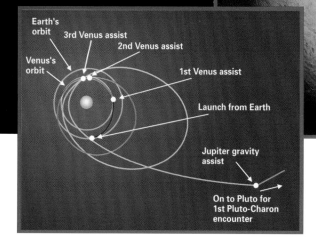

Earth's orbit
3rd Venus assist
2nd Venus assist
Venus's orbit
1st Venus assist
Launch from Earth
Jupiter gravity assist
On to Pluto for 1st Pluto-Charon encounter

A possible trajectory for a probe to Pluto calls for three passes by Venus and one by Jupiter, using the gravitational pull of these planets to gain speed. Such a trajectory would enable the probe to build enough velocity to reach Pluto—4.2 billion kilometers (2.6 billion miles) from Earth at its closest—in only eight years.

pulled from their distant orbits beyond Pluto by the gravity of the giant planets. Pluto Express could be launched sometime in the early 2000's, reaching Pluto around 2010.

The relatively low cost and increasing sophistication of unmanned space probes ensure that they will serve as our eyes and ears in the solar system for some time to come. The next generation of probes will add to the already enormous body of knowledge about the solar system amassed by their predecessors. When human beings finally set foot on other planets and their moons, the terrain, geology, and atmospheric conditions of those worlds will already be known to them. Unmanned probes will have blazed the trail.

For further reading:
Beatty, J. K. and Chaikin, A., eds. *The New Solar System*. Sky Publishing Corp., 1990.

Additional resources:
Jet Propulsion Laboratory Home Page *(http://www.jpl.nasa.gov)*
  The home page for NASA's Jet Propulsion Laboratory, perhaps the world's leading center of solar system exploration, with many links to other web sites featuring the solar system.
The Nine Planets *(http://www.seds.org/nineplanets/nineplanets/nineplanets.html)*
  A Web tour of the solar system prepared by the University of Arizona Chapter of Students for the Exploration and Development of space (SEDS).

DOGS AT WORK

Dogs have helped people for thousands of years, and they continue to play an important role in the high-tech world of the 1990's.

By Benjamin L. Hart and
    Lynette A. Hart

Throughout a chilly night in April 1996, more than 50 search-and-rescue team members and 6 specially trained dogs combed the New Mexico foothills of the Sangre de Cristo Mountains and the banks of the Rio Grande searching for a missing 3-year-old girl. The child, accompanied by three neighborhood dogs, had wandered away that evening from her home in Pilar, a community 17 miles south of Taos. The next morning, a search-and-rescue dog named Samson spotted the child under a tree surrounded by the three dogs, who had kept her warm all night. Samson raced back to his handler, alerted him to the find, and led him to the child.

Dogs have been helping people for thousands of years. They were first used to guard property, help people hunt, and pull sleds or carts. In more recent times, dogs have been trained to sniff out drugs, explosives, illegal food substances, and even termites; to help people who are blind, deaf, or disabled, or who have epileptic seizures; and to enrich the lives of people living in institutions or troubled by emotional or psychological problems.

What qualities make dogs work so well, and so willingly, with people at such a wide variety of tasks? And how do certain kinds of dogs pass on to their offspring specific traits—such as Newfoundlands with their love of water or border collies with their instinct to herd anything in sight? Scientists have been working to find the answers to these questions for many years. They have learned much about the ancestors of dogs and how to choose and train the best dogs for specific tasks. Then, in the 1990's, researchers began trying to determine how dogs' behavior may be coded in their genes.

How dogs joined human society

Dogs belong to the *family* (group of related animals) called the Canidae. The domestic dog, *Canis familiaris,* was the first member of the Canidae to become fully tamed from its wild state. This family also includes foxes, wolves, jackals, and coyotes. Researchers believe that dogs descended from wolves, *Canis lupus,* because the two species are similar in many ways. Some dogs, such as huskies and German shepherds, resemble wolves in appearance. But regardless of physical appearance, these two species have many genes in common. Moreover, dogs and wolves show similar behaviors, and both species are more social animals than the other members of the Canidae.

The authors:
Benjamin L. Hart is a professor of physiology and behavior and Lynette A. Hart is an associate professor at the Center for Animals in Society, both at the School of Veterinary Medicine at the University of California at Davis.

Paleontologists have traced the relationship between canines and people back at least 400,000 years, when the bones of wolves first began to be mingled with human bones at habitation sites. Scientists theorize that individual wolves who were the least afraid of people had begun to scavenge for food at the sites and were gradually accepted into human communities. By 11,000 to 14,000 years ago, the descendants of those wolves had begun to evolve into domestic dogs. By 3,000 to 4,000 years ago, distinct breeds began to appear. But scientists are not sure how this process occurred. They do know that a modern wolf cannot simply be taken from the wild and tamed to become as docile as a dog.

The traits that help dogs help people

For thousands of years, people have chosen dogs as helpers more than any other domestic animal. Dogs' senses, body size, and social behavior make them uniquely suited to help people with a wide variety of tasks.

Hearing

Experiments show that dogs can hear certain sounds four times farther away than people. A dog's very mobile ears can work independently of each other to locate the source of a sound in as little as six-hundredths of a second. Their excellent hearing makes dogs useful in guarding people and property, alerting deaf human companions to sounds, and helping with police and search-and-rescue work.

Smell

Smell is a dog's strongest sense and the one it relies on most. While people have about 5 million scent receptors in their noses, dogs have an estimated 200 million. Dogs may be as much as 1 million times more sensitive to some smells than people, allowing them to sniff out drugs and bombs, locate people who are lost or injured, and track down fugitives.

Body size

Dogs' many different shapes and body sizes enable people to choose a breed best suited for a particular task. Large or medium-sized dogs are useful for tasks that require strength, stamina, or physical force, such as police work or search-and-rescue work. Smaller dogs are often used for such roles as providing hearing for people who are deaf and love and companionship for people with emotional or psychological problems.

Social behavior

Dogs' behavior is human oriented, making dogs especially willing to accept people as leaders, to take commands from people, and to respond to praise or play sessions as rewards. This behavior is one reason that dogs are easier to train than other animals and why they seem to derive pleasure from working with people.

Vision

In some ways, dogs can see better than people. For example, dogs with eyes that are widely spaced have better *peripheral* (side) vision than humans. Dogs also have better night vision than people, because their eyes are more sensitive to light. These traits make dogs useful in police and search-and-rescue work, as guard dogs, and as seeing-eye dogs for blind people.

Particular breeds for particular tasks

Dog trainers and behaviorists agree that an individual dog's temperament is usually more important than its breed in predicting how well it will perform a given task. Some mixed-breed dogs have outperformed pure-breds in various kinds of work. However, professional dog trainers have also found that certain breeds have characteristics that make them ideally suited for particular jobs.

Commonly used breeds and their work

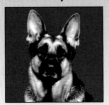

German shepherd
• Assistance
• Sniffing
• Search and rescue

Labrador retriever
• Asssistance
• Sniffing
• Search and rescue

Golden retriever
• Assistance
• Sniffing
• Search and rescue

■ German shepherds and Labrador and golden retrievers are the most popular dogs for assistance, sniffing, and search-and-rescue work. Dogs from these three breeds are strong, agile, persistent, and happy to work for such rewards as praise and play sessions.

Pembroke welsh corgi
• Assistance

Beagle
• Sniffing

German shorthaired pointer
• Sniffing

■ Pembroke welsh corgis are popular "hearing-ear" dogs. They are ever-alert and persistent in attracting their deaf human companion's attention to the source of a sound. Beagles, which have a good scenting ability and a nonthreatening appearance, are favored for sniffing out illegal agricultural items in air travelers' luggage. German shorthaired pointers make excellent drug sniffers.

English springer spaniel
• Sniffing

Bloodhound
• Sniffing
• Search and rescue

Newfoundland
• Search and rescue

■ English springer spaniels are often used for bomb and drug sniffing. Because of their small size, they are easily transportable and able to negotiate small or tight spaces. The bloodhound's particularly acute sense of smell makes it an excellent tracker. Newfoundlands, with their large, strong bodies and love of water, are excellent water-rescue dogs.

The friendliness of dogs toward human beings has always made them natural companions for people. But dogs also have other qualities that people have found extremely useful. One of those traits is an exceptional sense of smell. Lawrence J. Myers, founder of the Institute for Biological Detection Systems at Auburn University's School of Veterinary Medicine in Auburn, Alabama, investigated why dogs have a sense of smell that is so superior to that of humans. Based on research estimates that the average dog has 200 million scent receptors in its nose and the average person has 5 million, it would be logical to expect that dogs could detect smells about 40 times better than people. However, experiments Myers conducted with odors from various substances revealed that dogs can detect a scent at only one one-hundred-thousandth of the concentration required for human detection. Myers speculated that dogs may be up to 1 million times more sensitive to some odors than humans.

Besides having more scent receptors than people, dogs may also have a better sense of smell because their air-sampling processes—the mechanisms by which chemicals are moved from the air into a dog's nasal cavity and then to the scent receptors—are more efficient than people's. Furthermore, researchers speculate, the way that scent receptors relay nerve impulses to the brain may be superior in dogs.

Dogs have a sense of hearing that is also much more acute than that of humans. Scientists estimate that dogs can hear certain sounds four times farther away than a person. Moreover, a dog can turn its ears to locate the source of a sound in about six hundredths of a second.

In some ways, dogs see better than people do, too. Dogs with widely spaced eyes have more acute *peripheral* (side) vision than people. Dogs also have better night vision, in part because their eyes have more *rods* (cells that are sensitive to dim light) in their retina than people do.

Traits that set dogs apart

But superior senses of smell, sight, and hearing are not exclusive to dogs. Pigs and other mammals are just as sensitive as dogs to scents, for example. In Europe, pigs have long been used to sniff out *truffles*—an edible fungus favored by gourmets—under several inches of soil. Yet, people do not use pigs to sniff out drugs, explosives, or forbidden foodstuffs in airports. What makes dogs more valuable in such tasks than other animals? One factor is their convenient body size. Most working dogs are medium sized, weighing about 30 to 35 kilograms (70 to 80 pounds). In comparison, the average weight of a full-grown pig is between 135 and 230 kilograms (300 and 500 pounds).

Another reason that dogs are preferred in working with people is their human-oriented behavior. Unlike most other domestic animals, dogs are very cooperative, and they allow people to take the authoritative role. Behaviorists believe dogs inherited these traits from wolves. Wolves acknowledge one pack member as dominant, and they share food, hunt together, and guard the pack's terrritory. Dogs acknowledge people as dominant, guard people's "territory"—home and property—and work willingly with them. Even in our highly industrialized society, people have found that dogs, because of their physical characteristics and eagerness to please, are valuable helpers in many tasks.

The use of dogs is growing in a number of areas. One in particular is in fields that require "sniffers." A leading center for the training of sniffing dogs to be used by the armed forces, the Bureau of Alcohol, Tobacco and Firearms, and the Federal Aviation Administration is at Lackland Air Force Base in San Antonio. Trainers at Lackland conduct 12-week programs for bomb-sniffing and drug-sniffing dogs and their handlers. According to Walt Burghardt, a veterinary behaviorist who serves as a consultant to the program, a dog can learn to pick out a particular scent from a multitude of odors. Certified bomb-detecting dogs, for instance, can distinguish the scent of nine basic explosives even when the explosives are mixed with any of tens of thousands of other compounds.

During the training course the dogs are exposed to various substances such as cocaine (for dogs who will be used in drug-detecting) or nitroglycerine (for explosive-detecting dogs). The dogs are taught to detect the odor of the substance from up to 2 meters (6 feet) away and are rewarded with praise and a food treat for finding it. Many of the dogs chosen for the program are Labrador or Chesapeake Bay retrievers, German shepherds, and Belgian Malinois. These breeds tend to be quick learners, persistent searchers, and hardy enough to work in rugged terrain. Trainers note, however, that the qualities of an individual dog, such as its drive and eagerness to work, are usually more important than its breed. A mixed-breed dog can perform as well as—and sometimes better than—a purebred dog.

Putting those sensitive noses to good use

One of the places where sniffer dogs were being increasingly used in the 1990's was at airports, to screen luggage for smuggled drugs and terrorist bombs. Dogs can sniff an entire baggage area or waiting room, making them much more flexible in their ability to uncover drugs or explosives than a stationary scanning machine. The importance of dogs to national security has not gone unnoticed by the federal government. In October 1996, President Bill Clinton signed the Federal Aviation Reauthorization Act, which requires the operators of the 50 largest airports in the United States to supplement existing bomb and weapons-detection facilities with dogs. Congress set aside $8.9 million for the training of more than 100 explosive-detection dog teams.

Dogs are also used at airports to find agricultural products that some travelers might bring into a country illegally. In the United States, for example, a number of such items, including many fruits, vegetables, plants, and seeds, have been banned because they often harbor diseases or insects that can infect plants and animals on American farms. Beagles are the dogs most often used for this task, carried out by the U.S. Animal and Plant Inspection Service, because of their excellent sniffing ability. And most passengers view beagles as less threatening than some other breeds of dogs.

The low-tech, but highly effective, canine nose was also being used more frequently in the 1990's by termite inspectors. Dogs, especially beagles, can be trained to detect the odor of termites and carpenter ants, among other insects. The dogs can alert human inspectors to the presence of termites and other damaging insects living in the soil around building foundations and other hard-to-inspect places.

Their keen sense of smell has long made dogs valuable for search-and-rescue work. Federal agencies and city police departments, as well as private organizations, train dogs to do such work. When the federal building in Oklahoma City was bombed in 1995, German shepherds from the Rocky Mountain Rescue Dogs helped search for victims in

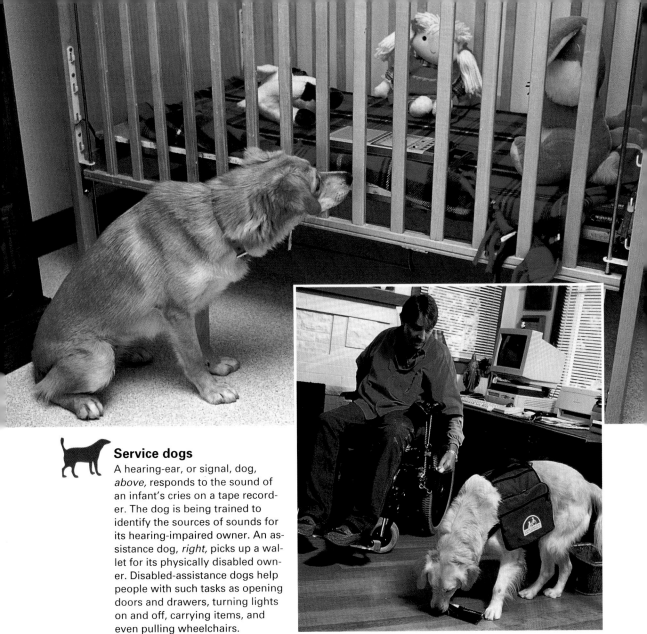

Service dogs

A hearing-ear, or signal, dog, *above*, responds to the sound of an infant's cries on a tape recorder. The dog is being trained to identify the sources of sounds for its hearing-impaired owner. An assistance dog, *right,* picks up a wallet for its physically disabled owner. Disabled-assistance dogs help people with such tasks as opening doors and drawers, turning lights on and off, carrying items, and even pulling wheelchairs.

the rubble. Iin the search for the Pilar, New Mexico, child, it was a dog from the Los Alamos Mountain Canine Corps that found her.

Just as with sniffing dogs, a dog's breed is not considered as important for search-and-rescue work as its individual temperament. Nevertheless, German shepherds, Labrador and golden retrievers—and Newfoundlands for water search-and-rescue—are among the most popular breeds. In addition to being intelligent and having a good nose, a search-and-rescue dog must be willing to master many training exercises; it must be agile and hardy, because it may need to search in wilderness areas or through rubble or snow; and it must be able to stay calm and focused in frightening or distracting situations. Perhaps most important, the dog should be eager to please its handler, so that it will

Sniffing dogs

A beagle, *right,* sniffs a piece of one of the illegal fruits and vegetables it is being trained to find in air travelers' luggage. A fully trained dog, *below,* sniffs a traveler's bag under the direction of its handler. The United States Department of Agriculture uses beagles for such tasks, in part because most passengers view beagles as less threatening than some other breeds of dogs.

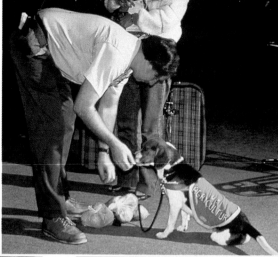

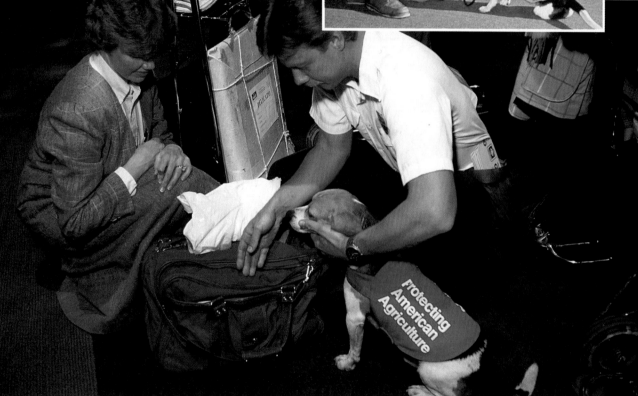

persevere in searches that yield no rewards for hours or days at a time.

Some search-and-rescue dogs begin training as puppies; others are older when they enter a training program. All dogs must first pass a basic obedience course. Then they learn to find people and objects and develop agility. They climb ladders, jump hurdles, crawl through pipes, and perform other maneuvers that may be needed in an actual search.

One of the most important skills of search-and-rescue dogs is tracking or scenting. Dogs *track* (follow a scent on the ground) when the trail of a fugitive or lost person is visible or when clothing worn by the person being sought can be used. Many times, however, a person's tracks have already been obscured by the tracks of others, or the starting point and path the person took are unknown. Then, dogs must *scent* (follow a smell through the air) in order to find the individual.

Search-and-rescue dog trainers have learned that people shed about 40,000 dead skin cells, called *rafts*, per minute. The rafts contain bacteria and vapors unique to each individual. Wind currents carry the rafts away from people and spread them in a roughly cone-shaped volume of air. Dogs learn to detect this cone of scent and follow it. That is why dogs on a scent typically move back and forth across an area—they are staying within the boundaries of the cone as they follow it to its source.

Some police dogs are trained in search-and-rescue work, but they must master many other tasks as well. In addition to following the scent of fugitives, police dogs must protect officers from hidden threats—a task for which dogs' excellent peripheral and night vision are of great help. Often dogs can see the slight movement of a suspect in dark shadows and alert the officer in time to prevent an ambush. Police dogs can also be trained to find hidden caches of drugs.

German shepherds are one of the most popular breeds for police work because of their intelligence, strength, persistence, and eagerness to work. A police dog stays with the officer it has been paired with almost around the clock and lives with the officer's family. German shepherds, like wolves, seem to need the close social contact that living with their "pack" provides. This social bonding also benefits the officers, according to a 1997 study of California police officers conducted by one of the authors, animal behaviorist Lynette Hart of the University of California's School of Veterinary Medicine at Davis, and police officer and dog trainer Sandy Bryson of the Alpine and El Dorado County, California, Sheriff's Department. They found that officers who let their dogs sleep indoors liked their jobs and trusted their dogs more than officers who kept their dogs outside. A close relationship at home with a dog seemed to improve the working partnership.

Helping disabled people

Very different skills are needed by dogs who work with people with disabilities. These dogs help people who are blind, deaf, or physically disabled to lead more independent lives.

The first dogs to guide blind people were trained in Germany in 1916 to help soldiers injured in World War I (1914-1918). The first guide-dog school in the United States, The Seeing Eye in Morristown, New Jersey, began training dogs in 1929. At first, German shepherds were the only dogs used for such work, but trainers later found that such dogs as golden and Labrador retrievers, and sometimes mixed breeds, make excellent guide dogs as well. It is not any particular sensory skill that makes a good guide dog, but rather the guarding behavior acquired through training and the bond the dog forms with its caretaker. The training includes teaching the dog to ignore an owner's command when it sees a danger that the blind person is unaware of.

The use of dogs to help physically disabled people dates to 1975, when Canine Companions for Independence (CCI), the first center for training these dogs, was founded in Santa Rosa, California. Service dogs for the disabled are taught to perform practical tasks, helping people with serious medical conditions such as muscular dystrophy, cerebral palsy, and spinal cord or head injuries to lead more independent lives. For this kind of work, German shepherds and Labrador and golden retrievers once again became the dog of choice.

The first dogs for people with hearing disabilities, called hearing-ear or signal dogs, were trained in 1976 by the American Humane Association in Denver, Colorado. Hearing-ear dogs learn to respond to such sounds as doorbells, telephones, or a baby's cries, and then to alert their owner. Hearing-dog programs often train adult dogs that are already in homes or dogs found in animal shelters. Dogs of many breeds, and often mixed breeds as well, make effective hearing dogs, though CCI, which began training hearing dogs in 1986, favors Welsh corgis and border collies. Signal dogs need not be large or strong, but they must be alert and quick to respond when they hear certain sounds.

Training dogs to help people with disabilities

By the late 1990's, dozens of organizations had been formed to train seeing-eye dogs, signal dogs, and dogs to assist people with physical disabilities. Each group differed somewhat in its methods and standards. However, the programs generally followed the same basic sequence.

Most of the dogs in these programs begin their training as puppies, living with a volunteer "foster family." The puppies learn basic commands, such as "sit," "lie down," and "stay." And they go everywhere the family members go, to become accustomed to a variety of places and activities. When they are about 13 or 14 months old, the puppies are moved to a training school, where they learn their service skills.

Guide dogs learn to wear a harness and practice such skills as stopping at curbs and leading a blind person around obstacles. Hearing-ear dogs learn such tasks as waking their owner when the alarm clock goes off and running to the door when the doorbell rings. A signal dog must not only master tasks, as seeing-eye dogs do, but must also learn to perform the tasks without a command from its human partner. Dogs that assist the physically disabled learn about 60 to 80 specific commands, including picking things up carefully, opening and shutting doors and drawers, turning lights on and off, and pulling wheelchairs. Training programs for guide and hearing dogs take about five or six months. The training of disabled-assistance dogs takes about eight months, because these dogs need to master a greater number of tasks.

Once the guide, hearing, or disabled-assistance dog has been trained, the dog is placed with an owner based on the person's needs and on the compatability of the temperament of the dog and the new owner. Owners review and reinforce commands with their dogs regularly, so that the dogs will continue to perform specific tasks.

One intriguing trait of some dogs that help people is the dogs' ability to detect and warn their owners of an epileptic seizure before it occurs. Usually, the dog uses some uncharacteristic behavior—such as whining for a dog that never whines—to alert the person of an im-

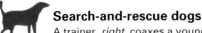

Search-and-rescue dogs

A trainer, *right*, coaxes a young search-and-rescue dog toward a pipe—a common refuge for lost children. Search-and-rescue dogs must be familiar with a wide variety of obstacles and be agile enough to overcome them on a real search mission. A handler at the site of the bombed-out federal building in Oklahoma City in 1995, *below*, pauses to allow her search-and-rescue dog to check the rubble for survivors.

pending seizure. The warning gives the person with epilepsy time to sit or lie down in a safe place. No one is sure how the dogs sense that a seizure is about to occur. However, studies published by British veterinarian Andrew Edney in 1993 suggest that a dog may detect an odor that a person produces at the time that a seizure is beginning. Or, the dog may note some slight changes in the owner's behavior that neither the person nor other people present are aware of. Collies, retrievers, terriers, and mixed-breed dogs are among those that have this ability.

Researchers have found that guide, hearing, and disabled-assistance dogs benefit their owners in ways that go far beyond helping with everyday tasks. In a 1996 study by Lynette Hart and her colleagues, deaf individuals with assistance dogs reported feeling less stress and loneli-

Research on dogs

A scientist at Auburn University's Institute for Biological Detection Systems in Alabama, *right,* holds a dog as it sniffs a flask of diluted clove scent. Researchers at the Institute have learned much from such experiments about why a dog's sense of smell is so superior to that of humans. At the Fred Hutchinson Cancer Research Center in Seattle, a researcher, *below,* works on isolating and sequencing canine genes as part of the Canine Genome Initiative. The project seeks to decipher the dog genome (the sum of canine genetic material) and to correlate the information with dog behavior.

ness than they did before they had dogs. The owners of hearing dogs said the animals made it easier for them to meet new people. They explained that because a hearing dog makes the disability of the owner more evident to other people, social situations became less stressful for them. In other studies, psychiatrists James Lynch and Aaron Katcher at the University of Pennsylvania in Philadelphia and psychologist Erika Friedmann at the City University of New York's Brooklyn College found that interacting with a dog can actually slow people's heart rate, lessen their muscle tension, and make their breathing more regular.

Dogs themselves have been the subject of much research. In the 1980's, for example, Lynette Hart and her husband, Benjamin Hart, also an animal behaviorist at the University of California at Davis, conducted a study of canine behavior. They sought to learn how specific traits, such as aggressiveness, excitability, and sociability, may have changed in various breeds when dogs were bred for certain physical attributes or specific tasks. The Harts interviewed nearly 100 authorities —mainly dog show judges and veterinarians—and documented what dog fanciers had always claimed: dogs display an incredibly varied range of behavior.

Studying canine genes

Scientists now want to learn whether dogs' behavior is transmitted in their genes, and if so, how. To find out, geneticist Jasper Rine at the University of California at Berkeley and biologist Elaine Ostrander at the Fred Hutchinson Cancer Research Center in Seattle, Washington, launched the Canine Genome Initiative in 1992. The project seeks to decipher the dog genome—the sum of canine genetic material—and to relate that information to the behavior of various breeds.

Rine began by breeding dogs from two species known for several very obvious traits. He and his colleagues then began to explore which gene or genes might be responsible for the traits. Rine chose his own male border collie, Gregor, and his wife's female Newfoundland, Pepper, for the experiment. Border collies weigh about 18 kilograms (40 pounds), are work-oriented, and are passionate about herding sheep. Their behavior includes crouching, staring, and driving the sheep—or any other creatures that they may encounter. "Newfies," on the other hand, can reach 65 to 70 kilograms (140 to 150 pounds), love water, are people-oriented, and are known for their water-rescue abilities.

Rine and his collaborators mated Gregor and Pepper, and then the seven dogs that were born to them. By early 1997, the matings had produced 23 grandpuppies of the original dogs. Each of the young dogs exhibited a different combination of identifiable traits. One dog, for example, had the intent stare of the border collie but, like a Newfoundland, also loved people. Two grandpuppies that differed in almost all behavioral and physical traits shared Pepper's love of water. Rine and his colleagues then began correlating these various characteristics with the dogs' genetic makeup to identify the gene that determines each trait. But the process is complex and time consuming, and it was expected to occupy the scientists for many years to come.

Someday, people may know enough about dogs and their genes to breed animals with the exact physical and behavioral traits they desire. However, regardless of how future dogs may look or act, it is virtually certain that they will continue to be the helpers, companions, and "best friends" to people that they have been throughout the ages.

For further reading:

Derr, Mark. *Dog's Best Friend*. Henry Holt, 1997.
Hart, Benjamin L., and Hart, Lynette J. *The Perfect Puppy: How to Choose Your Dog by Its Behavior*. W. H. Freeman, 1988.
McCaig, Donald. "The Dogs That Go to Work, and Play, All Day—for Science." *Smithsonian*, November 1996, pp. 126-137.
Serpell, James, ed. *The Domestic Dog*. Cambridge Univ. Press, 1995.

Digital Flicks

Using computers, moviemakers create spectacular special effects in film and bring new realities to the big screen.

BY HERB BRODY

H erds of jungle animals stampede through a city street. Ferocious dinosaurs terrorize visitors at an advanced-technology zoo. Dragons talk and fly. A group of toys create a community. Intrepid "storm chasers" pursue rampaging tornadoes. Movie characters chat with historical figures, such as President John F. Kennedy.

These are just a few of the amazing special effects that dazzled motion-picture audiences in the 1990's. Moviegoers love dramatic visual effects, but these fantastic creations of the filmmaker's art are certainly far from new—in fact, they are as old as the movies themselves. One of the classics in special-effects cinematography—King Kong clutching the screaming Fay Wray in his hand while scaling the Empire State Building —dates back to 1933. Although this giant gorilla may not have looked and moved like a real creature, it was believable enough to capture the imagination of audiences.

What set the special effects of the 1990's apart from those of the 1930's was that they did look real. Whereas accepting the reality of King Kong required considerable suspension of disbelief, no such mental effort is required for the meat-eating dinosaurs of *Jurassic Park*. The tyrannosaur and velociraptors populating director Steven Spielberg's groundbreaking motion picture look like living, breathing—and thus terrifying—creatures.

Computers in Hollywood

The realism of modern special effects is due largely to computer technology. The computer has become an indispensable tool in the motion-picture industry, creating visual effects that once would have been impossible. And in many recent movies, the special effects are at least as much a draw as the story or the actors. Blockbusters of 1996 and 1997 that relied heavily on computer technology included *Twister,* starring tornadoes that never existed in nature; *Independence Day,* a special-effects extravaganza featuring epic battles with alien spaceships; and the rereleased versions of the *Star Wars* trilogy, in which new creatures were inserted in some scenes and other special effects were fine-tuned.

Small wonder that a mini-industry is booming in Hollywood, with companies full of computer experts competing with one another to see who can produce the most dramatic images for the big screen. Some people have dubbed this new industry sector Siliwood, a name derived from silicon—the material of which computer chips are made—and Hollywood. At companies such as Industrial Light and Magic, Digital Domain, Boss Film Studios, Kleiser-Walczak Construction Company, Mass Illusions, Pacific Data Images, and VIFX, teams of computer programmers work closely with artists and film directors to craft ever more dazzling visual effects. As these electronic wizards continue honing their skills, and as computers continue to gain in power, motion-picture special effects are certain to become more astonishing still. Eventually, even many "human" actors in movies are likely to be computer creations.

Computer technology plays two basic roles in special-effects production. Special-effects artists can manipulate, combine, or add details to

Preceding pages:
The 1996 film *Dragonheart* featured Draco, a creature designed entirely on a computer and integrated into live-action footage.

The old-fashioned way

Special-effects artist Ray Harryhausen, *right,* positions a monster for the 1958 film *The Seventh Voyage of Sinbad.* Harryhausen used a technique called stop-motion animation, in which one or more models of creatures are photographed one frame at a time and moved slightly for each frame. For the 1933 film *King Kong, below right,* actors are filmed in front of a screen onto which a river scene is projected. This technique, called rear-screen projection, created the illusion of the actors rowing down the river.

filmed images that were shot with a traditional camera; or they can create entirely new images that have no physical reality. The latter technique has resulted in some truly spectacular effects, including the dinosaurs of *Jurassic Park* and the tornadoes in *Twister.* These computer-generated images were then inserted in scenes that had been photographed conventionally. But the animated feature *Toy Story* (1995) consisted entirely of computer-generated images, with no live-action film.

The illusion of motion

Creating images of things that don't really exist is a form of visual trickery—but, then, so is all of moviemaking. The "motion" in a motion picture is an illusion created by the projection, in rapid succession, of still images. Each still frame in a reel of film differs slightly from the one before it. A movie projector flashes 24 frames on the screen every second, and the eye perceives the separate still images as a continuous flow of motion.

Over the years, moviemakers have come up with many ways to extend this basic trickery. In slow-motion photography, for example, the film runs through the camera quickly, exposing more than 24 frames per second. When the film is projected at normal speed, motion appears slower than it was in reality. Slow-motion filming is sometimes used to add some drama to a scene, but filmmakers more often employ the technique to

The author:
Herb Brody is a senior editor at *Technology Review* magazine.

make viewers think they are seeing a special effect in normal time. To simulate the explosion of a building, for instance, a small model of the building is blown up with tiny explosive charges. The model, however, flies apart much faster than the real building would, so the explosion must be filmed at a higher camera speed. On the movie screen, the slow-motion explosion of the model looks like the real-time explosion of a large building.

Some classic special-effects techniques

Another technique, called compositing, which involves combining scenes that were not filmed at the same time, has been a staple of filmmaking for decades. In one method of compositing, known as rear-screen projection, actors play a scene in a studio in front of a screen on which previously filmed background action is projected from behind.

One of the most sophisticated compositing methods is the blue-screen process. Typically, the actors are filmed playing a scene with a plain blue screen as a backdrop. The background that is to appear in the finished movie is shot separately. The film of the actors is first printed through various filters onto high-contrast black-and-white film to create frames called mattes. For every original frame of film, there are two mattes. One is completely clear except for a black silhouette of the actors; the other is completely black except for a clear silhouette of the actors. The final version of the film is then printed in two stages. To print the scenery, the filmmakers use the matte with the black silhouette of the actors to block exposure of the "acting" area of the film. In the next step, the clear silhouette of the "acting" area allows only the image of the actors to be exposed.

For decades, a special-effects technique called stop-motion animation was indispensable in creating the monsters that rampaged across the big screen. King Kong; Godzilla, the star of several Japanese monster movies; and a fire-breathing dragon in *The Seventh Voyage of Sinbad* (1958) are just a few of the creatures that have been brought to life by stop-motion animation. In this time-consuming process, a sequence is photographed one frame at a time. A model of the monster is photographed in one position, then moved slightly and photographed again for the next frame. The result on the screen, however, generally falls far short of a realistic effect. The motion appears jerky, because in each frame the model is stationary. In comparison, when a real moving object is filmed, the image is blurred slightly in each frame. By eliminating blur, stop-motion photography sacrifices an important tool for fooling the eye.

Some special effects have simply relied on the use of large mechanical objects. For the close-up shots in *King Kong*, several people worked inside full-scale versions of the gorilla's head and hand, where they pulled levers to move Kong's eyes, mouth, and fingers. To create the tornado in *The Wizard of Oz* (1939) that swept Dorothy up from Kansas and deposited her in the land of Oz, the filmmakers built an 11-meter (35-foot)

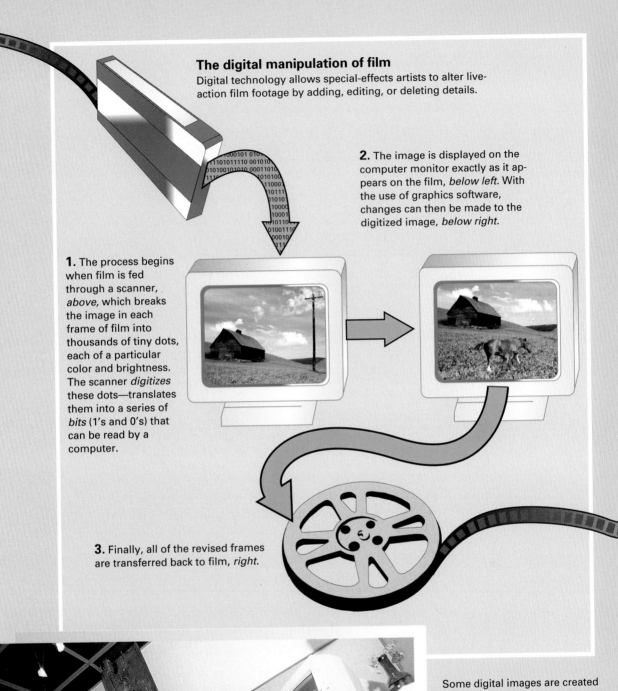

The digital manipulation of film
Digital technology allows special-effects artists to alter live-action film footage by adding, editing, or deleting details.

1. The process begins when film is fed through a scanner, *above,* which breaks the image in each frame of film into thousands of tiny dots, each of a particular color and brightness. The scanner *digitizes* these dots—translates them into a series of *bits* (1's and 0's) that can be read by a computer.

2. The image is displayed on the computer monitor exactly as it appears on the film, *below left.* With the use of graphics software, changes can then be made to the digitized image, *below right.*

3. Finally, all of the revised frames are transferred back to film, *right.*

Some digital images are created directly on the computer. A special-effects artist develops a space alien for the movie *The Arrival* (1996) using a small model of the creature, arrow, as a guide. The first renditions of the creature are simple-looking models with minimal detail. The artist will later add color, texture, and lighting information. The computer then draws the final images that will be inserted into the movie.

muslin funnel that moved back and forth in the studio as dust blew through it.

Comparisons between the tornado in *The Wizard of Oz* and the tornadoes in *Twister* reveal the drastic difference that computer technology has made to special-effects artistry. But the computer's contribution to the motion-picture industry began long before the making of *Twister* and other special-effects spectaculars of the 1990's.

Refining the craft—introducing computers to film

Many experts date the beginning of the computer revolution in movies to the first episode of *Star Wars*. In the original version of this 1977 film, directed by George Lucas, the computer's main contribution was not in altering the details of shots or creating characters but in controlling the motion of the cameras. The stunning battle scenes in *Star Wars* were made possible because computer-controlled cameras could follow exactly the same path repeatedly as they photographed the many spaceship models used in the movie. Some scenes called for the camera to perform multiple movements, including complex tilts, pans, and rolls. With the ability to repeat such motions precisely time after time, Lucas could shoot the same battle scene as often as he wished, each time adding a different element to the scene. When the resulting film images were combined, everything in the scene looked as if it had been shot at once.

Computer-controlled movement also made it possible to improve the effect of stop-motion animation. In the making of the 1981 film *Dragonslayer*, a model of a two-headed dragon was rigged with mechanical rods that were controlled by a computer. The computer directed the model to move slightly while the shutter of the camera was open for each frame. With this technique, dubbed go-motion animation, the blur in each "still" shot resulted in more natural movement.

In 1982, two motion pictures—*TRON* and *Star Trek II: The Wrath of Khan*—introduced computer technology that led to the spectacular effects of later movies. In *TRON*, most of the action takes place inside a computer game. The actors playing electronic beings within the game were photographed separately and combined with digitally created sets. *The Wrath of Khan* features an entire planet created on screen, evolving from a sphere of dust and rock to a lush, green world. Computer graphics gave this so-called "Genesis" sequence a more vivid and realistic look than was possible with conventional hand-drawn animation. Motion-picture historians see the production of these two films as the true beginning of the age of computer-generated special effects.

To create special effects with a computer, the visual information must be in the language that computers understand. That language is a digital one—information is expressed as a series of *binary digits*, or *bits* (0's and 1's). Conventionally filmed images are converted to digital language by scanning each frame of film with a device that breaks the image up into a series of tiny dots, called picture elements or pixels. Each pixel is then translated into a number that corresponds to its exact brightness and

Special-effects breakthroughs

A stained-glass knight, *above,* attacks a startled priest in the 1985 film *Young Sherlock Holmes.* The knight was the first completely computer-generated character to appear in a live-action motion picture. In the 1985 fantasy *Willow, right,* a magic wand transforms a creature into a tiger and finally a woman. This technique, called morphing, enables filmmakers to fluidly change one digitized image into another.

color. Once this has been done, the images become putty in the hands of the movie's creators. Special-effects artists can alter colors, fill in backgrounds with objects that were not there during filming, reposition objects, or combine scenes that were filmed separately.

After everything is where the director wants it, the computerized images are transferred to film. This is done by feeding the digital information to a device that controls variations in the brightness of a beam of light that is scanned across unexposed film three times. Each exposure uses a different color filter—red, green, or blue—to create a full color image. The film is then developed and printed using the conventional techniques of film production.

The manipulation of digitized live-film footage allows moviemakers to achieve more effectively and less expensively some of the tricks that have long been standard movie fare. Rather than constructing a set depicting a city street of the 1800's, for example, moviemakers can shoot scenes on a modern street and use digital techniques to wipe out intrusive objects. Power lines and TV antennas can be electronically snipped out and replaced with gas lamps, for example.

Computers have also made compositing much easier. For example, in the climactic chase in the 1996 film *Mission: Impossible,* the character played by Tom Cruise leaps from a helicopter onto the back of a speeding train. In reality, Cruise was wearing a harness and was supported by cables, and he made the jump in front of a blue screen in the safety of a studio. Before the advent of digital technology, special-effects artists would have created several mattes to remove the cables and harness and combine the image with the background scenery—with only a moderately realistic effect. But by digitizing the footage of Cruise and of the helicopter and train, the special-effects artists could remove the support cables and combine the two scenes with convincingly realistic results.

The 1994 film *Forrest Gump* pushed such compositing techniques to new heights. The title character, played by Tom Hanks, was introduced into real archival footage of news events. In one famous scene, Gump shakes hands and speaks with President John F. Kennedy. To create this shot, Hanks first shook hands with a stand-in against a blue-screen backdrop while reciting his lines. This scene was digitized, as was footage of Kennedy shaking hands and talking with someone else. A computer was then used to erase the individual in the news shot and insert Hanks. Computers were also used to form Kennedy's mouth to match the words that the movie script called for.

Another way that computers can be used to manipulate scenes is for a technique called morphing, first used in a feature film in the 1985 fantasy *Willow.* Morphing achieves the illusion of one object fluidly transforming into another. To achieve this effect, footage of the two objects is digitized. Then the first image is progressively altered in shape and color in successive frames until it matches the final image.

Creating objects that never were

In addition to manipulating images that were filmed conventionally with a camera, computers can also create entirely new objects that exist only in the minds of the artists and the programmers. The first completely computer-generated motion-picture character appeared in the 1985 film *Young Sherlock Holmes.* In one scene, a knight in a stained-glass window comes to life, steps out of the window, and enters the action of the human characters. Although the animated knight still looked like a flat piece of stained glass, this effect marked a significant advance in the use of digital technology.

A 1989 release, *The Abyss,* advanced this technology by creating the first truly lifelike computer-generated creature: the pseudopod, an eerie, snakelike ocean monster that could take on a human face. The pseudopod began as a small sculpture, which was scanned with lasers that translated the creature's shape and proportions into a three-dimensional image on the computer. This digital version of the creature provided the special-effects artists with guidelines to create a so-called wire-frame model, a rough three-dimensional sketch of the pseudopod on the computer screen. The filmmakers made an animated sequence with the wire-frame model and then inserted the sequence into a digitized version of the live-action film. Lastly, the artists used other computer graphics software to add color, lighting, and texture to the creature's surface in the final image.

The techniques used in *The Abyss* became the basic tools for creating other-worldly creatures, but since the pseudopod was a fantasy creature, the special-effects artists did not have to worry about making the creature's movement "natural." That task was faced, however, by the makers of the 1991 film *Terminator 2: Judgment Day*. The Terminator is a formidable villain, a creature who smoothly changes from a human form—actor Robert Patrick—to a liquid-metal robot, which was generated on the computer.

Producing realistic motion in the computer

Although the creation of this effect depended largely on morphing techniques used in *Willow,* the filmmakers took it a step further. To get the metallic robot to move like Patrick, the special-effects artists drew a network of grid lines on the actor's body and filmed him as he performed the same motions that the robot would go through on-screen. When this film was scanned to create a digital file, the grid provided reference data that enabled the computer to analyze the motion of every part of Patrick's body. In other words, the grid served as a sort of moving wire-frame model for creation of the liquid-metal Terminator.

This technique, known as motion-capture, was soon refined by other filmmakers. Instead of marking actors with grid lines, they dressed them in clothing studded with sensors that could be tracked by optical detectors or magnetic recording devices. An actor outfitted in this way generates a stream of data with each motion. The data is stored in a computer and later plugged into the computer-generated character, which obediently follows every move the actor made.

Motion-capture has also been used for orchestrating the movements of nonhuman characters. The 1995 motion picture *Species* was filmed with the aid of a mechanical model of the creature named Sil—a hideous reptilian monster. The model was wired with a number of sensors, each one corresponding to a point on a computer version of the creature. When the model was moved in any way, the computer translated the electronic data from the sensors into identical movements of the digital creature on the screen. In addition to saving time in making the digital creature move realistically, the immediate translation of movement from the model to the screen allowed the director to work with the creature as though it were a regular actor.

Creating computer-generated effects

Special-effects artists use a variety of software programs and tools to create effects completely in the computer.

The kitchen scene from *Jurassic Park* (1993) began with a digitized version of the film, *upper left.* Next, artists drew "wire-frame" models of the velociraptors and plotted out their basic movements for the scene, *upper right.* The models were then added to the kitchen scene, *lower left.* In the final stages of production, *lower right,* artists completed the coloring of the dinosaurs, matched the lighting on the creatures to the lighting on the real set, and added details to their movement.

One of the tornadoes in *Twister* (1996) began as a wire-frame model, *top right,* to plot out the path of destruction and the flying debris. Special-effects artists used software that could animate millions of particles to create the whirling dust and clouds in the final image, *bottom right.*

Capturing motion for the computer

Motion-capture devices help special-effects artists give computer-generated creatures realistic movement. An actor, *right,* is a stand-in for a computer-generated creature. The actor's blue suit is studded with reflective material that can be tracked with an optical recorder.

The reflectors provide information about the position and movement of the actor during a fight scene, *left.* The optical recorder feeds this information into a computer that translates the actor's movements into the exact same movements of a computer-generated creature.

Special-effects artists then digitally remove the stand-in actor from the live-action film and insert the computer-generated creature into the scene.

The digital marvels of *Jurassic Park*

By the time *Species* was made, digital motion-picture technology had already entered a new era. In 1993, the motion picture *Jurassic Park* set a new standard for the creation of computer-generated creatures. With its stunningly believable dinosaurs, *Jurassic Park* was the first movie to bring realistic digital creatures to the screen and blend them seamlessly with live action.

Jurassic Park's computer-generated dinosaurs began as wire-frame models on the computer screen. The special-effects artists at Industrial Light and Magic (ILM) then experimented with ways of making the digital models move in a believable fashion. To model the motion of the huge, lumbering brachiosaurs, the effects makers studied the way elephants walk and then applied the same general patterns of movement to the plant-eating dinosaurs.

But the most memorable dinosaurs in *Jurassic Park* are the fleet-footed velociraptors and the tyrannosaur. Spielberg and his fellow filmmakers took into account the latest scientific thinking that dinosaurs were warm-blooded and that some of them, including the tyrannosaur and velociraptors, could run and jump. Because these motions were incorporated into the computer-generated dinosaurs, the public may never again think of all dinosaurs as slow, dull-witted beasts.

One problem confronting the makers of *Jurassic Park* was how to program the motion of a herd of fast-running, ostrichlike dinosaurs. The special-effects producers at ILM came up with an ingenious solution. They videotaped a large group of their fellow employees running back and forth across the company parking lot and then analyzed patterns of motion on the tape. Those patterns were applied to the digital creations to produce the scene in which the stampeding herd almost tramples the movie's main human characters. The special-effects artists needed to construct just one animal. They then duplicated it dozens of times with slight variations to create the entire herd.

In some scenes, the special-effects artists added small but lifelike movements—the blinking of an eye, the tapping of a claw on a hard floor, or the twitching of a tail—to enhance the dinosaurs' realism. In addition, in a technique similar to go-motion animation, the artists added a slight amount of blur to the outline of the dinosaurs to give them fluid movement.

Pushing the technology in new directions

Once *Jurassic Park* showed Hollywood and film audiences how convincingly real computer-generated creatures could be, moviemakers started to use the technology routinely. The 1995 film *Casper*, for example, features a set of computer-generated ghosts. The ghosts are on screen for far longer than the *Jurassic Park* dinosaurs, an advance made possible by the rapid increase in computer power. Computer graphical processes that had taken hours could be done in seconds. And Draco, a huge flying dragon starring in the medieval epic *Dragonheart* (1996), appears throughout the movie.

Dragonheart also represents a step in giving computer-generated beasts personalities. The tyrannosaur and velociraptors in *Jurassic Park* display only predatory ferocity; Draco has a humanlike character. To create this unusual dragon, the filmmakers had to do more than simulate a reptilian skin and conjure up an image of how such a huge beast would fly. They also had to give Draco facial expressions that conveyed emotions and to make its mouth move in such a way that it seemed to really say the words recorded by actor Sean Connery. In fact, the special-effects artists created the dragon at the outset to reflect Connery's style of speaking. If the producers had needed to replace Connery, the artists would have had to recreate Draco's face. In order for the artists to achieve such precise details, the digital model of Draco's face had more points of computer control than the model for the entire *Tyrannosaurus rex* in *Jurassic Park*.

Confronting other technical challenges

In creating dinosaurs, water-monsters, ghosts, and other smoothly contoured creatures, computer artists were dodging a tough technical problem: how to simulate animal hair. The realistic depiction of hair requires an enormous amount of computational power and vast amounts of patience. The first movie to take on this challenge on a large scale was *Jumanji* (1995), in which a magical board game conjures up a veritable menagerie of furry jungle animals, including lions and monkeys.

To create authentic-looking animal hair, the special-effects artists at ILM developed software that allowed them to get around modeling every hair individually. The software allowed them to set certain variables, such as the number of hairs per square inch, hair color, degree of transparency, and the tendency of hairs to clump together or to remain free. The special-effects artists then tinkered with these elements until they got the desired look. While experimenting with the lion, for example, the creators had to make adjustments because the lion's mane at first looked either blow-dried or like dreadlocks.

In 1996, special-effects artists overcame another major challenge—creating a computer-generated natural disaster. In *Twister,* the filmmakers began with some of the same software tools used to animate creatures. They designed wire-frame models of a tornado and the objects that it picked up and tossed around. These models helped the artists plot out the basic path of the tornado and its debris as it moved across a landscape. Filling in the details of a digital tornado presented new problems, however, because a tornado is not a solid object like a dinosaur—or even a lion—but a whirling mass of clouds and dust that varies in density and transparency. Rather than animating and coloring a single object, the artists had to animate many points and duplicate them by the millions to create layers of furiously rotating material.

At about the same time that *Twister* was being produced, the animated motion picture *Toy Story* established another milestone in the history of computerized filmmaking. For the first time, an entire feature-length movie had been created with a computer. Nothing was drawn by hand,

Batman leaps from a 60-story building in the 1995 film *Batman Forever*. In order to show the superhero through the entire fall, the special-effects artists created a computer-generated version of the character to perform the stunt.

nothing was shot with a camera. All of *Toy Story*'s 79 minutes—more than 114,000 frames, totaling more than 500 billion *bytes* of data—originated in a computer. (A byte is a unit of data consisting of eight bits.) While the movie was intended to appear cartoonlike, it demonstrated subtleties of form, lighting, and texture that could serve well in creating the ultimate in digital motion pictures: a completely computer-generated "live-action" film.

Digital actors

Many digitally created characters that appeared in movies before 1997 were clearly fantasy creatures: dragons, dinosaurs, alien creatures, and cartoon characters. But electronics experts foresaw the day when computer-generated images could replace live human actors. Filmmakers already were using computers to duplicate images of low-paid extras in order to multiply the number of people in crowd scenes. And several movies hinted at other possibilities. In *Batman Forever* (1995), for example, the caped crusader leaps off a 60-story skyscraper and dives into a manhole. The Batman figure is seen full frame for the entire fall. Clearly, no director could ask an actor or stuntman to attempt anything so lethally dangerous, and a dummy or miniature would not have looked real enough. So the special-effects artists at Pacific Data Images created a computer-generated version of the Batman character to perform the stunt.

But special-effects experts believed that continued advances in computing technology, and the corresponding drop in the costs of special effects, would someday enable movie producers to cast "virtual actors" in leading roles. These computer-generated actors are likely to debut in action-adventure films, where dramatic effects are more important than nuanced character development.

Many of the basic techniques for making a virtual actor had been developed by the late 1990's. In movies such as *Jurassic Park* and *Dragon-*

heart, computers proved that it was possible to create a living creature that looks indistinguishable from one that had been photographed. But to extend such photorealism to human actors, moviemakers faced a tough challenge. People know instinctively how other humans look, move, and speak, so audiences are likely to recognize fakery in a synthetic human actor far more readily than in a computer-generated dragon or dinosaur.

While the creation of a fully computer-generated "movie star" was still years in the future in 1997, filmmakers had begun using computers in a related special effect: bringing the stars of old back to cinematic life. Once digitized, old film footage becomes a mother lode of acting talent. The faces of long-deceased actors can be extracted from vintage movies and electronically pasted onto three-dimensional digital models of human forms. In a 1995 episode of the TV series *Tales from the Crypt,* this method brought Hollywood legend Humphrey Bogart back to life using scenes from his movies, including the 1941 film *The Maltese Falcon.*

Despite the sophistication of digital technology of the 1990's, some special effects were still too difficult to create in the computer. Besides the challenges involved with creating virtual actors, the simulation of fire, flowing water, smoke, and explosions required more computing power than filmmakers had at their disposal. Therefore, special-effects artists continued to rely on many tried-and-true techniques from the past. The most famous scene of the 1996 blockbuster *Independence Day,* for instance, shows an alien spaceship blasting the White House to smithereens. Although the movie's creators depended heavily on computer graphics in other scenes, here they did things the old-fashioned way: They built a precise scale model of the Executive Mansion complete with tiny pieces of furniture.

Then, with the cameras rolling, they blew it up.

For further reading:

McCarthy, Robert E. *Secrets of Hollywood Special Effects.* Focal Press, 1992.
McGee, Mark T. *Beyond Ballyhoo: Motion Picture Promotion and Gimmicks.* McFarland & Co., 1989.
Powers, Tom. *Special Effects in the Movies.* Lucent Books, 1989.
Rimmer, Ian. *The Great Book of Movies F/X.* Rourke Enterprises, 1989.
Scott, Elaine. *Movie Magic: Behind the Scenes with Special Effects.* William Morrow & Co., 1995.
Vaz, Mark Cotta and Patricia Rose Duignan. *Industrial Light & Magic: Into the Digital Realm.* Ballantine Books, 1996.

Tour boats navigate the waters of the Galapagos Islands. By the mid-1990's, tourism accounted for more than half of the income of island residents. But the growing number of visitors was taking a toll on the islands' natural resources.

A pair of strange-looking sea birds meet along a gravel pathway. The male begins to raise and lower his bright blue webbed feet. The female responds in a like manner. Every few seconds, the birds fold back and raise their wings and point their beaks skyward. The male emits a shrill whistle; the female, a guttural honk.

   This is the courtship dance of the blue-footed booby, a famous resident of the Galapagos Archipelago, a group of islands that lie across the equator in the Pacific Ocean, 970 kilometers (600 miles) west of the coast of Ecuador. These isolated islands are also home to giant tortoises and a host of other species found nowhere else in the world.

The Galapagos— Endangered Isles

Charles Darwin called the Galapagos Islands a "living laboratory of evolution." But tourism and economic development threaten the islands' wildlife.

BY ARTHUR G. TRESSLER

English naturalist Charles Darwin, who visited the Galapagos in 1835, called the islands a "living laboratory of evolution." Today, the laboratory is in trouble. The archipelago has become a center of confrontation and international attention. The wildlife population shares the islands with a growing human population, and the result has been a conflict between wildlife and people.

The situation reached a boiling point on Sept. 1, 1995, when the president of Ecuador vetoed a measure that would have shifted administrative power over the Galapagos Islands from the federal government to local residents. The residents, eager for economic opportuni-

Terms and Concepts

Archipelago: A group of islands.

El Niño: A dramatic change in weather patterns caused by altered ocean currents off the west coast of South America.

Endemic species: Plants and animals that exist in a certain locality and nowhere else.

Magma: Molten rock beneath the Earth's crust or outer skin.

Natural selection: The process by which inherited traits beneficial to a plant or animal become more widespread in a species; natural selection is the driving force of evolution.

Tectonic plates: Pieces of the Earth's crust that move at a slow but steady rate, driven by heat within the Earth.

The author:
Arthur G. Tressler is a free-lance science writer and a former executive editor of *Science Year*.

ties, wanted increased hotel construction in the islands and a freer hand in using the islands' natural resources. Although the president's veto pleased scientists, conservationists, and nature-tour operators, a small but vocal group of Galapagos residents were outraged. The next day, they retaliated by forcing one of the islands' two airports to close and by blockading the administrative offices of Galapagos National Park and the Charles Darwin Research Station. They also threatened to kill giant tortoises, take tourists hostage, and burn parts of the national park.

The economic goals of the growing number of Galapagos residents and international business ventures threaten the very existence of the islands' unique plants and animals. Scientists are greatly concerned and are trying to protect the islands while there is still time.

An important province

Politically, the Galapagos are 1 of 21 provinces that form the South American nation of Ecuador. Like each mainland province, the islands are headed by a governor appointed by the president of Ecuador.

Geographically, the Galapagos consist of 13 major islands varying in size from 14 square kilometers (5 square miles) to nearly 4,700 square kilometers (1,800 square miles), together with more than 100 smaller islands, islets, and rocks. About 97 percent of the land area of the Galapagos Islands and all of the waters surrounding the islands up to a 28-kilometer (17-mile) boundary have been set aside by the Ecuadorean government as a national park.

Scientifically, the Galapagos are of major importance because of their unique animals and plant life. One of the first people to study and observe the course of life in the Galapagos was Darwin. His 1835 stopoff at the islands was part of a round-the-world voyage aboard the H.M.S. *Beagle*. What he saw during the five weeks he spent at the Galapagos was evidence that, in order to survive as species, animals and plants must adjust physically and behaviorally to changes in their environment. In each generation, he theorized, individual animals and plants possessing the most beneficial traits are the most likely to survive and produce offspring. In this way, certain traits become more widespread and species evolve into new species. This process, which Darwin called *natural selection* (and which is often referred to as "the survival of the fittest"), formed the basis for his theory of evolution. Darwin realized that natural selection is not evolution, but the mechanism that leads to evolution. Natural selection may take place within a generation, but evolution takes many generations to occur.

During his stay at the Galapagos, Darwin noted that the plants and animals vary from island to island and from the lowlands to the highlands of each island. Because of the islands' isolation for hundreds of thousands of years, many of their species are *endemic*—they exist only on the Galapagos and nowhere else on Earth. This is true of about 30 percent of the nearly 600 species of plants in the Galapagos. More than 80 percent of the land-based animals that inhabit the islands are en-

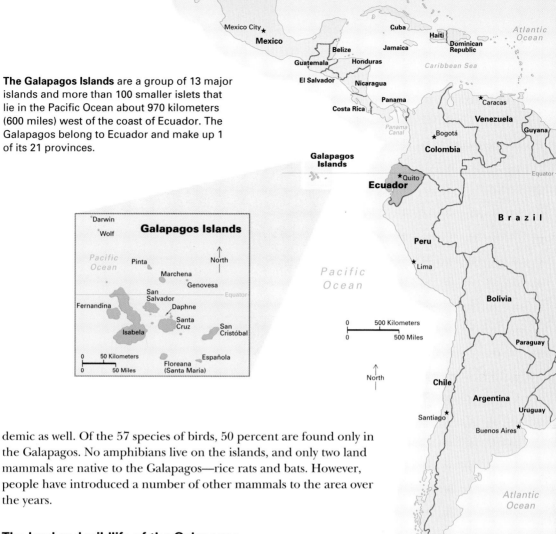

The Galapagos Islands are a group of 13 major islands and more than 100 smaller islets that lie in the Pacific Ocean about 970 kilometers (600 miles) west of the coast of Ecuador. The Galapagos belong to Ecuador and make up 1 of its 21 provinces.

demic as well. Of the 57 species of birds, 50 percent are found only in the Galapagos. No amphibians live on the islands, and only two land mammals are native to the Galapagos—rice rats and bats. However, people have introduced a number of other mammals to the area over the years.

The land and wildlife of the Galapagos

Much of the Galapagos land area is covered with hardened lava, because the islands are volcanic in origin. The islands were formed by a dynamic process beneath the Earth's *crust,* its rocky outer "skin." The crust is composed of about 20 *tectonic plates,* pieces of the continental and ocean floors that move at a slow but steady rate. The Nazca plate, on which the islands ride, passes over a *hot spot,* an intense source of heat deep within the Earth that melts the crust, giving birth to an underwater volcano. Through continuous lava flow and build-up, a volcanic island is born. As the Nazca plate continued to move, the hot spot created more volcanic islands, eventually forming the Galapagos chain.

The Galapagos Islands are relatively young. The oldest—Española and San Cristóbal, to the southeast—are just 3 million to 5 million years old. The youngest island—Fernandina, in the northwest—is less than 700,000 years old. Volcanoes on Fernandina and Isabela still periodically pour out molten rock that cools and hardens.

Today, the islands are a favorite stop for so-called ecotourists. The blue-footed boobies charm the tourists and offer wonderful opportunities for close-up photographs. Like many Galapagos animals, the boo-

Darwin and the finches

Charles Darwin was 26 years old when he visited the Galapagos Islands in 1835. During his stay, Darwin noticed that the size and shape of the beaks of finches from the same species varied according to the types of seeds that the finches ate. This observation helped Darwin formulate his theory of evolution: that species change over time, developing traits that help them survive changes in their environment.

bies seem fearless and make no effort to move out of the way. The nesting habits of these birds are quite casual, too—they lay and incubate their eggs on the ground, sometimes in the middle of visitor footpaths.

Another famous resident that awes tourists and scientists alike is the Galapagos tortoise, for which the islands were named. ("Galapagos" is the Spanish word for saddle, which describes the shape of the tortoise's shell.) These huge reptiles—some weighing more than 225 kilograms (500 pounds)—have a long life span. Scientists estimate that they can live to be at least 150 years old. So a visitor in the 1990's could be looking at a tortoise that Darwin saw as a hatchling.

Many of the islands' beaches are dotted with sun-bathing sea lions. They, too, seem to ignore human visitors on shore. Snorkelers, however, often encounter these playful marine mammals swimming close by and even occasionally tugging on a swim fin. The islands' beaches are also home to prehistoric looking creatures called marine iguanas. These cold-blooded lizards, which use their surroundings to control their body temperature, grow to about 1 meter (3 feet) in length. Their dark-colored skin absorbs heat from the sun and from the sun-warmed lava on which they lie. Marine iguanas are the only lizards in the world that feed in the sea, and they are found only in the Galapagos. Land iguanas live on several islands as well. These are more colorful than the marine iguana—yellow and brownish-red.

The waters off-shore teem with colorful undersea life—parrot fish, angel fish, grunts, white tipped and hammerhead sharks, and moray eels. Dolphins can be spotted riding the bow-wave of ships that ferry visitors between islands. And in the northern and western waters, visitors may see sperm, minke, humpback, or killer whales. The fur seal, along with penguins, seems out of place on these equatorial islands.

There are also many species of Galapagos birds. Small bright-yellow warblers and vermilion flycatchers live inland; graceful red-billed tropic birds with long streaming tails haunt the island cliffs. Herons and flamingos populate the lagoons. Gulls, pelicans, penguins, doves, finches, and the Galapagos hawk are part of the islands' bird life.

Inland on the various islands are plants and animals that have adapted to the drought conditions that prevail much of the year. Plants include giant prickly pear and several other species of cactus, along with leafy plants such as the Galapagos tomato and the passion flower. The land iguana lives among the prickly pear cactuses and feeds on their pads, fruit, and spines. In an evolutionary response, the prickly pear cactuses, over a period of centuries, have grown taller and developed tougher bark to protect themselves.

The highlands are a world of their own. Because of the islands' peculiar weather patterns, there is enough moisture above 300 to 600 meters (1,000 to 2,000 feet) altitude for more lush vegetation. Here, many species of ferns grow, and tree trunks and shrubs, as well as the ground, are frequently covered with moss.

The influence of ocean currents

The Galapagos Islands are very dry but not particularly hot because of the ocean currents and trade winds that bathe them. From July to December, a flow of ocean water called the Peru Current (also known as the Humboldt Current) streams north along the west coast of South America, bringing the cold waters of the Antarctic to the islands. The cold water cools the air above it, creating a *temperature inversion layer,* an area in which warm air rests on top of cold air. (The usual atmospheric situation, in any part of the world, is for air to be warmer at lower elevations and colder at higher elevations.) When evaporating water from the sea surface reaches the warm air of the inversion layer at the moisture level, it causes a continuous mist, called *garúa,* that keeps the highlands lush and green. The lowland areas remain dry and cool.

From January to June, the winds that drive the Peru Current die down, and the warmer waters of the Panama Current bathe the islands. The inversion layer breaks up, rain falls on the coastal areas, and a more typical tropical climate prevails.

Sometimes, these climatic patterns are broken by an *El Niño,* a period of greatly altered weather conditions caused by changes in ocean currents. An El Niño occurs when no trade winds form to bring the Peru Current to the Galapagos. Then, the Panama Current warms the waters of the islands much longer, increasing the annual rainfall.

The additional rain benefits the islands' plants and the land animals that feed on them, but it is a danger for the sea birds and other animals that depend on the ocean for food. Fish feed on nutrients that come to them through *upwelling,* the rise of seawater from lower depths to the surface. This process diminishes when the surface waters warm. Fewer nutrients in the surface waters means fewer fish, and that in turn means less food for seabirds and marine mammals that feed on fish, such as fur seals and sea lions. Following a severe El Niño, large numbers of birds and mammals perish from starvation.

Creatures of the Galapagos

The peculiar weather conditions on the Galapagos create a tropical climate in the highlands and drought throughout much of the lowland area. These differences in moisture are the reason that the Islands are home to such a wide variety of creatures—some of them found no place else in the world.

Galapagos tortoises, *above,* rest in the cool comfort of a highland pool. The giant tortoises—several species of which are *endemic* to the Galapagos (they exist nowhere else on Earth)—have become endangered. Scientists at the Charles Darwin Research Station have begun a hatchling-raising program for the tortoises, hoping to increase their numbers. Blue-footed boobies, *right,* make their nests and raise their hatchlings right in the middle of a gravel pathway for visitors.The blue-foots live in the coastal lowlands of the islands.

A pair of Tripplefin Blenny fish, *right,* skim the ocean floor in the waters surrounding the Galapagos. The Blennys are also endemic, as are marine iguanas, *below,* warming themselves on sun-baked rocks along the Galapagos coasts. These iguanas are the only lizards that feed in the sea. Lava cactus, their bright yellow tips indicating new growth, flourish in the warmth of the lava rocks as well.

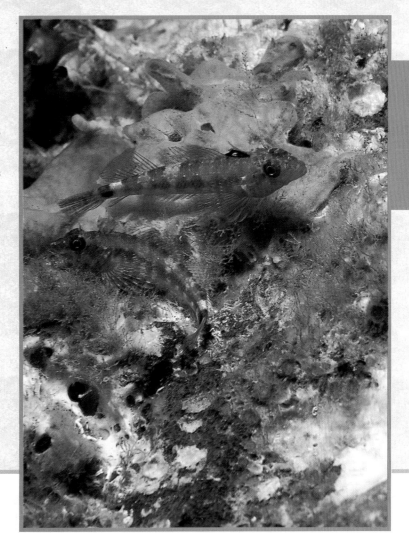

How the first plants and animals reached the Galapagos

The abundance of life in the Galapagos has always been a puzzle to scientists, considering the remoteness of the islands and their unpredictable, and frequently extreme, climate. Biologists theorize that most of the species originated in and around South and Central America. Water creatures—fish, fur seals, sea lions, sea turtles, dolphins—would have been able to ride the ocean currents to the islands. Birds presumably arrived on the winds, as did the seeds and spores for the first plants. The reptiles, which have skins that can withstand salt water and the hot sun, and which can go for long periods without food and fresh water, probably rode in on some kind of vegetative raft. Amphibians and land mammals, being less sturdy than reptiles, could not have survived such a long journey. Thus, it is not surprising that there are no amphibians and just two native land mammals on the islands.

For the plant-eating land animals and land-birds to survive once they got there, plant life must have preceded them. Windborne bacteria, algae, and fungi may have been followed by lightweight seeds and spores. The first plants to flourish may have been lichens and mosses, and later ferns and grasses. The remains of these plants, along with weathered rocks, became the early soil of the Galapagos.

Survival in harsh surroundings

The first animal settlers probably did not find ideal living conditions on the islands, and most of them did not survive. They either arrived before their food supply was established or were wiped out during periods of severe weather. Survival into succeeding generations was equally chancy. A male and a female tortoise, for example, had to land on the same island and find each other for offspring to follow. For much of the life on the islands, it has been "survival of the lucky."

This harsh environment was an ideal place for Darwin to study evolution in isolation. By the time the *Beagle* reached the Galapagos in 1835, near the end of a mapping expedition of South America and selected Pacific Islands, Darwin had become familiar with many South American plant and animal species. More than the similarities, it was the differences in related species on the Galapagos that puzzled him.

Darwin was particularly interested in the Galapagos finches. He noted thirteen distinct species on the four islands that he visited. The species varied in size, but otherwise were very much alike, with one notable exception—their beak structure. The size and shape of a bird's beak depends on what it eats. For example, finches with long pointed beaks feed on cactus flowers. Those with shorter but heavier beaks use them to break up seeds. Other shapes serve finches that dine on insect larva. Over time, the finches' beaks adapted to their food needs through the process of natural selection and evolution.

Since Darwin's time, many scientists have visited the Galapagos to study its wealth of plant and animal life and observe natural selection in action. One of the most exhaustive studies of Galapagos finches (which everyone now calls Darwin's finches) was made by biologists

Peter and Rosemary Grant, of Princeton University in New Jersey, and their associates. Beginning in 1973, the British-born Grants followed more than 20 generations of the birds. By the mid-1990's, the research team had caught, measured, and leg-banded about 20,000 finches.

Through these long-range studies, the scientists observed the effects of extreme climatic changes on the birds. For example, in 1977, the normal wet season turned out to be a period of drought. By the end of the year, some 1,400 of one of the most common species of finches on the island of Daphne Major had been reduced to fewer than 300.

During the drought, the seed-eating birds ate all of the small, soft seeds that were available, until only larger, harder ones were left. The biggest finches with the largest, strongest beaks were the only ones able to crack open and eat those seeds. Consequently, more large finches than small ones survived the drought. In addition, many more males than females survived. The females who lost their mates, for the most part, chose males with larger bodies and larger beaks. So succeeding generations of finches were larger and had larger beaks. Rarely had such a dramatic change in a species been observed in so short a time.

The impact of human activity

The plants and animals of the Galapagos have had to contend with the islands' unpredictable climate for tens of thousands of years. In more recent times, however, the greatest pressures on Galapagos species have come from human activity.

The first humans to make a significant impact on the islands were British buccaneers of the 1500's and 1600's. They stopped at the islands to recover from battles with the Spanish and to replenish their supplies of water and meat—the latter provided by the giant tortoises. During the 1800's, whalers and sealers from Great Britain and the United States hunted whales and fur seals in the seas off South America to near extinction. They also came close to wiping out the giant tortoises. Tortoises can go for months without food and water, so sailors would capture them, stack them upside-down in the holds of their ships, and enjoy fresh meat during their many months at sea.

The sailors also introduced many new species of animals and about 300 new plants to the islands—some deliberately, some by accident. The men released cattle, goats, and pigs on some islands before sailing away so that the animals could graze and fatten. On their return, the sailors would capture some of the animals and be assured of fresh meat while at sea. Cats, dogs, rats, and mice, which also began to populate the islands, may have escaped from ships and been marooned.

Many of the introduced animal and plant species became competitors with, or even predators of, the native plants and animals, which had little or no defense against them. The goats—whose numbers at one time reached 100,000—eat the plants on which tortoises and land iguanas feed. The pigs trample the native plants and eat tortoise eggs and land and marine iguanas. Wild dogs eat iguanas, young fur seals, and penguins. An ornamental shrub called the lantana, brought to the

The impact of people on the Galapagos
Sea lions, *left,* sunbathe peacefully on a Galapagos beach, largely ignoring the tourists wandering among them. The sea lions, like most animals of these isolated islands, show no fear of people, because they have had little exposure to humans. Sharks, *bottom left,* many with their fins already cut off, lie in the bottom of a fishing boat in the waters of the Galapagos. The great demand for shark fins by soup-making enterprises in Asia has dangerously depleted shark populations in the ocean surrounding the islands.

Galapagos in 1938 for a family garden, spread so quickly that it has endangered the local lantana species by competing with it for the limited amount of available water. Even in the early 1990's, new species continued to be introduced to the islands. Native fishermen landing on uninhabited islands to process their catch often brought goats and other animals with them. And tourists traveling between the islands inadvertently carried seeds and insects with them.

More than nonnative species, however, it is people themselves that pose the greatest danger to the Galapagos. After Ecuador annexed the Galapagos in 1832, mainlanders began to colonize the islands. The early inhabitants fished, mined salt, collected moss to make dyes, and harvested giant tortoises for their oil. The human population stabilized at about 600 until the mid-1900's, when it more than doubled. A substantial increase in human population began again in the 1980's, fueled by the nature-tourism industry. By 1997, about 16,000 people were permanent residents of the islands, and the population was still growing.

The four islands on which people live—Santa Cruz, Floreana, San Cristóbal, and Isabela—are overpopulated. Municipal services, such as waste disposal and the provision of drinking water and electricity, are being pushed to the limit. Employment opportunities are also limited. Agriculture is marginal because of the poor soil on these volcanic islands, and fishing, long an important source of income, is threatened. Like the whales and fur seals in the 1800's, populations of fish and other edible sea creatures are now in peril. International fishing vessels, which are licensed to catch particular fish, such as tuna, also take great quantities of other species for which they are not licensed.

In addition, large international factory ships sail to the Galapagos area, where they purchase the catches of local fishermen. This source of cash encourages the islanders to fish illegally in coastal areas that were set aside as a marine reserve, and which are now part of the national park, and to exceed the quotas of fish they are allowed to catch. Sharks, in particular, are in danger of being depleted. High prices for shark fins, which are used in the making of some Oriental soups, have enticed fishermen to catch tens of thousands of sharks each year and cut off their fins.

Lobsters, crabs, shrimp, and other crustaceans are also in jeopardy, as are creatures called sea cucumbers. Sea cucumbers, which belong to a group of spiny-skinned sea animals called *echinoderms,* are prized in Asian countries as an aphrodisiac and a thickening and flavoring agent for soups. Though the government of Ecuador has prohibited the taking of any more sea cucumbers, Galapagos divers have continued to gather them, and in many areas of the islands the animal has all but disappeared.

Today, the largest source of revenue on the islands is the tourism industry. Providing services for tourists and tourist vessels accounts for more than half of the residents' income. For Ecuadoreans struggling to earn a living on the mainland, the impression that great amounts of foreign currency can easily be made in the islands lures more people to the Galapagos than the economy and land can handle.

Taking steps to protect the islands

There are rules that all visitors to the Galapagos must adhere to: No one may disturb or remove anything from the islands, even a rock or sea shell; no one may touch or feed the animals; all visitors must stay on marked trails and be accompanied by trained tour guides; and tourists may visit only the 45 approved visitor sites. Nonetheless, about 60,000 people visited the Galapagos annually in the 1990's, and their collective presence adds to the strain on the islands' resources.

Beyond the regulation of tourism, many organizations, both national and international, are working together to try to solve the problems in the Galapagos. At the Charles Darwin Research Station (CDRS) on Santa Cruz Island, scientists are achieving some success with a hatchling-raising program for giant tortoises in an attempt to increase the numbers of this endangered species. The CDRS is the research arm of

Hope for the tortoises
Game wardens at Galapagos National Park measure the size of a young tortoise's shell. By raising tortoise hatchlings in special pens on Santa Cruz Island and then releasing them, scientists hope to increase the numbers of this endangered species.

the Charles Darwin Foundation for the Galapagos Isles (CDF), an organization founded in 1959 by an international group of scientists who had become concerned about the destruction of Galapagos wildlife. The foundation operates under the auspices of the United Nations Educational, Scientific and Cultural Organization (UNESCO), the IUCN (the World Conservation Union)—a multinational conservation and wildlife management organization—and the government of Ecuador. The purpose of the CDF is to advise the government on conservation strategies for the islands and to operate the CDRS. Scientists at the CDRS gather data on the marine environment of the islands, study the effects of recently introduced plants and animals, and develop environmental education programs.

In 1968, Ecuador established the Galapagos National Park Service (GNPS) to implement the conservation goals set by the CDRS and to oversee Galapagos National Park. In 1986, the government established the Galapagos Marine Resources Reserve. The reserve consists of more than 70,000 square kilometers (27,000 square miles) of waters surrounding the islands, defined by a 28-kilometer (17-mile) boundary. In November 1996, Ecuador's National Institute for Forestry and National Parks declared the marine reserve a part of Galapagos National Park. No commercial fishing is allowed within the area, and traditional fishing is allowed only in certain parts of it. In addition, regulations govern the size and type of fish and sea creatures that may be taken, so that young and reproducing members of a species are left to ensure the long-term survival of the islands' sea life. Many conservationists in the mid-1990's contended, however, that the federal government failed to adequately patrol the marine reserve and enforce the regulations. Conservationists hoped that the national park service would be better able to enforce the existing regulations.

There has been other support for protecting the Galapagos as well.

In 1978, the World Heritage Commission of UNESCO designated Galapagos National Park a World Heritage Site, recognizing the park as a unique area of natural importance. In December 1996, representatives of the World Heritage Commission expressed concern over the environmental problems of the park. The commissioners stated that, unless the government of Ecuador adopts effective measures to control the growing migration of settlers to the park, the introduction of new species to the islands, and the destruction of wildlife by fishermen, the islands will be placed on the World Heritage Sites in Danger List.

Johannah Barry, executive director of the CDF, agrees with the World Heritage Commission on the three most important issues facing the Ecuadorean government:

- The migration of people to the islands must be controlled. This may be a difficult policy to enforce because, like Americans who are free to move from state to state, Ecuadoreans expect to be able to relocate at will from province to province.

- The introduction of nonnative species must be stopped. Even if this is enforced, however, the extensive travel to the islands by ships and airplanes increases opportunities for insects, rodents, or other nonnative animals to come in as stowaways.

- Economic exploitation of the islands must be strictly controlled. The fishing industry is not the only problem. Trees, sand, gravel, and even lava are being removed from several islands for use in construction projects.

Environmental experts agree that solving the problems of the Galapagos will be costly. For example, the cash-strapped government of Ecuador needs funds to build or buy enough ships and aircraft to successfully patrol the islands. Many scientists and environmental activists believe that the financial burden should not be borne by Ecuador alone. They feel that a world concerned about the Galapagos' problems should be willing to share the costs of solving them. With international cooperation, they say, this world treasure can be preserved. And it should be—not just for its importance to science but also for the pleasure and wonder the islands provide to all who visit their shores.

For further reading:

Boyce, Barry. *A Traveler's Guide to the Galapagos Islands.* Galapagos Travel, 1994.

Jackson, Michael H. *Galapagos: A Natural History.* University of Calgary Press, 1993.

Let's Go: The Budget Guide to Ecuador and the Galapagos Islands. Ed. by Katherine R. Unterman. St. Martin's Press, 1997.

Litteral, Linda L. *Boobies, Iguanas, and Other Critters.* American Kestrel Press, 1994.

Weiner, Jonathan. *The Beak of the Finch.* Vintage Books, 1995.

Exploring the theories of quantum physics and relativity, scientists search for a combined theory to explain the origin of the universe.

Beyond the Big Bang

BY ALAN H. GUTH

Few of us can look into the starry sky on a clear night without experiencing a sense of awe. We can see that our world—the planet Earth with all its mountains, oceans, forests, cities, and villages—is part of a vastly larger universe. Gazing at the faraway stars, many barely visible, we think we can feel the immensity of the universe, but in fact, we have no real sense of its size. We cannot see that our sun and all the stars within our view are part of a giant pinwheel of more than 100 billion stars, a galaxy known as the Milky Way. And we have no reason even to suspect that other galaxies exist. Astronomers have found, however, that space is teeming with galaxies, about 100 billion of them within the reach of our most powerful telescopes.

How did this vast and magnificent universe come to be? That is a question that *cosmology*, the branch of science that studies the universe as a whole, seeks to answer. Cosmologists have made tremendous strides since the early 1900's. We have advanced from the belief that the Milky Way is an "island universe," a solitary galaxy surrounded by a sea of emptiness, to the picture of a universe filled with galaxies. We have also progressed from the belief that the universe is motionless to the view that it has expanded from a dramatic explosion, the big bang, which astronomers think occurred 10 billion to 15 billion years ago. But despite these advances, the most fundamental questions about the universe remain unanswered.

For example, the traditional form of the big bang scenario does not attempt to address questions about the very beginning of the universe. Although it is called the big bang theory, it is really only a theory of what happened after the big bang explosion. The theory describes how the early universe expanded and cooled and how a nearly uniform cloud of gaseous matter condensed into clumps to form stars and galaxies. But the theory gives not even a clue about what the universe emerged from, or what caused it to explode into being.

Today many cosmologists are looking for ways to go beyond the big bang theory, to describe the very moment of creation in terms of the laws of nature. Although our understanding of these laws is still incomplete, there has been much progress in constructing a theory of how the universe may have come into existence. If the new ideas are correct, then the universe is far older than 15 billion years—and vastly larger than had been previously thought. Furthermore, the new ideas imply that the big bang occurred not just once, but countless times. Each big bang produced a huge expanse of space, often called a "bubble universe." These bubble universes are similar to the *observable universe* (the region within the reach of our telescopes), but they are separate from it, and possibly much larger.

The beginning of modern cosmology

The modern view of cosmology is based on the work of Edwin P. Hubble, an American astronomer. In 1929, he discovered that all the galaxies in the universe are rushing away from one another, which means that the universe as a whole is expanding. Since matter is known to cool as it expands, cosmologists concluded that the universe began in an immensely hot, dense state, often called the primordial fireball.

The theory of the primordial fireball, also called the big bang theory, has become widely accepted because a number of its predictions have been confirmed by observation. The first strong evidence that the universe had a fiery birth came in 1965. That year Arno A. Penzias and Robert W. Wilson, researchers working at Bell Telephone Laboratories in New Jersey, discovered that weak microwave radiation is arriving at Earth from all directions in space. Cosmologists interpreted these microwaves, now called the cosmic background radiation, as the faint glow that survives today from the blazing heat of the primordial fireball. Today we know, based on data obtained from the Cosmic Background Explorer (COBE) satellite in the early 1990's, that the properties of the background radiation agree precisely with what we would expect from the glow of hot matter in the early universe.

In addition, physicists have studied how the nuclei of atoms would have formed in a fireball as it cooled. They found that the nuclei in the universe would be mainly of the lightest known types: two *isotopes* (forms) of hydrogen, two isotopes of helium, and an isotope of lithium. The amounts of these elements that astronomers have measured in our universe agree well with what the theorists calculated. Cosmologists believe that heavier elements formed much later, in the interior of stars, so they do not provide a test for the big bang theory.

Rethinking the big bang theory

Despite the success of the big bang theory in accounting for the present state of the universe, there is strong evidence that the theory is incomplete. Because the theory describes only the aftermath of the primordial explosion, and not the explosion itself, there are mysteries that the big bang theory leaves unresolved. Most importantly, the theory gives no explanation for two remarkable properties of the observable universe: its uniformity and its average density of mass.

> ### Writing big numbers
> Scientists use *scientific notation*, a kind of numerical shorthand, to write very large or very small numbers. For example, 10^6 is an easier way to write a 1 followed by 6 zeros, or 1,000,000. The number 6 is called the exponent. 10^{-6} is a shorthand way to write a decimal point, followed by 5 (not 6) zeros, and then a 1, or .000001.

If the big bang had been an ordinary explosion, like a blast of dynamite or a nuclear bomb, we would not expect the universe to be uniform. Objects would be distributed randomly and unevenly. However, that is not the case—the universe appears to be remarkably uniform. If we could imagine stepping back and looking at the very big picture, we would find that the distribution of stars and galaxies is very much the same throughout the universe. The most striking evidence for the uniformity of the universe comes from the cosmic background radiation. Precise measurements have shown that the intensity of the radiation is almost exactly the same from every direction in the sky.

Cosmologists usually discuss the average density of mass in the universe in terms of its effect on the fate of the universe. Recall that the universe is expanding and that the expansion is being slowed by the gravitational attraction that exists between any two masses. If the average mass density is greater than a certain value, called the critical density, the force of gravity will eventually halt the expansion of the universe and cause it to collapse into what is sometimes called the "big crunch." If the average density is less than or equal to the critical density, the universe will continue to expand forever.

Unfortunately, it is very difficult to measure the density of mass in the universe. Cosmologists only know that the average density lies somewhere near the critical value. Nonetheless, they have calculated that the slightest variation from the critical density soon after the birth of the universe would have had a significant effect on its development. At one second after the big bang, for example, the average mass density must have been less than 1.000000000000001 times the critical value, or else the universe would have stopped expanding and collapsed in on itself before reaching its present age. But the density must have been more than 0.999999999999999 times the critical value, or else the matter in

The author:
Alan H. Guth is the Victor F. Weisskopf Professor of Physics at the Massachusetts Institute of Technology in Cambridge, Massachusetts.

Looking back to the birth of our universe

Observations of our universe led cosmologists to develop
a theory of how it came into being.

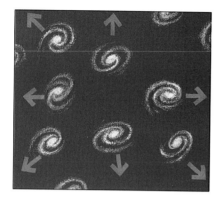

The galaxies in the universe today
are moving away from each other.
As they move away, the density of
the matter in the universe decreases, the universe cools, and the
force of gravity between the galaxies weakens. Astronomer Edwin
Hubble first observed this expansion of the universe in the 1920's.

If the universe is expanding, then in the past, the
galaxies must have been
closer together. The den-
sity of matter must have
been greater and the uni-
verse hotter.

Tracing the expansion
backwards in time, cos-
mologists theorized that
at some point there
must have been an in-
stant of extreme density
and temperature, when
the universe exploded
into being. They call this
the big bang theory.

the universe would have flown apart so quickly that stars and galaxies
would never have formed.

Because the traditional big bang theory could not explain why the
universe is so uniform or why the density of the primordial fireball was
so extraordinarily close to the critical value, cosmologists realized that
the theory would have to be refined. In the 1980's, they developed a
new theory that accounted for these two phenomena—the inflationary universe theory. The theory proposes that just an instant after it
emerged into being, the infant universe was propelled by a force called
inflation. In just an eyeblink of cosmic time, the universe increased in
size by a factor of trillions of trillions. The theory was first suggested by
me in a form which did not quite work. The first fully successful version
of inflation was proposed by Andrei Linde, then at the Lebedev
Institute in Moscow, and independently in a publication by Andreas
Albrecht and Paul Steinhardt at the University of Pennsylvania.

The inflationary universe

The inflationary universe theory was developed by combining ideas in cosmology with findings from another area of study, particle physics. The connection between these two fields at first seems odd, since the goal of cosmology is to understand the largest objects that we know of, while the goal of particle physics is to understand the smallest. Particle physicists study the protons, neutrons, and electrons that combine to make atoms, as well as a host of other particles, such as the quarks that join to form protons and neutrons. The relationship between the two fields, however, arises naturally from the big bang theory, which implies that the early universe was far hotter than any furnace that can be produced on Earth. Our only hope to understand the behavior of matter at these extreme temperatures is to understand the particles from which the matter is made, and the forces by which the particles interact.

The crucial concept from particle physics that makes inflation possible is the predicted existence of a peculiar form of matter, called a *false vacuum,* that can turn gravity on its head. Gravity is normally an attractive force between any two objects, but a false vacuum produces a gravitational force that repels. A false vacuum was still just a theoretical idea in 1997, as the energy needed to produce it was much larger than anything available. Nonetheless, particle physicists were reasonably sure that this form of matter can exist.

The inflationary theory proposes that the infant universe, or some small patch of it, was filled with a false vacuum. The repulsive gravitational force of the false vacuum would then have set off an extremely rapid expansion. In a period of time much shorter than we could ever imagine—perhaps 10^{-37} second—the region of false vacuum doubled in size. (The time span 10^{-37} second is a fraction of a second—written out as a decimal point followed by 36 zeros and the numeral 1.) Then in the same amount of time, it doubled again, and then again and again at least 100 times. This is called exponential expansion. In a twinkling, the universe became at least 10^{30} (1 followed by 30 zeros) times larger than it had been. While any ordinary form of matter would have been diluted to a negligible density by such a gargantuan increase in volume, the peculiar properties of the false vacuum imply that its density of energy was unaffected by the expansion. The total energy in the false vacuum, therefore, grew enormously during the period of inflation.

The entire period of inflation lasted just a tiny fraction of a second because the false vacuum is unstable, just as the nuclei of radioactive elements are unstable. An unstable nucleus of uranium, for example, will decay by breaking up into a nucleus of thorium and a nucleus of helium. So, too, a false vacuum "decays" into other forms of matter. It converts its huge store of energy into a tremendously hot gas of essentially all the elementary particles. The gas is so hot that the particles cannot combine even to form protons or neutrons.

This expanding hot soup of particles, produced by the expansion and subsequent decay of the false vacuum, is exactly the form of matter that the traditional big bang theory had assumed made up the primordial fireball. Thus, the inflationary theory provides the detailed description of the initial explosion that was absent from the original form of the big bang theory. The description of the universe after the decay of the false vacuum is the same in both the theory of inflation and the older form of the big bang theory.

The inflationary universe theory can explain the nearly uniform distribution of matter throughout the universe, because the enormous burst of expansion makes it possible for the universe to have started out much smaller than had been previously thought. Just before inflation began, the region of space that we call the observable universe would have been more than a billion times smaller than a proton. Since the region was so small, both the temperature and the distribution of matter had a chance to become uniform before inflation kicked in. This uniformity would have been preserved as inflation expanded this tiny region to an immensely larger volume.

The inflationary theory can also explain why the average mass density in the universe is so close to the critical value. As the universe evolves, both the mass density and its critical value change, since the critical density is determined by the rate of expansion. (If the rate of expansion were high, for example, then a strong gravitational force would be needed to reverse it, and the critical density would be high.) During inflation, the expansion rate of the universe was controlled by the gravitational repulsion of the false vacuum, which according to calculations had exactly the needed strength. Whatever the conditions were before inflation—whether the average mass density was greater or less than the critical value—the inflationary expansion would have adjusted the balance between the rate of expansion and the mass density. When the period of inflation ended, after 100 or more doublings in the size of the universe, the mass density would have been extraordinarily close to the critical value.

Because inflation is the only known explanation for the uniformity of the universe and the fact that the universe's mass density is very close to the critical value, cosmologists are fairly certain that the universe did indeed go through a period of inflation. Nonetheless, the theory of inflation is not the final word in cosmology, for at least three reasons. First, although inflation describes the universe at an extraordinarily early moment in time, it does not explain the actual origin of the universe—time zero. Second, inflation is not a unique theory, but rather a class of theories. Most of the versions present the same basic scenario of the early universe, but they differ in their details. There was still much work to be done in 1997 to determine which version of the theory, if any, is correct. And third, though inflation is a persuasive theory, decisive tests of its predictions were still needed.

Eternal creations

Nonetheless, the inflationary theory has led to new speculation about the nature of our universe. One of the most fascinating new ideas is the possibility that inflation never ends.

To understand how this could be so, recall that inflation is driven by a false vacuum and ends when the false vacuum decays. The false vacuum, however, does not decay all at once. In most versions of the inflationary theory, it decays with a fixed half-life, like a radioactive material. The half-life is the time it takes for half of a radioactive substance or a false vacuum to decay. Imagine that we could sprinkle a region of false vacuum uniformly with hundreds of tiny probes. After one half-life, half of the probes, on average, would be in regions that still contain false vacuum. The other half would be in regions in which the false vacuum has decayed into a hot soup of particles. The decay of the false vacuum would look just like the big bang in our own past, so each region in which the false vacuum decayed would become a new universe. Cosmologists call these universes "bubble universes," and many think our own universe is such a bubble.

Although a radioactive material will eventually decay completely, a false vacuum behaves differently. While the false vacuum is decaying into bubble universes, it is also exponentially expanding. The time it takes for the false vacuum to double in size—

An instant of rapid expansion

The uniform expansion of the universe from an initial state of extraordinary density and temperature, as proposed by the traditional big bang theory, does not completely explain the universe as we observe it today. As an improvement to this theory, cosmologists have proposed that a tiny fraction of a second after the moment of creation, the universe went through a brief period of rapid expansion. About every 10^{-37} second, the size of the universe doubled. At the end of this period, which is called inflation, the universe had doubled in size at least 100 times, becoming trillions of trillions times larger. After the inflationary expansion stopped, the universe continued to expand, but at an ever-decreasing rate.

One of many universes

The theory of inflation is based on an unusual form of matter called a false vacuum, which creates a gravitational force that repels instead of attracts. Cosmologists working with inflation have theorized that our universe may be only one of countless universes that resemble bubbles, each born from its own big bang. This revolutionary scenario is called eternal inflation.

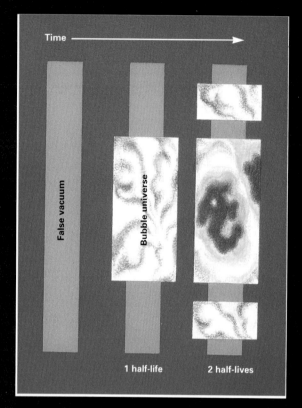

A false vacuum can be understood only in mathematical terms, so it is impossible to even imagine what a false vacuum might look like. But let's suppose the far left bar represents a region of false vacuum.

The second bar represents the same region after a certain period of time, the *half-life* of the false vacuum, during which half of it decays into normal matter. The steady expansion of this normal matter amounts to a traditional big bang, evolving into a bubble universe. Each of the two remaining regions grows to be as large as the original region.

In the third bar, another half life has elapsed. The two regions of false vacuum in the second bar have decayed, creating two new bubble universes. But now there are four regions of false vacuum, and each would be as large as the original region. Eventually these decay to create new bubble universes, and the process endlessly repeats itself. Each bubble universe evolves according to the big bang theory, undergoing a period of inflation and a uniform expansion, just as our universe is doing.

The possibility of innumerable bubble universes challenges our beliefs about the uniqueness of our own universe. Cosmologists usually assume that the underlying laws of nature are the same in all the bubbles, because otherwise we would have nothing to guide our thinking. But, the underlying laws may not require that the *apparent laws of nature,* those that would actually be observed in a bubble universe, be the same. It is possible, therefore, that the apparent laws would be different in each bubble universe. The space inside them could have more or fewer than the three dimensions of space that we observe. Many of the universes may be dark and empty. But some, just like our own, may be filled with stars and planets.

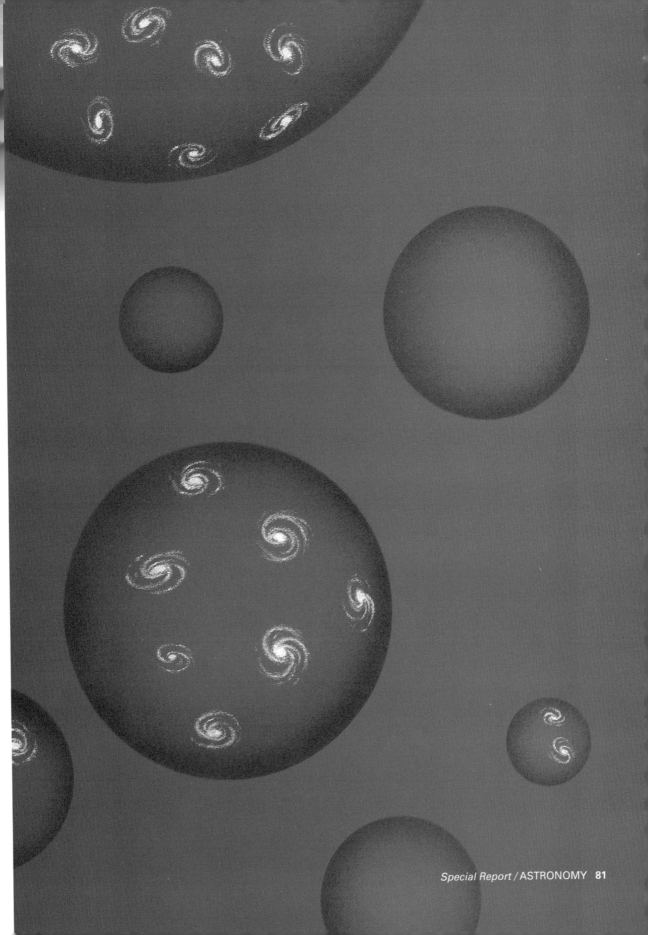

perhaps 10^{-37} second—is much shorter than the false vacuum's half-life. Thus, despite continually losing regions of itself to decay, the remaining false vacuum grows ever larger, and inflation never stops. The result is the eternal creation of an infinite number of bubble universes as the false vacuum goes on inflating and decaying. Each bubble universe continues to expand at an ever-decreasing rate for billions of years as it evolves. The fate of each bubble universe is determined by how much mass it contains. Some bubble universes will eventually collapse by the force of gravity into a big crunch; others will expand forever, becoming cold and dark. According to the theory, however, the overall universe—the false vacuum and all the bubbles that it spawns—continues forever.

The theory of eternal inflation invites us to ask further questions about the origin of the universe. For example, if the universe includes an infinite number of bubble universes, are the laws of physics the same within all of them? If inflation can continue without end, is it possible that it is also without beginning? If not, then how did the universe begin? To describe what cosmologists are thinking about these questions, we need to summarize what physicists have learned about the fundamental laws of nature.

The laws of physics—searching for a better understanding

Although the world around us appears unimaginably complex, most physicists believe that it is governed by an underlying simplicity. They attribute the spectacular complexity to the huge numbers of atoms and molecules that make up every object that we see and touch.

The interactions among subatomic particles appear to be governed by four known forces of nature. In the order of their strength, the first of these forces is simply called the strong force. It is responsible for binding quarks together to form protons and neutrons. It also holds protons and neutrons together inside an atomic nucleus. The electromagnetic force holds electrons in orbit around the atomic nucleus. The weak force is responsible for some types of radioactive decay. These forces are transmitted by particles. For example, photons transmit the electromagnetic force and gluons transmit the strong force.

Surprisingly, the weakest known force of all is gravity. The force of gravity between two elementary particles is so weak that it has never been detected. Gravity appears strong, however, because gravity is long-range and always attractive. The weight of a refrigerator, for example, is caused by the attraction between all its 10^{28} particles and all 10^{52} particles of the Earth. For similar reasons, gravity is the dominant force controlling the evolution of the universe.

Cosmologists believe that in the first moments of the universe, there existed only one master force. As the universe expanded and cooled, the master force split into the four forces known today. A major goal of modern physics is to understand the mathematical relationships that unify all the forces. So far, we have been able to develop a theory that unifies the strong, electromagnetic, and weak forces. But we have been only partially successful with gravity.

Under most circumstances, gravity is accurately described by the law formulated by the English physicist and mathematician Isaac Newton in the 1600's. Newton said that gravity is a force by which any two masses attract each other. In 1916, however, the German-Swiss physicist Albert Einstein invented a new theory of gravity, the general theory of relativity, which was found to be more accurate, especially when very large masses are involved.

Einstein said gravity is not a force, but a distortion in the geometry of space and time. Previously, physicists had concerned themselves only with the motion of matter and treated space as merely a fixed backdrop. But in general relativity, Einstein saw space as an elastic material, with the ability to bend, twist, and stretch. General relativity is completely adequate for describing the revolutions of planets and other large-scale motions, but it is not a candidate for being part of the truly fundamental laws of nature. The problem is that general relativity is not consistent with the quantum theories that physicists have developed to explain the behavior of atoms and elementary particles.

The key difference between quantum theories and so-called classical theories of physics, such as Newton's and Einstein's, concerns the question of predictability. A classical theory can be used to make clear predictions for every property of a system at any time in the future. A quantum theory, in contrast, can be used only to calculate the probabilities of different outcomes. Physicists are now convinced that the underlying laws of nature are all properly phrased in terms of quantum theory, and that they have found a successful quantum description of the strong, electromagnetic, and weak forces. Now they want to explain the origin of the universe by developing a quantum theory of cosmology. A major step in that direction would be a successful quantum theory of gravity.

Superstring theory

The need to develop a quantum theory of gravity has bedeviled theoretical physicists since the 1940's, and one approach after another has met with failure. However, after decades of frustration, many physicists now believe that we are well along the road to a solution, in the form of a quantum theory called superstrings. As its name suggests, the theory conceives of fundamental particles, such as electrons or quarks, not as pointlike objects but rather as tiny strings, with lengths of about 10^{-33} centimeter. The particles that transmit forces between particles of matter are also viewed as strings. The theory holds that the force of gravity is conveyed by a looplike particle called a graviton, and all the various kinds of particles exist in a 10-dimensional realm—the 4 dimensions we are familiar with in our everyday world (height, width, depth, and time) and 6 extra dimensions.

Why, then, do we not see these extra dimensions? The answer can be understood by thinking about an ordinary soda straw. By looking closely at the straw, you can see that it is a curved two-dimensional surface. However, if you look from a distance, you cannot see the thickness, and the straw looks like a one-dimensional line. Superstring theo-

In search of creation

In order to more completely understand what happened before the big bang, cosmologists must find a way to unite the laws of physics that explain the world of the atom and the laws that explain the expanses of the universe.

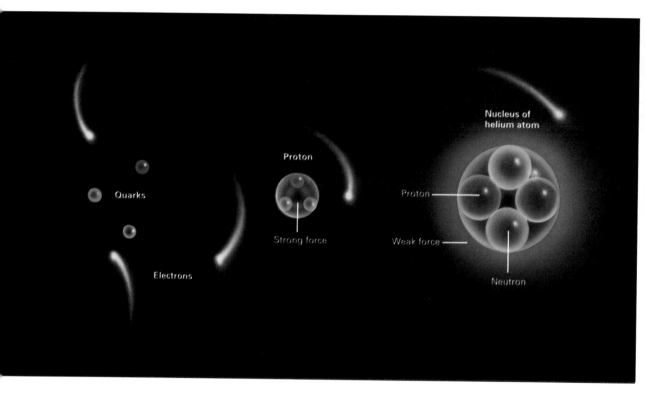

Quarks

Electrons

Proton

Strong force

Nucleus of helium atom

Proton

Weak force

Neutron

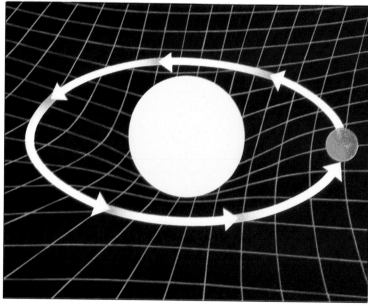

The paths of the planets, stars, and galaxies are controlled mainly by the force of gravity and can be calculated using the theory of general relativity, developed by Albert Einstein. According to Einstein, what we perceive as the force of gravity is actually caused by the bending of space and time. For example, just as a bowling ball would press into a soft mattress, the sun pushes against the "fabric" of space-time, creating a sloping depression that holds the Earth and other planets in orbit.

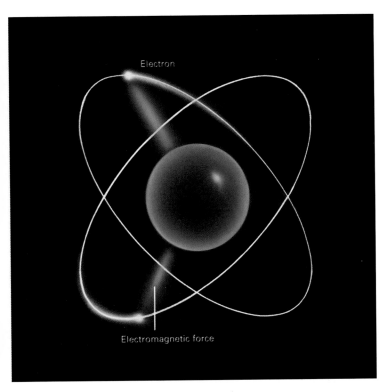

Electron

Electromagnetic force

Three forces control the fundamental particles of matter and are described by quantum theory. The strong force binds quarks into protons and neutrons. It also binds protons and neutrons to make up atomic nuclei. The weak force is responsible for some types of radioactive decay. The electromagnetic force holds electrons in orbit around the nucleus.

Scientists do not yet fully understand how to combine general relativity with quantum theory. General relativity accurately describes the evolution of the universe after inflation. Quantum theory explains how inflation may be possible and even suggests how the universe may have materialized from absolutely nothing. A detailed explanation of the origin of the universe, however, must await an ultimate theory that describes the force of gravity and the forces controlling subatomic particles in the same terms.

ry proposes that the 6 extra dimensions are curled in this way, with a circumference of about 10^{-32} centimeter. Unfortunately, the mechanism that causes this curling is not well understood.

While superstring theory was invented as a quantum theory of gravity, it appears to be much more far-reaching than anyone had anticipated. If the superstring theory is right, it could very well be the conclusion of our search for the fundamental laws of nature.

New speculation about our universe

We can now return to the question of whether the laws of physics within all the bubble universes can be expected to be the same. Observations of light from distant galaxies show that the laws of physics appear to be the same throughout the visible universe, but this of course says nothing about other bubble universes. In addressing this question, cosmologists usually assume that the truly underlying laws of nature are the same everywhere, because otherwise we would have no clue about how to proceed. Nonetheless, the apparent laws of physics—those that we actually observe—may not be uniquely determined by the underlying laws. In string theory, for example, there may be more than one way that the six hidden dimensions can curl up, so the apparent laws of physics may depend on how the curling happens to have occurred in our bubble universe. Indeed, it is even conceivable that the space-time of other bubble universes may not seem four-dimensional.

If inflation can continue without end, we might also ask if it could occur without a beginning? If so, there would be no need to seek a theory of the actual origin of the universe. The issue is not definitively decided, but calculations indicate that even eternal inflation cannot remove the need for a beginning.

In considering a scientific theory of creation, one crucial issue is the starting point. Any account of the creation of the universe must begin with an initial state in which there is no universe—but what does that mean? One might consider starting with empty space, but in the context of general relativity, empty space is essentially a material, capable of twisting and stretching like a piece of rubber. To most cosmologists, therefore, empty space is a kind of universe. To discuss a starting point with no universe, cosmologists speak of a state they call *absolute nothingness,* in which neither matter, space, nor time exist.

If the universe originated from nothing, an issue that must be understood is the conservation of energy. The laws of nature, physicists believe, imply that energy is never created or destroyed, so the total amount of energy can never change. But the total energy of the universe seems to be huge, so how could the universe have begun from nothing? The answer hinges on the fact that the energy of a gravitational field is negative. If the average gravitational field of the universe is strong enough, then the negative energy of gravity can cancel the positive energy of everything else, so that the total energy is zero. The inflationary theory, and especially the theory of eternal inflation, depend on the fact that whole bubble universes can arise with no input of energy.

Although an accepted theory of the creation of the universe from nothing does not exist, serious speculations have been proposed by four noted cosmologists: Alexander Vilenkin of Tufts University in Massachusetts, Andrei Linde of Stanford University in California, and working collaboratively, Stephen Hawking of Cambridge University in Great Britain and James Hartle of the University of California at Santa Barbara. These proposals use the unpredictability of quantum theory to explain the origin of the universe as the random creation of space and time out of a state of absolute nothingness. The ideas are only approximate, based on our imperfect understanding of the quantum version of general relativity. While one hopes that someday the origin of the universe will be addressed by superstring theory, at present the theory is not understood well enough to make this possible.

Likewise, the theory of inflation itself, though it seems valid, must be put on a more solid footing before it can confidently be called the correct description of the very early moments of our universe. More work is needed to test the predictions of inflation, and to determine which version of the theory, if any, is correct. For example, most versions of the theory predict the creation of slight variations in the density of the universe, which can be explored by measuring the very faint nonuniformities in the cosmic background radiation. Cosmologists had high hopes in 1997 that some of these questions would be answered by the Microwave Anisotropy Probe, a highly sensitive satellite that was to make further measurements of the cosmic background radiation. The satellite was scheduled to be launched by the National Aeronautics and Space Administration in about the year 2000. The European Space Agency was planning to launch an even more sensitive probe, called Planck, in 2004. The measurements provided by these probes might leave us totally baffled, or they could help settle the inflation issue.

It is an exciting time in cosmology, and the stakes are high, because if the creation of our universe can someday be described by the laws of physics, we would be left with just one great mystery of existence: What was it that determined the laws of physics?

For further reading:

Guth, Alan H. *The Inflationary Universe: The Quest for a New Theory of Cosmic Origins.* Addison-Wesley Publishing, 1997.

Halliwell, Jonathan J. "Quantum Cosmology and the Creation of the Universe." *Scientific American,* December 1991, pp. 76–85.

Hawking, Stephen. *The Illustrated Brief History of Time,* Updated and Expanded Edition. Bantam Books, 1996.

Linde, Andrei. "The Self-Reproducing Inflationary Universe." *Scientific American,* November 1994, pp. 48–55.

Morris, Richard. *Cosmic Questions.* John Wiley & Sons, 1993.

Silk, Joseph. *A Short History of the Universe.* Scientific American Library, 1994.

Frozen in Time

Fossils preserved in the solidified
resin of ancient trees offer a rare
look at many prehistoric organisms.

BY DAVID DREIER

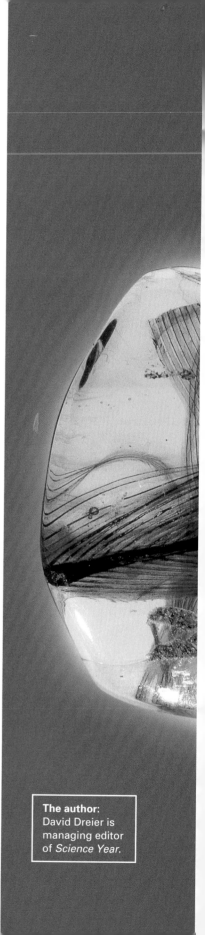

Visitors to natural-history museums are usually astonished when
they see pieces of prehistoric amber containing fossils of ancient insects, plants, and other organisms. The specimens are
often so perfectly preserved, it seems impossible that the organisms
could have died tens of millions of years ago.

Such is the preservative power of amber, the solidified resin of pine
trees and various other *coniferous* (cone-bearing) and tropical broad-
leaf trees. These trees produce resin—a sticky, usually yellowish substance—when they suffer any sort of injury. The resin slowly hardens
and provides an enduring protective covering for the exposed wood.
Long after a tree has died, pieces of the tree, with deposits of resin,
may survive. Over thousands of years, the resin hardens further into a
substance called copal. And after millions of years, it becomes amber.

Sometimes insects, spiders, bird feathers, or leaves—even young
frogs or other small animals—get stuck in a flow of resin and entombed. This happened countless times in the dense forests that covered the Earth in prehistoric times. Compounds in the resin killed bacteria in the plant and animal tissues, protecting them from decay. The
chemicals also dehydrated the tissues without shrinking them, thereby
keeping them in a lifelike state.

The dehydration process in amber also preserved the DNA of many
organisms. DNA (deoxyribonucleic acid) is the molecule genes are
made of. Scientists have extracted segments of DNA from the amber-
preserved tissues of various prehistoric insects and plants. The genetic
material makes it possible to study how present-day organisms evolved
from long-extinct ancestors. (Some researchers contend, however, that
any DNA found in amber is modern genetic "contamination.")

Prehistoric amber is almost always found buried in ancient ocean
sediments—some now far inland—where it was protected from the destructive effects of oxygen in the atmosphere. The best-quality amber
comes from about 20 deposits around the world, including the Baltic
region, the Dominican Republic, and New Jersey. New Jersey amber,
which dates from more than 90 million years ago, is some of the oldest
containing complete organisms. Baltic amber dates from about 40 million years ago, and Dominican amber is about 25 million years old.

The specimens shown in these pages are greatly enlarged.

The author:
David Dreier is
managing editor
of *Science Year*.

Portions of three flight feathers from an unknown type of bird are encased in a piece of Dominican amber. At the time that the feathers were preserved, about 25 million years ago, modern-type birds had been in existence for about 40 million years.

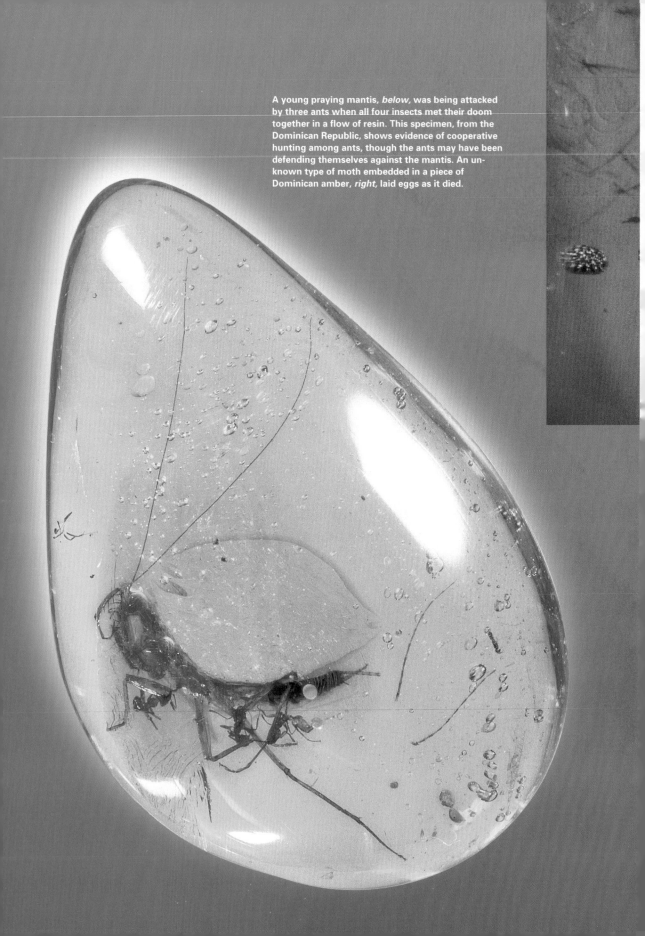

A young praying mantis, *below,* was being attacked by three ants when all four insects met their doom together in a flow of resin. This specimen, from the Dominican Republic, shows evidence of cooperative hunting among ants, though the ants may have been defending themselves against the mantis. An unknown type of moth embedded in a piece of Dominican amber, *right,* laid eggs as it died.

Amber in its natural state is covered by deep grooves and must be polished to reveal fossils. This piece of Mexican amber—about the same age as Dominican amber—is shown approximately one-third actual size.

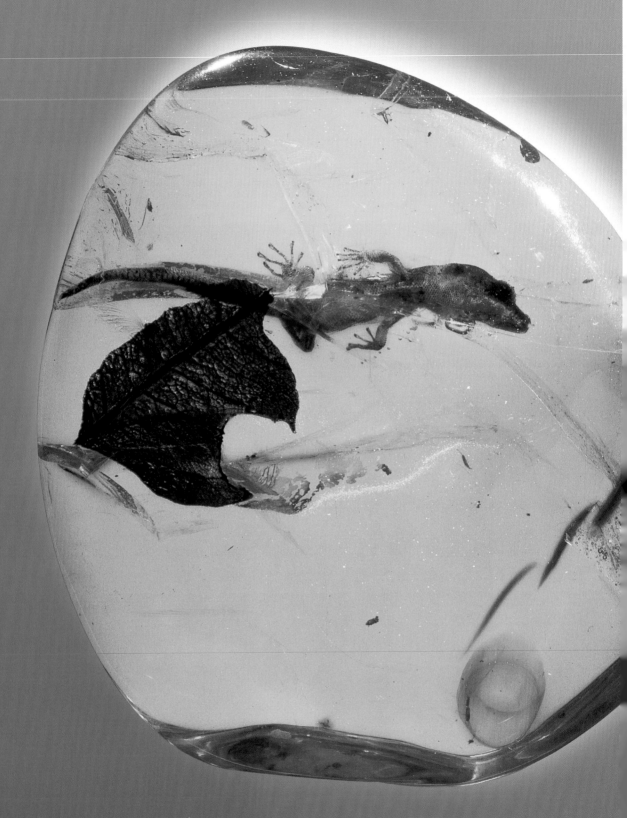

A small lizard called a gecko appears to be going for a swim in this piece of Dominican amber, *left.* Next to it is a leaf that had been gnawed on by an insect, perhaps a leaf-cutter bee. X-ray analysis of the fossil revealed that the gecko's back was broken in several places, evidently from the animal's struggle to escape the resin that had trapped it. *Vertebrates* (animals with backbones) such as this one are rare finds among amber fossils. Rarer still is amber containing mammal bones. The first authenticated fossil of an early mammal in amber was reported by scientists in 1996. The specimen, *above,* is a piece of Dominican amber containing the backbone and ribs of a small mammal, probably a shrewlike animal or a creature distantly related to the opossum.

More than 200 tiny insects, spiders, and plants are preserved in a piece of Dominican amber just 3.75 centimeters (1.5 inches) long. Such amber "menageries" provide valuable information about the kinds of organisms that were living at the same time in prehistoric forests. But most organisms found in amber, like these, are very small. Although young frogs and lizards did sometimes become entombed in amber, such animals—and most larger ones— were usually strong enough to free themselves from pools of tree resin. Likewise, the plants most likely to end up being deposited in resin and encapsu- lated were ones that were small enough to be blown about by the wind.

A cluster of flowers from an oaklike tree that lived about 90 million years ago, preserved in New Jersey amber, *left,* are the oldest blossoms ever found in amber. The flowers are surrounded by air bubbles, which were often trapped in resin along with plants and animals. The oldest mushroom ever found, *above,* dates from the same period and was also found in New Jersey amber. A piece of Baltic amber about 40 million years old contains an ancient pine cone, *below,* perhaps from the same tree that produced the resin.

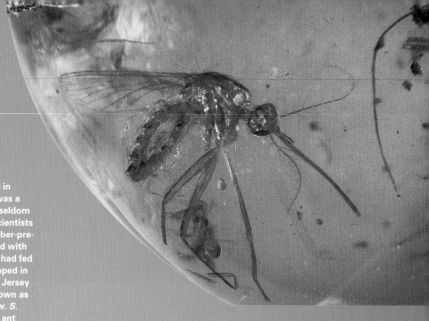

A female mosquito sealed in Dominican amber, *right,* was a rare find. Mosquitoes are seldom found in amber, though scientists have discovered a few amber-preserved mosquitoes bloated with the blood of animals they had fed on just before getting trapped in tree resin. A piece of New Jersey amber contains an ant known as *Sphecomyrma freyi, below. S. freyi* is the most primitive ant ever found.

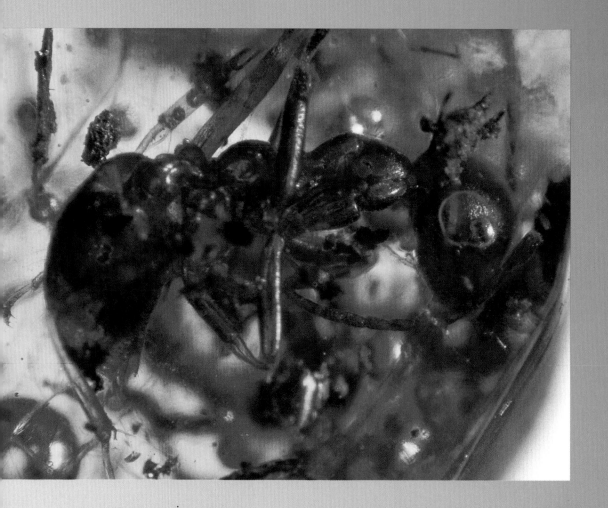

A scorpion embedded in Dominican amber has been identified as belonging to the family Buthidae. Modern scorpions of this family are commonly found under loose tree bark. The ancient scorpion may have chosen the same habitat—and paid for it by becoming a victim of the tree's resin defenses.

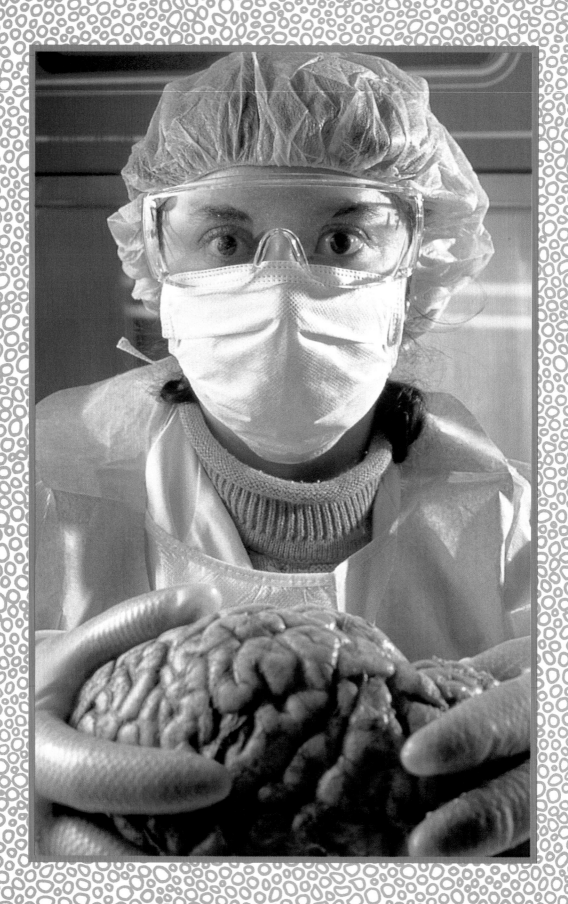

Abnormal protein molecules called prions
are involved in several devastating brain
disorders, including "mad cow disease," but
some scientists are skeptical about the idea
that these proteins cause illness on their own.

Rogue Proteins

BY KARYN HEDE GEORGE

The worst fears of people in the United Kingdom were confirmed
in October 1996 when a group of British neuroscientists reported their findings about a recent outbreak of a terrifying brain
disease. The illness appeared to be a new form of a rare human disorder called Creutzfeldt-Jakob (*KROYTS fehlt YAH kahb*) disease (CJD),
which robs people of their thoughts, memories, and power of speech
and ends in death. CJD usually strikes in late middle age, but of the 14
people (later increased to 17) known to be afflicted by the new disease,
most were in their teens and 20's. The British researchers confirmed
an earlier report that these individuals had probably contracted their
illnesses by eating beef from cattle infected with a similar brain disorder called bovine spongiform encephalopathy (BSE), or "mad cow disease." The cattle had contracted BSE from feed containing meat and
bone meal from sheep that had been suffering from essentially the
same disease—called scrapie in sheep.

In their October announcement, the scientists reported that they
had found strong evidence linking BSE to the cluster of human illnesses. Laboratory studies, they said, had revealed that an abnormal
protein extracted from the patients' brains after death resembles a
protein thought to cause mad cow disease. This finding suggested that

Opposite page:
A pathologist holds the
brain of a person who
died of Creutzfeldt-
Jakob disease, a rare,
fatal brain disorder in
which prions have been
implicated.

the new human brain disorder and BSE are in fact the same disease.

The type of protein associated with CJD, mad cow disease, and scrapie—as well as several other human and animal brain diseases—is known as a prion (*PREE on*). Prions, to put it simply, are protein molecules that have "gone bad," acquiring the ability to cause disease. Normal proteins are long strings of building blocks called amino acids, and they must fold into just the right structure to function normally. Prions are theorized to be proteins that fold the wrong way and that have the ability to bind to other proteins and cause them to also fold incorrectly. This causes an abnormal protein-folding "domino effect" that both causes disease and produces more infectious material.

That at least is the theory, and by the late 1990's there was considerable evidence to support it. Nonetheless, some researchers expressed doubts about the idea. Although they agreed that prions are obviously associated with certain brain diseases, they said the proteins may not actually cause the illnesses. The skeptics argued that some sort of microorganism, perhaps a virus, must be involved in prion diseases. Many other experts, though, predicted that the prion theory would be confirmed. They also speculated that other, more common, neurological disorders such as Alzheimer's disease and Parkinson's disease might also be caused by rogue proteins, though of a different sort.

A molecular assault on the brain

The handful of diseases known to be associated with prions are known collectively as *transmissible spongiform encephalopathies* (TSE's) because they are infectious and because the brains of people or animals that die from them are often found to be spongelike—riddled with small holes. Encephalopathies are any diseases of the brain.

Among animal TSE's are disorders affecting minks, mule deer, elk, and cats. Until the British mad cow scare, however, the best known prion disease in animals was scrapie, which occurs only in sheep. Sheep with scrapie become so uncoordinated they frequently fall over for no apparent reason. In some cases, they also develop an intense itch that causes them to rub against objects and scrape off their wool (hence the name "scrapie"). In 1936, researchers showed that scrapie could be transmitted to healthy sheep by injecting them with scrapie-infected brain material. The disease can also be transmitted in this manner to certain other animals.

TSE's that strike humans include, in addition to CJD, a brain condition called Gerstmann-Sträussler-Scheinker syndrome (GSS), characterized by shaking and a loss of coordination followed by *dementia* (deterioration of mental abilities); and fatal familial insomnia, a disorder that begins with sleeplessness and progresses to dementia. They also include a bizarre brain disease that was noted among an ethnic group called the Fore in the highlands of Papua New Guinea. It was there, in 1957, that the study of human prion diseases began.

That year, two physicians—D. Carleton Gajdusek of the National Institutes of Health (NIH) in Bethesda, Maryland, and Vincent Zigas of the Australian Public Health Service—journeyed to the Fore homeland to study the strange, fatal illness that other Westerners had described. Those earlier visitors had named the mysterious ailment kuru, which is a Fore word meaning to shake or be afraid. People afflicted with kuru lost their coordination, developed tremors, and finally became demented and died. The Fore called the disease the "laughing death" because in its later stages it caused fits of giggling.

Gajdusek and Zigas discovered that people contracted the disease through ritual cannibalism: The Fore tribe honored their dead relatives by eating their brains. The Fore abandoned cannibalism soon thereafter, and kuru has all but disappeared.

Gajdusek decided to do further research on kuru. In mid-1960's, he and his fellow investigators at the NIH found that chimpanzees injected with brain material from people who had died of kuru developed the disease. Clearly there was some sort of infectious agent involved in the disease. In 1976, Gajdusek won the Nobel Prize in medicine for his research on kuru.

After Gajdusek reported his findings about kuru, researchers found that several other human and animal brain diseases could also be transmitted via injections of brain material. Gajdusek himself showed that CJD was infectious in this way. But what was transmitting the infection in these illnesses, which were now being called TSE's? Some scientists proposed that an unknown type of virus was at work. Because TSE's take months or years to develop after infection, a so-called slow virus was suggested as the infectious agent. A few such viruses, which reproduce much more slowly than the typical virus, were already known to medical researchers, and TSE's appeared to fit the profile of

Mad cow disease
In 1996, "Mad cow disease"—bovine spongiform encephalopathy (BSE), a fatal brain condition of cattle—was linked to a similar human disorder that struck more than a dozen people in the United Kingdom. The individuals were thought to have contracted their illnesses by eating beef from BSE-infected cattle. Both the BSE and the human disease were linked with *prions*, abnormal proteins that are involved in several human and animal brain diseases.

Prions—a new agent of infection?

Prions are abnormal protein particles found in the brains of humans and animals afflicted with several devastating brain diseases. Unlike viruses and bacteria, which contain genes, prions apparently can both infect cells and *replicate* (duplicate) themselves—thus spreading the infection—without genes. If so, this represents a new kind of infection, because genes had always been thought essential for replication.

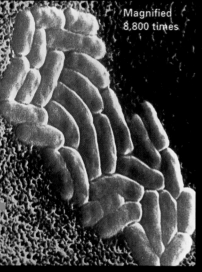

Magnified 8,800 times

Magnified 82,500 times

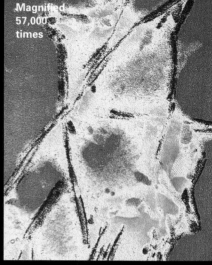

Magnified 57,000 times

Bacteria

Bacteria are one-celled organisms. While some bacteria are helpful, others, such as the pneumonia bacterium, *above*, cause disease. Bacteria replicate rapidly and can cause illness in hours or days. A typical bacterium has several thousand genes.

Viruses

Viruses—such as the adenoviruses, *above*, which cause respiratory illness in animals—are extremely tiny microorganisms that are a major cause of disease. A virus consists of a few to several hundred genes wrapped in a protein envelope. A viral infection can be rapid, though some take months or years to develop.

Prions

Prions, such as ones extracted from the brain of a cow stricken with BSE—blue strands, *above*—are incorrectly shaped versions of normal proteins. As of 1997, no one had been able to find any genetic material in prions. Prion diseases usually take years to develop but can progress rapidly once symptoms start.

diseases caused by these microorganisms. Yet no one had been able to find any sort of virus in brain material from a person or animal that had died of a TSE.

The mystery deepened in 1966 and 1967, when researchers in England reported that the infectious agent causing scrapie might lack *nucleic acids*, the genetic material—called DNA and RNA—that carries coded instructions for all life processes. Specialized molecules in cells follow those instructions to manufacture a large variety of proteins needed by the body. The British scientists had exposed scrapie-infected brain matter to radiation, which usually destroys nucleic acids, and found that it could still transmit scrapie. If the scrapie infectious agent truly did not possess any nucleic acid, it couldn't be a virus or any other known microorganism, all of which contain DNA or RNA (or both).

At about the same time, a British mathematician named J. S. Griffith made a remarkable suggestion. Griffith said it might be possible for a protein to fold itself in an abnormal way and act as an infectious agent. This notion was so contrary to accepted ideas about how infections occur that it was ignored for many years until further research indicated that Griffith might have been right.

The discovery of prions

In 1982, a research team at the University of California at San Francisco (UCSF), led by neurologist and biochemist Stanley B. Prusiner, published a startling research paper in the journal *Science*. Prusiner and his colleagues reported that they had succeeded in purifying a substance, extracted from the brains of hamsters infected with scrapie, that was made almost entirely of infectious material. They claimed that the material contained no nucleic acids, because they had subjected the extract to procedures that destroy DNA and RNA. Nonetheless, the scientists said, the extract still had the power to cause scrapie. On the other hand, when they exposed the brain material to substances known to damage or destroy protein, it became less infectious.

From these results, the researchers deduced that the infectious material must be a protein, which they named a "prion," for "proteinaceous infectious agent." They said this unusual protein apparently had the ability to reproduce itself, and thereby spread an infection, in the absence of genetic material. This was a radical idea, because it was universally accepted among biologists that only nucleic acids are capable of self-duplication.

Isolating this unusual protein was the next step in Prusiner's research. He and his associates continued to purify the infectious brain material until they had reduced it to copies of a single protein, which they called PrP, for "prion protein." But the protein was a mystery to the investigators. They knew nothing about its characteristics, where it came from, whether it operated on its own or was carried by a virus, or how it made more of itself.

New findings about PrP were not long in coming, however. In the mid-1980's, researchers in the United States and Switzerland found that hamsters and mice have a gene in their cells that *codes for*—carries instructions for making—PrP. Other scientists later found the same gene in the cells of other mammals, including human beings. This finding indicated that PrP is produced routinely in the brains of mammals to carry out some necessary, though still unknown, function.

Research by Prusiner's group—and independent work by another American biochemist, Byron W. Caughey—soon showed that a disease-causing prion is an abnormal form of PrP. To distinguish between the two forms of the protein, they called the normal form "cellular PrP." But how, investigators now wondered, does cellular PrP become a disease-causing prion? And how does it then wreak havoc in the brain? In an effort to answer those questions, some scientists turned their attention back to human TSE's, particularly CJD and GSS, which they thought might also be caused by prions.

CJD was first described in the early 1920's by two German physicians, Hans G. Creutzfeldt and Alfons M. Jakob. This rare disease usually strikes people in their late 50's to 60's, and most sufferers die within a year of being diagnosed. Most cases seem to be *sporadic*—that is, they occur randomly, just as cancer often does. About one person in a million develops CJD in this way each year. Doctors further noted that about 10 to 15 percent of CJD cases run in families, an indication that the disease is sometimes caused by an inherited genetic *mutation* (molecular change). In addition, a few people have contracted CJD from a transplant of the cornea of the eye, a brain-tissue implant, or treatment with contaminated surgical instruments. Such cases, and the fact that scientists had succeeded in transmitting CJD to animals, showed that the illness can also be infectious.

GSS, another rare condition, provided other clues to the prion puzzle. This malady is similar to CJD except that it works more slowly, taking up to six years to kill its victims. GSS is usually inherited, but again, researchers had been able to transmit the disease to animals by injecting infected brain material into them.

Prusiner and his colleagues wondered whether prions might be involved in all cases of CJD and GSS, regardless of whether the diseases arise spontaneously, are inherited, or are contracted by infection. They set out to investigate that hypothesis.

New insights from a flawed gene

In 1988, Prusiner and neurologist Karen Hsiao studied the PrP gene from a man dying from an inherited case of GSS and compared it with PrP genes from normal, healthy people. They found that the sick man's gene contained a mutation. Then, working with geneticists Tim J. Crow of Northwick Park Hospital in London and Jurg Ott of Columbia University in New York City, they analyzed the PrP gene from a large number of other GSS patients. The researchers found the same mutation in all the genes. Because so many sick people had the same genetic defect, it was likely that this one small error—which produced a corresponding error in the protein coded for by the gene—meant the difference between good health and a deadly brain disease. In other words, abnormal PrP—a prion—was the apparent cause of these inherited illnesses.

In 1989, Prusiner and Hsiao followed up on that study with experiments in mice that had been genetically engineered to carry the same mutation in the PrP gene. All of the animals eventually developed a disease similar to GSS and died. The researchers then injected material extracted from the brains of the diseased mice into mice and hamsters that did not have the PrP mutation. After eight months, some of those animals also got sick.

This result, together with similar findings by other researchers,

The prion diseases

Prion diseases make up a group of fatal brain illnesses called *transmissible spongiform encephalopathies* (TSE's). In all TSE's, prions build up in the brain and cause the brain to become spongy—riddled with holes—resulting in progressively severe neurological impairment and finally death.

Infection	Host population	Mode of transmission	Symptoms
Scrapie	Certain breeds of sheep that usually are more than four years old; found in all parts of the world except Australia and New Zealand.	Unknown.	Irritability and restlessness; later scratching, biting, and rubbing of the skin, from which the name derives; patchy loss of wool, tremors, weight loss, weakness in the hindquarters.
Bovine spongiform encephalopathy (mad cow disease)	Mature cattle, mainly in the United Kingdom.	Commercial feed supplements containing ground-up tissues from sheep infected with scrapie. Might be transmitted from an infected cow to her calf.	A stumbling or high-stepping gait, changes in temperament, scratching, and weight loss.
Kuru	Members of an isolated ethnic group in Papua New Guinea called the Fore (very few new cases occurring).	Eating infected brain tissue of dead relatives (ritualistic cannibalism—no longer practiced).	Neurological weakness, palsy, uncoordinated movements, and dementia.
Creutzfeldt-Jakob disease	People in late middle age, though a new form in the U.K. in 1996 struck people in their teens and 20's.	Some cases occur spontaneously; others result from infection or from an inherited genetic flaw.	Dementia, followed by loss of coordination (though sometimes the reverse).
Fatal familial insomnia	People in late middle age.	An inherited genetic flaw.	An inability to sleep, developing later into dementia.
Gerstmann-Sträussler-Scheinker syndrome	People in late middle age.	Some cases occur spontaneously; others result from infection or from an inherited genetic flaw.	Shaking and loss of coordination, followed by dementia.

Sources: Encyclopaedia of Microbiology; Susan Lindquist, Ph.D., University of Chicago.

How prions may infect the brain

Researchers have proposed a theory of how prions infect cells and replicate themselves in the absence of genes. The theory contends that prions convert normal brain proteins to abnormal ones—new prions—simply by coming in contact with them and causing them to change their shape.

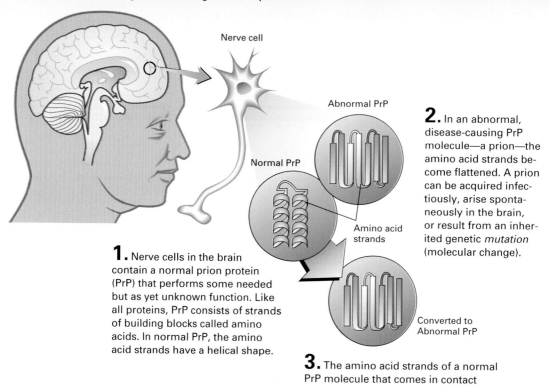

Nerve cell

Abnormal PrP

Normal PrP

Amino acid strands

Converted to Abnormal PrP

1. Nerve cells in the brain contain a normal prion protein (PrP) that performs some needed but as yet unknown function. Like all proteins, PrP consists of strands of building blocks called amino acids. In normal PrP, the amino acid strands have a helical shape.

2. In an abnormal, disease-causing PrP molecule—a prion—the amino acid strands become flattened. A prion can be acquired infectiously, arise spontaneously in the brain, or result from an inherited genetic *mutation* (molecular change).

3. The amino acid strands of a normal PrP molecule that comes in contact with a prion take on the same abnormal shape as the prion. According to the prion theory, these altered proteins then change still other normal PrP molecules, and the damage spreads.

strongly bolstered the idea that prions cause disease by themselves, unaided by viruses or any other microorganisms. Several PrP mutations were discovered in the following years, each associated with a different disease.

Also supporting the prion theory was the fact that the abnormal proteins appear to be "invisible" to the immune system, which does not attack them as it does viruses or bacteria. But if Prusiner was correct, it meant that prions cause disease in a way that is different from all other known infectious agents. The next challenge was to explain what that mode of infection might be.

In 1994, Prusiner and another UCSF colleague, biologist Fred Cohen, worked together to seek the answer to that question. And they soon found it. A prion, they reported, apparently has the ability to convert normal cellular PrP into abnormal PrP—new disease-causing prion particles, each identical to the original. A prion seems to carry out this bit of molecular sabotage by simply coming into contact with normal PrP and causing it to change its shape.

Studies at Prusiner's laboratory and by Byron Caughey indicated that normal PrP has an amino-acid "backbone" shaped like a *helix* (coil), whereas in a prion this helical structure has become flattened. Cellular PrP that is touched by a prion unwinds and mimics the flattened form of the protein, thereby becoming a prion. This change starts a chain reaction in which each newly created prion, in turn, converts other cellular PrP molecules into prions. The prions slowly accumulate in the brain, causing the characteristic damage seen in TSE's and leading to dementia and death.

Whether prions really do set off this cascade of events in the brain had yet to be proved. But an experiment reported later in 1994 by Caughey and another American biochemist—Peter T. Lansbury of the Massachusetts Institute of Technology in Cambridge, Massachusetts—indicated that they do. The researchers showed that if prions are mixed with cellular PrP in a test tube, the normal proteins change their shape to match that of the prions.

Infection with a prion can evidently start this process as soon as the sinister protein makes its way to the brain. With inherited TSE's, however, the fatal chain reaction is probably delayed for years, otherwise anyone inheriting a PrP mutation would be dead before reaching adulthood. Prusiner speculated that the protein produced by a mutated PrP gene, though slightly different in its biochemical makeup, contains a helical backbone and usually functions normally. Each such protein molecule, however, has a potential for "flipping" to the flattened configuration. Eventually, one of the protein molecules assumes the flattened state, becoming a prion. It then begins converting other PrP molecules to prions, and the damage multiplies until finally the outward symptoms of the disease begin to appear. A similar sequence of events is most likely involved with sporadic cases of TSE's.

Puzzling questions about prion diseases

Some aspects of prion diseases still puzzled researchers in 1997. For one thing, scientists had found that prions with the same mutation can produce different illnesses. This means that there must be variant types—what biologists call "strains"—of prions. But all previously known strains in infectious disease were due to genetic differences in the infectious agent. If prions truly have no genetic material, some other mechanism must be at work.

Scientists who favored the prion theory speculated that PrP might be able to fold itself into several different abnormal shapes, each resulting prion capable of causing normal PrP to fold in the same wrong way. Caughey and Lansbury tested that idea with hamster prion strains. They mixed normal hamster PrP molecules with different forms of abnormal hamster PrP in separate test tubes and found that in each batch of PrP, the normal proteins did indeed fold themselves to match the particular prion strain they were mixed with.

One human disease that seems to be caused by a variant prion strain is fatal familial insomnia (FFI). This rare hereditary disease, like other TSE's, usually strikes in middle age. In 1992, researchers at Case Western Reserve University in Cleveland and the University of Bologna in Italy linked this unusual illness to a PrP gene mutation in several Italian families afflicted with FFI. The mutation was found to be the same one that had been found in some people with inherited CJD. The researchers theorized that variations in abnormal protein folding—the phenomenon that had been demonstrated by Caughey and Lansbury—must be the explanation for how the same genetic defect could cause two diseases that are so dissimilar. As of 1997, researchers were still trying to prove this hypothesis.

They were also trying to explain why prions made by one animal species often have difficulty causing disease in another kind of animal. In the 1960's, for example, researchers discovered that it is difficult to transmit scrapie from sheep to mice. This phenomenon is known as a "species barrier." How easily various kinds of prions can cross the species barrier is very important to learn because of the link between mad cow disease and the cluster of CJD cases in the United Kingdom in 1996. Researchers want to learn if those cases were a fluke or if the prion that causes scrapie can infect humans as easily as it does cattle. No one could say for sure in 1997 whether the threat from mad cow disease was over or if thousands of people in Britain might eventually succumb to the new form of CJD.

Challenges to the prion theory

Also far from settled in 1997 was the prion theory itself. Although virtually all researchers agreed that prions are intimately involved in TSE's, some scientists still could not accept the idea that a protein molecule can by itself cause disease. The skeptics continued to search for the elusive nucleic acids that they believed must be present for prions to reproduce themselves.

Most critics of the prion theory predicted that a virus would eventually be found lurking within the abnormal proteins. Others proposed that prions consist of a protein linked with a strand of nucleic acid. They dubbed this combined viruslike particle a "virino."

One of the most active research teams looking for viruses and virinos was at the Yale University School of Medicine in New Haven, Connecticut. In May 1995, neuropathologist Laura Manuelidis, leader of the Yale group, published a research article that indirectly implicated a virus in CJD. Manuelidis reported that she and her colleagues had infected animals with brain extracts from CJD patients that were rich in prion proteins but low in genetic material. These extracts were infectious, but not very. On the other hand, extracts with a higher proportion of nucleic acids were extremely infectious, suggesting that genetic material may be necessary for a prion infection.

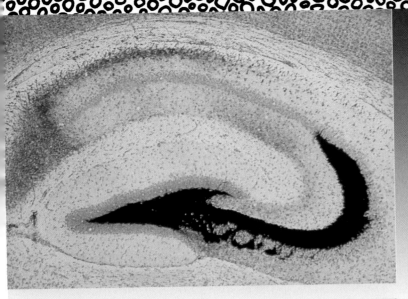

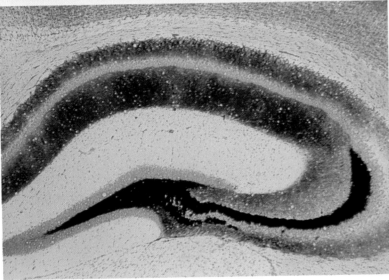

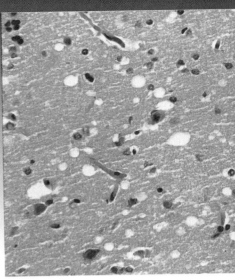

The ravages of prions

Prion diseases devastate the brain, producing a build-up of abnormal proteins and riddling the brain with tiny holes, giving it a spongelike appearance. Normal brain tissue from a sheep, *above left,* shows well-defined structures. Brain tissue from a sheep that had been suffering from a prion disease called scrapie, *left,* has visibly degenerated. Holes (white spots) are scattered through the brain tissue of a person who died of Creutzfeldt-Jakob disease, *above.*

Other research posing a challenge to the prion theory was reported in January 1997 by Dominique Dormont, a researcher at France's Atomic Energy Commission neurovirology laboratory in Fontenay-aux-Roses. Dormont and his colleagues injected healthy mice with brain matter from cattle with BSE and found that all the mice developed degenerative brain disease. But when the scientists examined the animals' brains, they could not find prions in all of them. The investigators then extracted brain material from each of the animals and injected the extracts into another set of healthy mice. Most of those mice also sickened and died—even if injected with an extract with no detectable prions—and the animals had a greater amount of prions in their brains than those in the first group. The procedure was repeated with a third group of mice, and the amount of prions increased fur-

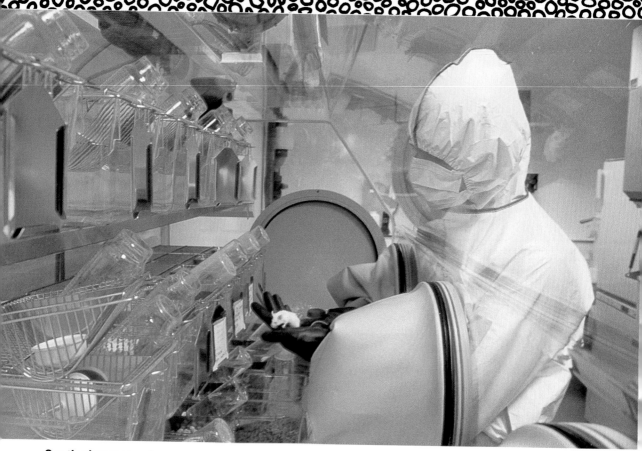

Continuing research

Swathed in protective clothing, a scientist handles a mouse infected with BSE. Researchers labored in 1997 to learn the true nature of prions. Many scientists predicted that the prion theory would be confirmed, while others maintained that prions would eventually be found to contain genetic material. Some investigators theorized that the abnormal proteins harbor a virus, while others speculated that prions are linked with strands of genes, forming infectious particles called virinos.

ther. Dormont concluded from these results that prions might be intimately involved in TSE's and cause much of the brain damage associated with them but not be the actual cause of the diseases. Some "unidentified agent"—presumably a virus or virino—may be at work in TSE's, Dormont said.

The prion debate seemed fated to continue until researchers can make a demonstration of prions' ability to cause infection that completely rules out the presence of nucleic acids. Scientists said the ultimate test would be to construct prions in the laboratory from biochemical building blocks and then show that the synthesized proteins can produce brain disease in animals. As of 1997, however, no one had been able to make prions from scratch.

If prions could be shown to cause TSE's on their own, researchers would finally have a starting point for treating or preventing these devastating illnesses. Prusiner suggested, for example, that it might be possible to develop drugs that stabilize abnormal PrP molecules produced by mutated genes, preventing the proteins from flipping to the prion shape.

Ongoing research may also help determine whether other proteins that can change their shape are involved in more common nervous system diseases, such as Alzheimer's disease, Parkinson's disease, and amyotrophic lateral sclerosis (ALS, or Lou Gehrig's disease). Although these diseases are definitely not infectious, they have certain similarities to human TSE's: They usually occur later in life; they can run in families but also occur sporadically; and they cause severe damage to brain or nerve cells and form deposits of abnormal proteins.

Research indicates that once abnormally folded protein molecules start to accumulate in the brains of people with these illnesses, they cause other proteins of the same type to flip to the same incorrect configuration. Over time, larger and larger amounts of the abnormal proteins build up in the brain. These proteins, though noninfectious, have the same flattened amino-acid strands seen in prions. Scientists hope that findings about these abnormal proteins will lead to a better understanding of prions—and vice versa.

Insights into abnormal protein folding have also come from research on yeast. Since the 1960's, geneticists have puzzled over the ability of these one-celled organisms to inherit certain characteristics from their "mother" cells that couldn't be attributed to genetics. In 1994, an NIH yeast researcher, Reed B. Wickner, reported that the passing of these particular traits from one generation of yeast to the next might be explained by the inheritance of abnormally folded proteins, which he called yeast prions.

Wickner and other researchers later reported that yeast cells do indeed contain abnormal proteins. And like the prions associated with TSE's, the yeast prions seem able to cause other proteins of the same type to fold abnormally. Unlike human and animal prions, however, the abnormal folding pattern is not passed from one cell to another except when yeast cells divide—that is, the yeast prions are not infectious. Yeast prions seem to represent a new form of inheritance based on protein structure rather than genes. This finding suggests that self-perpetuating changes in protein folding my be common in nature. Scientists studying yeast hoped their studies might come to supplement those of researchers investigating TSE's and other degenerative brain diseases and provide insights into how abnormal protein folding might be controlled.

And so research on prions continued—as did the controversy surrounding it. Whether the prion theory as espoused by Prusiner and his advocates, with its challenge to established scientific wisdom about the nature of infection, would finally be proved true or refuted was still very much an open question in 1997. Nonetheless, the unfolding tale had already taught researchers a humbling lesson: There are many more chapters yet unopened in the book of life.

For further reading:

Lanchester, John. "A New Kind of Contagion." *The New Yorker,* Dec. 2, 1996, pp. 70-81.
Prusiner, Stanley B. "The Prion Diseases." *Scientific American,* January 1995, pp. 48-57.
Mestel, Rosie. "Putting Prions to the Test." *Science,* July 12, 1996, pp. 184-189.

Scientists are investigating a strange world of exotic creatures, unique geology, and great mineral wealth—the deep ocean.

Exploring the
Ocean Abyss

By Peter R. Limburg

Opposite page:
The Johnson Sea Link, a four-person submarine, is just one of many different undersea vehicles that oceanographers are using to explore the deep ocean.

The deep ocean is a world that seems as alien to human beings as a planet in a science-fiction novel. It is a realm of absolute darkness, where sunlight never penetrates and the frigidly cold water exerts pressures measured in tons per square inch. The ocean floor is a landscape of rolling plains, deep canyons, and dramatic mountain chains, all formed by vigorous geologic activity. Here, molten rock from deep within the Earth forms new areas of sea floor and hot springs called hydrothermal vents belch clouds of superhot water and minerals from deep within the crust into the surrounding water. The vents and the areas around them are home to a wealth of strange creatures—microbes that feed on sulfur compounds erupting from the springs; six-foot, red-tipped worms fed by colonies of bacteria living within their guts; and bizarre animals that resemble limp dandelions.

In August 1996, scientists reported that the vents harbor a form of life that is truly alien to our world of air and sunlight. Researchers at The Institute for Genomic Research (TIGR) in Rockville, Maryland, announced that they had mapped the entire *genome* (genetic code) of a single-celled organism called *Methanococcus jannaschii*. Taken from the sides of a vent 2 miles (3 kilometers) beneath the Pacific Ocean in 1982, the organism resembled true bacteria in that it was composed of a single cell that had no nucleus. Genetically, however, it was in many ways closer to plants and animals—organisms whose cells have nuclei.

Terms and concepts

Abyss: The deep ocean beyond the continental shelves.

Abyssal hill region: Flat expanses of the ocean floor where mountains, ridges, and valleys have been buried under a heavy blanket of sediment.

Abyssal plain: Extremely flat plains on the sea bottom covered by thick layers of sediment.

Archaea: Microorganisms, resembling bacteria, that live in and around hydrothermal vents and which constitute a third branch of life on Earth.

Autonomous underwater vehicle (AUV): An unmanned exploration robot controlled by an onboard computer.

Continental shelf: A relatively shallow, gently sloping underwater plain that borders a continental coastline.

Hydrothermal vent: A sea-floor geyser that emits superhot water and clouds of minerals from deep within the Earth's crust.

Rift: A gap in the Earth's crust formed when adjoining crustal plates move apart.

Remote-operated vehicle (ROV): An unmanned exploration vessel controlled by a human pilot aboard a surface ship.

Satellite gravimetry: The use of radar from an orbiting satellite to measure the varying height of the ocean surface caused by differences in the gravitational pull of subsurface features on the surrounding water. The shape of the underlying sea floor is calculated from these variations.

Seismic reflection profiling: The reflection of artificially created sound waves off the ocean floor to discern subsea features.

The author:
Peter R. Limburg is a free-lance writer.

Furthermore, it lived under conditions that no bacterium could survive. The TIGR scientists concluded that *M. jannaschii* belongs to a third kingdom of organisms—literally, a new kind of life form—the *Archaea*. The significance of this discovery was not completely understood in 1997, but it was already causing a revolution in biological thinking. As one researcher remarked: "It shows how little we know about life on this planet."

It is remarkable, but not surprising, that we could have shared the planet with a third branch of life for so long while knowing nothing of its existence. Even as scientists study the features of Mars and Venus, the deepest recesses of our own ocean remain largely a mystery. The ocean covers more than 70 percent of the Earth's surface—more than twice as much as all the land masses combined—and yet human beings have explored only a tiny fraction of it. But that is changing. The pace of undersea exploration is increasing, and the benefits of studying the ocean are moving beyond the realm of theory. By the mid-1990's, many geological features of the ocean floor had been mapped and many of the unusual creatures that inhabit its depths classified. Meanwhile, oceanographers were developing new tools and methods for exploring the deep, including a variety of advanced submersible vehicles. We are embarked on a real-life voyage to the bottom of the sea that promises to change the way we view the ocean.

The geology and life forms of the abyss

The ocean floor was long thought to be a barren, featureless "desert." It seemed unlikely that the cold, black depths could be hiding anything of interest or sustaining any form of life. People referred to the deep ocean as the abyss, from the Greek word *abyssos*, which means "without bottom." But as scientists began to explore ever farther beneath the ocean surface in the 1900's, it became clear that the abyss holds many interesting secrets and that its geology is strikingly varied.

If all the water could be removed from the world ocean, the continents would look like high plateaus rising above the sea floor, each bordered by a relatively shallow, gently sloping plain called a continental shelf. The continental shelves are hundreds of miles wide in some places, and nearly nonexistent in others. At a depth of about 90 to 180 meters (300 to 600 feet), the continental shelves drop off steeply to the abyss. The average depth of the ocean beyond the continental shelves is about 4,800 meters (16,000 feet), but this figure is somewhat deceptive because the ocean floor includes many tall submerged mountains as well as trenches that can be 5 to 11 kilometers (3 to 7 miles) deep.

About 10 percent of the ocean floor consists of abyssal plains, which marine geologists believe are the flattest areas on Earth. The abyssal plains are found in several regions, where solid particles from rivers and from the shells of tiny marine organisms settle to the bottom to form thick, smooth layers of sediments. Farther out in the ocean, most sediment comes from the shells of tiny marine organisms. The shells drift slowly down through the water when the organisms die and accu-

mulate on the bottom. The lower layers of the sea-floor sediments become packed hard by the weight of the sediment above them. The deepest sediments are several kilometers thick and nearly 200 million years old.

Abyssal hill regions, which cover an estimated one-fourth to one-third of the deep-sea floor, are almost as flat as the true abyssal plains, but they are underlain by mountains, ridges, and valleys. These features are buried under a heavy blanket of sediment. Here and there, the top of a particularly lofty peak protrudes from the sediment.

The most prominent feature of the deep-ocean floor is the Mid-Ocean Ridge, an enormous undersea mountain chain. When explorers first discovered evidence of the Mid-Ocean Ridge in the mid-1800's, they thought there were many separate ridges in each ocean, so they gave each part of the ridge they found a different name, such as the Mid-Atlantic Ridge, which divides the Atlantic Ocean nearly down the middle. Since then, they have learned that the Mid-Ocean Ridge is a single formation stretching about 60,000 kilometers (37,000 miles) around the globe. However, the original names for its various segments are still often used.

The Mid-Ocean Ridge marks a line along which major plates of the Earth's crust are pulling apart at a rate of 1 to 2 centimeters (0.4 to 0.8 inch) a year to form new ocean floor. As the plates separate, molten lava rises up from below to fill the *rifts* (gaps), solidifying as it meets the icy-cold seawater. As the oceanic plates move away from the rifts, the valleys between the ridges slowly become filled with sediment until, after millions of years, they become abyssal hill regions.

Where an oceanic plate collides with a continental plate, a subduc-

More than 70 percent of the Earth's surface lies beneath the sea. The ocean bottom has varied geologic features. Continental shelves, which border the continents, are places where the ocean floor is relatively shallow. Beyond the shelves, the sea floor drops steeply downward. A chain of mountains called the Mid-Ocean Ridge stretches for about 60,000 kilometers (37,000 miles) along the ocean floor. The ridge marks the boundaries between the huge individual plates that make up the Earth's crust.

About the Abyss:
Geologic features

- The Mid-Ocean Ridge, a chain of peaks, ridges, and valleys formed by volcanic action, stretches about 60,000 kilometers (37,000 miles) around the globe.

- Ocean-floor sediment accumulates very slowly. Although most sediment is soil carried to the ocean by rivers and the remains of marine organisms, scientists have found that some sediment is dust from outer space.

- Abyssal hill regions are areas of the ocean floor where undersea mountains and valleys have been buried under sediment.

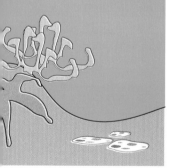

tion zone is formed. At a subduction zone, the dense oceanic plate is forced downward, beneath the lighter continental plate, and begins a slow descent back into the Earth's interior, where it is melted down again. The colliding plates and heat make subduction zones regions of volcanic activity and earthquakes.

Subduction zones are marked by deep trenches hundreds of kilometers in length. A trench is formed when an oceanic plate drags some of the crust downward with it as it dives beneath a continental plate. Most of the world's oceanic trenches are found in the Pacific; the only major one in the Atlantic is the Puerto Rico Trench. This is the deepest point in the Atlantic Ocean: 8,648 meters (28,374 feet) below sea level. The deepest known spot on Earth is the Challenger Deep of the Mariana Trench in the central Pacific Ocean, measured at 11,033 meters (36,198 feet) below sea level.

The water pressures at such depths are incredible. At the bottom of the Mariana Trench, the 11 kilometers (7 miles) of overlying water exert a pressure of more than 1,100 kilograms per square centimeter (16,000 pounds per square inch). At that pressure, an unprotected human being would be crushed to death. And yet, even in such a hostile environment there is life, including a primitive type of shrimp.

At lesser depths of the deep ocean, marine biologists have found hundreds of life forms, ranging from single-celled microorganisms to crabs, worms, and fish. There are no plants because there is no light to support *photosynthesis,* the process by which plants use the energy of sunlight to grow. Most of the food that sustains life at the bottom is organic debris that drifts down from the waters nearer the surface. Also, hydrothermal vents and *cold seeps* (areas where methane escapes from deeply buried deposits) support dense populations of specialized bacteria that live by *chemosynthesis*—the manufacture of nutrients from hydrogen sulfide or methane. Animals that live near the vents feed on these bacteria and on each other.

The beginning of deep-sea exploration

The knowledge we currently have about the deep ocean has been a long time coming. The exploration of the deep ocean floor began in 1856, with the laying of the first telegraph cable across the Atlantic Ocean. To lay the cable correctly, it was necessary to make detailed depth measurements of the sea floor along the cable's 3,200-kilometer (2,000-mile) route between Newfoundland and the southwest corner of Ireland. These readings were made with a *sounding line,* a strong, thin cord with a heavy sinker at one end. The line was marked at regular intervals, like a giant measuring tape, to indicate depth.

The first major oceanographic expedition—for the sake of science rather than for commercial or military purposes—was made by the British naval ship HMS *Challenger.* From 1872 to 1876, the *Challenger* sailed the Atlantic, Pacific, Antarctic, and southern Indian oceans. Its scientists took water temperature readings at various depths, collected water for chemical analysis, dredged up samples of deep-sea sediment, much of it rich in plant and animal life, and made numerous soundings. The *Challenger*'s voyage aroused interest in deep-sea exploration, and in the following years several countries, including Germany and the United States, launched oceanographic expeditions.

New technologies add to knowledge of the sea floor

Deep-sea research got a boost with the invention of sonar in 1914. Developed to detect icebergs at night or in fog, sonar quickly proved to be an excellent depth-finder, much faster than the old sounding line. Sonar is based on the principle that sound travels through water at a rapid and fairly constant rate. A "pinger" mounted underwater on a ship's hull sends out periodic bursts of sound. The sound waves bounce off obstacles and get reflected back to the ship. By measuring how long it takes for the reflected waves to return to the ship, the distance to an obstacle can be calculated.

During World War I (1914-1918), Britain, France, and the United States refined sonar for use against German submarines. By the mid-1920's, most of the world's navies were equipped with sonar, and by the 1930's oceanographers were using it to map the sea floor. With experience, researchers learned that the speed of sound through seawater can be affected by changes in the water's temperature, pressure, and *salinity* (amount of salt), resulting in erroneous readings, so they worked out methods to correct these distortions. This refinement allowed oceanographers to accurately map portions of the sea floor. But because the ocean bottom is vast, only a small percentage of it could be mapped in this way.

In the 1930's, oceanographers also began adopting a technique called *seismic reflection profiling*, developed originally for use in oil exploration. In seismic reflection profiling, a large burst of sound is generated at the surface, and the sound waves that reflect from the ocean floor are picked up by an array of floating receivers. Originally, an explosive charge was used to create the sonic blast, but today a powerful air gun is used instead. Because the sound wave it produces is so strong, seismic reflection profiling not only reaches greater depths than sonar, it also penetrates sediments to give a true picture of the underlying bedrock.

Another frequently used exploration method is *coring*, which enables researchers to obtain cross-sections of sea-floor sediment. Coring is done by rapidly lowering a narrow, heavy, open-ended tube to the bottom. The tube plunges into the sediment and encloses a section of it. When the surface crew hauls the tube back up, a flap at the bottom end closes and prevents the sediment from falling out. Variations in the different layers of sediment reveal information about the history of the sea and of Earth's climate.

Core samples from bedrock are obtained by drilling into the rock, using equipment adapted from oil-well derricks. Drilling is done from special ships able to hold a constant position and equipped with sophisticated computers to guide the drill. The rock cores yield valuable

About the Abyss:

Island building

- A seamount is an undersea mountain that forms from lava when plates of the sea floor pass over "hot spots" in the Earth's crust.

- Over thousands of years, a seamount may eventually break the surface of the water to form an island. Both the Galapagos and Hawaiian island chains were formed in this way.

Exploring the Abyss

A number of manned and unmanned submersible vehicles have visited the extreme depths of the ocean abyss. During their dives, these vehicles have discovered some interesting creatures that dwell in the depths.

Alvin

Alvin, an American submersible, began exploring the deep ocean in 1964. It has been rebuilt and upgraded many times. *Alvin* can achieve a maximum depth of 4,500 meters (14,750 feet).

Trieste I

The *Trieste,* a type of submersible known as a bathyscaphe, in 1960 set a record for the deepest dive ever. The *Trieste* carried two men to a depth of 10,740 meters (35,800 feet) in the Challenger Deep of the Mariana Trench.

Glass sponge

Standing about 40 centimeters (16 inches) tall, a deep-sea sponge rises above the ocean floor on a stalk made up of glasslike strands of *silica* (silicon dioxide). These creatures are found at depths of about 2,000 to 4,000 meters (6,600 to 13,200 feet).

15,000 feet

20,000 feet

25,000 feet

30,000 feet

35,000 feet

Angler fish

A deep-dwelling species of angler fish is one of many deep-sea species to use *bioluminescence* (light generated by chemicals in its body). The fish uses a glowing lure on its head to attract prey close to its gaping mouth. Angler fish are found at depths of about 1,000 meters (3,300 feet) and below.

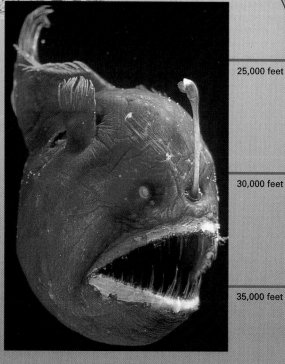

Kaiko-10000

Kaiko is an un-manned Japanese remote operated vehicle (ROV) piloted from a surface ship. In 1995, *Kaiko* descended into the Challenger Deep and came to within 0.6 meter (2 feet) of equalling the *Trieste*'s all-time depth record.

Shinkai 6500

Shinkai is a Japanese manned submersible used extensively in studies of the deep-sea trenches off the Japanese coast. *Shinkai*'s maximum depth capability is 6,500 meters (21,000 feet).

Jason

This unmanned ROV is carried partway down to the sea floor by a sled towed by a surface ship. In 1985, *Jason* took part in the historic discovery of the wreck of the *Titanic,* at a depth of 3,962 meters (13,074 feet). *Jason* is designed to reach a maximum depth of 6,000 meters (19,700 feet).

Tube worms

These creatures were first seen by the submersible *Alvin* in 1977, clustered around hydrothermal vents near the Galapagos Islands. Tube worms grow up to 1 meter (3.3 feet) in height and are 2 to 3 centimeters (0.8 to 1.2 inches) in diameter. They live at a depth of about 2,000 to 4,000 meters.

Opisthoproctus soleatus

This strange fish is about 10 centimeters (4 inches) long. Its tubular eyes stare upward, enabling the fish to detect the silhouettes of its prey from below, using the extremely faint light coming from the surface. These creatures live at a depth of about 1,000 meters (3,300 feet).

About the Abyss:

Creatures of the abyss

- Some oceanographers estimate that there are several million deep-ocean species—as many different types of species as are found in tropical rain forests or on coral reefs.

- To survive in the darkness of the abyss, many deep-sea species use *bioluminescence* (light generated by chemicals in their own bodies). They use light-producing organs to attract mates and prey, find food, or detect predators.

insights into the geological history of the deep-sea floor and of the Earth itself. For example, drill cores from the Mid-Atlantic Ridge contained proof that the Earth's magnetic field periodically reverses. The evidence was in magnetic patterns frozen in bands of lava that had flowed from each side of the Atlantic rift and solidified.

Like sonar maps, most maps of the ocean floor based on coring and drilling are compiled from data gathered from widely spaced swaths of the sea floor. Thus, the information they provide is patchy. The most comprehensive pictures of the ocean bottom are made by *satellite gravimetry*. Satellites in orbit around the Earth send out radar signals to measure the varying height of the ocean surface. These small but detectable variations are caused by differences in the gravity of underwater features. Massive objects beneath the sea exert more gravitational force on the surrounding water than small features do. Therefore, an underwater mountain pulls more water toward itself, forming a hump on the surface that may be up to 60 centimeters (2 feet) higher than the surrounding sea. Over a deep trench, on the other hand, the water forms a shallow trough. The shape of the underlying sea floor can be calculated from these slight variations.

Submersible vehicles carry researchers to the depths

But satellites and drilling rigs don't normally come to people's minds when they think of deep-sea exploration. For most people, undersea research means going down to the ocean bottom in a manned *submersible* (undersea exploration vessel). And many oceanographers agree that observations made from the surface can go only so far. A manned submersible enables them to get close to whatever they want to observe and see it with their own eyes. It also permits them to collect exactly the samples they want to study.

A submersible named the *Trieste I* holds the deep-diving record: a descent to a depth of 10,912 meters (35,800.5 feet) in the Challenger Deep of the Mariana Trench. The *Trieste* was not a true submarine, however, but a *bathyscaph* (from the Greek words for deep and tub). Like a hot-air balloon, it was designed to travel up and down. Not coincidentally, it was designed by Auguste Piccard *(oh GOOST pee KAHR)*, a famous Swiss designer of high-altitude balloons. The vehicle's cigar-shaped outer hull contained several large compartments filled with gasoline, which is lighter than water. For ballast, it carried some 8 metric tons (9 tons) of iron shot, attached to the hull by powerful electromagnets. To make the *Trieste* sink, the pilot released enough gasoline to lose buoyancy. To make it rise, he turned off one or more of the magnets long enough to drop the needed amount of ballast. The pilot and copilot sat in a pressurized steel sphere beneath the hull.

The *Trieste* made a series of successful dives beginning in 1953. On Jan. 23, 1960, it carried two men—Jacques Piccard, son of the inventor, and Lieutenant Don Walsh of the U.S. Navy—on the first-ever descent into the Challenger Deep. At the bottom of the trench, the men saw what appeared to be a bright-red shrimp and something they believed to be a type of flatfish. Most scientists, skeptical that fish could live at such a depth, insisted that the explorers had actually seen a strange type of creature known as a sea cucumber. Little information was gathered by the *Trieste*'s dive—all Piccard and Walsh could do was sit in one place and observe—but it demonstrated that descending to the deepest parts of the ocean was possible.

Long before the *Trieste* made its historic descent, scientists had discussed using small, maneuverable submersibles specifically designed for scientific observations to explore the ocean. It was Jacques-Yves Cousteau, coinventor of the original scuba-diving apparatus, who developed the first submersible used in undersea research. His little yellow *Soucoupe Plongeante* (Diving Saucer), launched in 1959, could carry two people to a depth of 300 meters (990 feet)—later increased to 410 meters (1,350 feet). The saucer's small size and maneuverability enabled it to travel along ridges and into canyons. Although a sphere is known to be the safest shape for a submersible's pressure hull, where its passengers ride, Cousteau opted for a flattened sphere for the Diving Saucer. This shape permitted the passengers to stretch out comfortably in a prone position rather than having to sit upright in a cramped spherical space.

Probably the world's most famous submersible is *Alvin*, operated by the Woods Hole Oceanographic Institution (WHOI) in Massachusetts. *Alvin* was launched in 1964, and was capable of diving 1,800 meters (6,000 feet). Its steel pressure hull was designed to carry a pilot and two scientists. Like all submersibles still operating, *Alvin* has been upgraded many times. Its newest hull, made of titanium, has a depth capability of 4,500 meters (14,750 feet).

Alvin has made many important dives. In the early 1970's, it took part in Project FAMOUS (French-American Mid-Ocean Undersea Study), a three-year study of the Mid-Atlantic Ridge in which oceanographers sampled, mapped, and photographed the gigantic undersea mountain range. In 1982, while investigating hydrothermal vents near the Pacific ridges, researchers on *Alvin* brought up the biological samples that turned out to be the mysterious *Archaea*.

The drawbacks of manned submersibles

But submersibles have their limitations. For one thing, they are designed to travel at speeds of 1.6 to 5.6 kilometers (1 to 3½ miles) per hour. This slow speed is sufficient for examining a small site, but it restricts a vehicle's range. Submersibles also take a long time to get to and from the sea floor. A typical dive may last six to eight hours, most of which is spent in vertical movement. Scientists become tired and uncomfortable after sitting in the cold, cramped pressure hull for several hours. Furthermore, the power supply of most submersibles is limited because they depend on batteries.

Expense is another limiting factor. Submersibles cost far too much to maintain and operate to simply go out and scour the ocean bottom, looking for interesting things. A submersible must be transported to a

About the Abyss: Unusual operations

- ROV's are capable of very delicate work. In 1989, an ROV named Jason used its mechanical arm to retrieve delicate ceramic objects from an ancient Roman shipwreck in the Mediterranean Sea without damaging them.

- The first important dive made by the submersible Alvin was not oceanographic at all; it aided in the recovery of an unarmed hydrogen bomb that fell into the Mediterranean Sea in 1966 when a U.S. Air Force B-52 collided with a refueling plane.

dive site aboard a surface ship, and another ship must first scout a proposed site with towed cameras and other instruments to make sure it is worth investigating firsthand. For example, a series of hydrothermal vents that *Alvin* visited in 1977 in the Pacific Ocean near the Galapagos Islands were first discovered by a towed temperature sensor, then double-checked with sonar, towed cameras, and laboratory analysis of water samples. Only then was the decision made to send *Alvin* down. Considering the work and expense involved with undersea exploration, it is not surprising that oceanographers often return to sites they have visited previously in order to study them more intensively. They are reluctant to visit a new site and come back with nothing.

Robotic vehicles gain in favor

The great expense of operating manned submersibles led inevitably to the development of cheaper and simpler alternatives. One is the *remote-operated vehicle* (ROV). An ROV is powered by an electrical cable from a mother ship on the surface and is piloted by an operator on the ship. ROV's can be equipped with every type of instrument a manned submersible carries. Video cameras on the ROV transmit images of the ocean bottom to screens in the control room. ROV's are smaller than manned submersibles, so they can explore places like small caves and narrow crevices. And, unlike manned submersibles, they can be operated for extended periods, because they are powered by generators on the mother ship and because the operator is not confined inside the vehicle. ROV's are also much cheaper to build because—since they do not carry a crew—they do not need a costly, heavy pressure hull. They need only compact pressure cases to protect their instruments.

Some ROV's are carried partway down to the bottom by an underwater launcher that is towed by a ship on the surface. The launcher is equipped with video cameras and sonar that scan the sea floor as the ship cruises along. When the launcher detects a site of potential interest, the operator releases the ROV, which then examines the site in detail. This two-stage procedure enables oceanographers to explore a much larger area of the sea floor than they can with an ROV alone.

The deepest-diving ROV is Japan's *Kaiko-10000,* a $50-million craft built by the Japan Marine Science and Technology Center, a research institution backed by government and industry. *Kaiko* is an example of a two-stage ROV: a launcher 5 meters (17 feet) long carries a 3-meter (10-foot) roving vehicle most of the way to the bottom. Designed to operate as deep as 10,000 meters (32,800 feet), *Kaiko* has actually been even deeper than that. In March 1995, *Kaiko* was piloted into the Challenger Deep, reaching a depth just 0.6 meter (2 feet) short of the *Trieste*'s record.

Another advance in undersea technology is the *autonomous underwater vehicle* (AUV). Like ROV's, AUV's are unmanned submersibles that must be transported to the dive site by a surface ship. Once it is in the water, though, an AUV operates independently, powered by batteries and controlled by a preprogrammed on-board computer. When its

High-tech exploration

Exploration of the ocean depths is benefitting from a variety of new technologies. Manned submersibles that can zip through the water, such as the prototype vehicle *Deep Flight I, right,* may one day enable researchers to reach even the most extreme depths in a short amount of time. Autonomous submersibles, such as ABE, *below,* are sent out to gather specific data on their own. They are extremely useful in situations where it would be unsafe or impractical to send a human explorer.

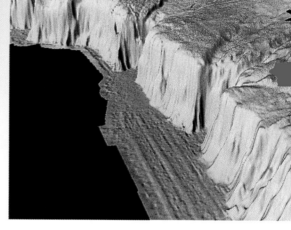

Computer modeling can convert data gathered by sonar into a three-dimensional image of a large segment of the ocean floor, such as the area along a continental shelf, *right.*

mission is completed, the AUV returns to the surface, where it deploys a buoy and a radio beacon so that it can be retrieved by its mother ship. An AUV named ROVER, operated by the Scripps Institution of Oceanography in La Jolla, California, crawls across sea-floor sediments on caterpillar treads and can function at depths up to 6,000 meters (19,700 feet). In 1996, ROVER descended to a depth of 4,100 meters (13,530 feet) some 200 kilometers (120 miles) off the coast of California to measure the oxygen consumption rate of organisms living in the top several centimeters of ocean-floor sediment. It gathered information that helped scientists estimate how much these creatures contribute to regulating the Earth's carbon supply, including the amount of carbon dioxide in the atmosphere.

A different type of AUV is WHOI's *autonomous benthic explorer* (ABE). The word *benthic* refers to the *benthos,* which is a technical term for the sea floor. Unlike ROVER, ABE is not a bottom crawler. Instead, it cruises above the bottom, taking photographs, water samples, or what-

About the Abyss:

Revelations at the vents

- The first hydrothermal vents (underwater hot springs) were found in the Pacific Ocean in 1977 near the Galapagos Islands.

- Life at the vents is based on energy derived from sulfur compounds. All other known living organisms depend on energy from the sun.

- Bacterialike organisms called Archaea that live in and around vents were declared a third branch of life in 1996. The other two branches include bacteria and all plants and animals.

ever else it has been programmed to do. In the summer of 1996, ABE gathered data on *geomagnetism* (the magnetic field generated by the Earth) on the Juan de Fuca Ridge off the coast of Oregon.

Like manned submersibles, ROV's and AUV's have their weaknesses. An ROV's cable can twist and malfunction or get snagged on obstructions on the bottom. The cable can also short out or snap, imperiling the crew on the deck of the surface ship. Also, AUV's are limited in the type of work they can do because they must be programmed in advance. If the vehicle encounters something unexpected, it cannot improvise as a human operator could. Furthermore, because working at sea is such an unpredictable enterprise, scientists who send an AUV out on a mission realize that the vehicle simply might not come back.

The benefits of deep-sea exploration

Whatever means are used, exploration of the abyss promises a variety of benefits. Several projects are currently underway to study the potential of the deep ocean for scientific and medical research, mineral and fuel supplies, and the disposal of hazardous waste.

Investigations along the Mid-Ocean Ridge, for example, have helped geologists understand how the Earth's crust is formed, provided clues about the deep structure of the planet, and greatly increased our knowledge about the nature of the Earth's magnetic field. And biologists are discovering animal species—and in the case of the *Archaea,* an entirely new branch of life—that were unknown just decades ago.

The unique physiology of deep-sea organisms, which have adapted to conditions found nowhere else on Earth, has led scientists to study whether they may yield new medicines. An increasingly serious problem for society is the growing number of disease-causing bacteria that over time have developed a natural resistance to antibiotics. Researchers, therefore, are turning to marine organisms in search of new substances from which they can develop medicines to treat bacterial illnesses. Scientists are hopeful that bacteria would take many years to develop a resistance to drugs derived from deep-sea organisms.

The ocean floor is also a vast storehouse of minerals. The most intriguing of these are manganese nodules, millions of which litter great swaths of the abyssal plains. Manganese nodules are metal-rich nuggets that range from half a centimeter to 25 centimeters (0.2 to 10 inches) in diameter. How they form is not fully understood. They consist chiefly of manganese but also contain iron, copper, cobalt, and nickel. Manganese is vital in making modern high-strength steels and other alloys. Cobalt and nickel, too, are used to make alloy metals. Manganese nodules could thus be an important source of some of these minerals. Several methods have been suggested for mining the nodules, including the use of remote-controlled, bottom-crawling robots.

Large concentrations of iron, *silica* (silicon dioxide, a common mineral), and other minerals, including gold, are known to exist in the deep ocean. But the value of these minerals is generally too small to justify the expense of retrieving them from the farther ocean depths.

Proposed sea-floor operations—and environmental concerns

Although the deep ocean floor may seem like an attractive source of metal ores, there are concerns about the possible harmful effects of sea-floor mining on marine ecology. For example, roughly 80 percent of the material brought up from the sea floor would be mud. After the valuable ore had been separated, the mud would be dumped back into the water, forming a large cloud of fine particles. This cloud would block light from *plankton* (microscopic marine organisms), which require sunlight to sustain themselves, resulting in massive die-offs of the microorganisms and disrupting the oceanic food chain. Because the sediment particles would be so fine, they could remain floating near the surface for months or years. And if ores were processed at sea, there is a risk that toxic wastes would be dumped into the water. Nonetheless, experts generally agree that the harmful effects of mining would affect only small areas of the ocean floor.

Oil is another important resource that the ocean floor may have in abundance. Offshore oil rigs have been drilling into the continental shelves—especially in the Gulf of Mexico and the North Sea—since the mid-1900's. Gradually, however, drilling operations have been moving into deeper waters. As of mid-1997, the deepest-drilling rigs operated in no more than 1,500 meters (5,000 feet) of water, but newer designs were in the works that would double that figure to 3,000 meters (10,000 feet). But if oil companies decide to drill for oil in the deepest parts of the ocean, completely new technologies will be required.

Like deep-sea mining, deep-sea drilling may also create ecological problems. Some experts warn that, as with any oil-retrieval operations, there would be a risk of breaks, leaks, and oil spills. Repairing such damage quickly at such depths would be extremely difficult.

Scientists are also studying the possibility of retrieving vast deposits of methane from the ocean floor. Methane, which ordinarily exists on Earth as a gas, burns more cleanly than coal or petroleum, and it may be an important fuel in the future. Methane is given off by the digestion process of bacteria living in ocean sediments. Scientists have found that the low temperature and extremely high water pressure at the sea floor traps methane in the form of *methane hydrates* (methane confined within ice crystals) in the sediment. Scientists drilling for sediment cores frequently hit pockets of methane hydrates. Nations like Japan, which have no oil of their own, are interested in tapping into these deposits, some of which are found off the Japanese coast.

But again, experts caution, the possible harmful effects on the environment would need to be examined. Methane is a powerful *greenhouse gas* (a gas that contributes to the warming of the atmosphere). If large quantities of methane were freed during the recovery process and allowed to escape into the atmosphere, there could be an unpredictable effect on the world's climate. Some scientists also suspect that the occasional melting of methane hydrate pockets causes huge underwater landslides, which in turn may trigger destructive *tsunamis* (huge waves caused by storms or underwater disturbances). Extracting methane from the sea might therefore contribute to even more landslides and

---

About the Abyss: Contents under pressure

- At the deepest part of the Mariana Trench in the Pacific Ocean, the pressure is about 1,100 kilograms per square centimeter (16,000 pounds—8 tons—per square inch).

- Crew members of Alvin's support ship create souvenirs by autographing styrofoam coffee cups, which are carried to the sea floor and back in the little sub's specimen basket. The pressure of the deep ocean squeezes the cups to a fraction of their former size.

8 TONS

The rewards of exploration

Researchers expect the exploration of the deep ocean to yield many valuable benefits:

- New biological knowledge, including the discovery of many deep-sea organisms, such as the *Archaea*.
- New scientific knowledge about how life developed and evolved on Earth.
- Greater understanding of the structure and geology of the Earth, including the nature of its magnetic field.
- New chemicals and other substances derived from deep-sea life.

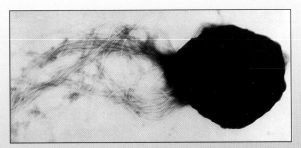

An Archaean organism, *Methanococcus jannaschii*.

- Possible safe disposal sites for nuclear and toxic wastes.
- New drugs based on deep-sea biology that may be used to combat infections or diseases of the immune system, such as arthritis.
- Vast deposits of manganese and other valuable alloy metals, in the form of nodules on the ocean floor.
- Fuel, including petroleum, methane, and hydrogen and diesel fuel synthesized from biological sources.

Manganese nodules

tsunamis. Other scientists, however, say that the possible adverse consequences of mining methane hydrates have been exaggerated.

Another potential use for the deep-sea floor is the disposal of such dangerous materials as nuclear wastes and toxic chemicals. Some experts have proposed using sites near the middle of large, stable oceanic plates, deeply covered with sediment, for this purpose. One suggested disposal method is to drill a deep hole in the sediment, pump the waste down in the form of a slurry, and push the sediment back into the hole. The clay particles of oceanic sediment present a formidable barrier to the movement of waste. They also have a great ability to capture and bind radioactive particles, trapping them permanently and preventing them from getting into the environment. Another strategy calls for encasing nuclear waste in heavy, dart-shaped containers called flechettes, which would be dumped from ships at specially selected ocean locations. The flechettes, weighing 4.5 to 5.5 metric tons (5 to 6 tons), would strike the soft sea floor at a speed of about 160 kilometers (100 miles) per hour, penetrating it deeply. The walls of the resulting hole would quickly collapse inward, burying the flechette.

Looking to the future

Most of these ideas for utilizing the deep sea have been around for many years. The idea of embarking on a new era of pioneering exploration—of the solar system as well as our own planet—became extremely popular in the 1960's and early 1970's. While space scientists envisioned colonies in orbit and on the moon, many oceanographers championed an "undersea NASA" effort to develop colonies on the ocean floor. But all these ideas fell victim to cuts in government funding in the 1970's. In the 1990's, however, the idea of exploring the deep ocean grew more popular again.

A potential new breed of manned submersibles was under development in California in the 1990's. An engineer named Graham Hawkes in 1996 successfully tested *Deep Flight I,* a prototype of a one-man submersible of revolutionary design, and *Deep Flight II* was in the planning stage. Instead of descending vertically to the sea floor, *Deep Flight II* would "fly" down, guided by winglike control surfaces. *Deep Flight II*'s expected top speed of 22 kilometers (14 miles) per hour would enable it to reach the bottom quickly and cover a great deal of territory. Thus, it could be useful for undersea exploration and photography.

Progress toward a permanent underwater base took a step forward in September 1996, with the installation of an unmanned facility called LEO-15 (for Long-term Ecosystem Observatory in 15 meters [50 feet] of water) in the Atlantic Ocean. LEO-15, a joint project of researchers and engineers from WHOI and Rutgers, the State University of New Jersey, is fastened to the sea floor at that depth off the coast of New Jersey. The observatory consists of two racks of instruments, each assembly surrounded by an outer shell of treated stainless steel secured to the sea floor by anchors. LEO-15 is intended to serve as a base for ROV's and for experiments that can be operated remotely by scientists anywhere in the world. While it is small and not designed for human habitation, LEO-15 takes advantage of computer technology to create a kind of virtual human presence in the ocean. Shallow-water experiments like LEO-15 may lead to similar projects at ever-greater depths.

In many ways, the course of deep-ocean exploration may parallel that of space exploration. Robotic vehicles have been investigating the solar system for decades, and in 1997, two U.S. space probes were scheduled to make the first visit to the planet Mars in more than 20 years. Closer to home, the Hubble Space Telescope has become a successful observatory in orbit, while the Russian space station Mir and the United States space shuttles have taken the first steps toward a permanent human presence in space. Similarly, the exploration of "inner space" will most likely involve the continued use of both manned and unmanned vehicles to explore the deep ocean in detail and of satellite and sonar imagery to map the sea floor on a wide scale. One day, these explorations could progress to the point where human beings might live and work in a permanent "inner-space station" beneath the sea.

For further reading:

Summerhayes, C. P. and Thorpe, S. A. *Oceanography: An Illustrated Guide.* John Wiley, 1996.
Ellis, Richard. *Deep Atlantic.* Alfred A. Knopf, 1996.

Crusader Against Delusion

An investigator of pseudoscience and claims of the paranormal talks about his work and the need for greater scientific literacy among the public.

AN INTERVIEW WITH JAMES RANDI
BY DAVID DREIER

*J*ames *Randi, known professionally as The Amazing Randi, had a long career as a magician and escape artist, but for years he has been better known as an exposer of frauds and an investigator of dubious claims and beliefs. Self-proclaimed psychics and healers, spirit channelers, and various other individuals claiming to have extraordinary powers have all come under Randi's scrutiny over the years. At the same time, he has labored to in-crease people's awareness of the scientific method and to discourage the casual acceptance of pseudoscience, which he views as a growing problem. Randi lec-tures internationally, makes numerous television appearances, and has written a dozen books. In 1996, with money donated by a computer-industry tycoon who asked that his support be kept anonymous, he established the James Randi Educational Foundation in Fort Lauderdale, Florida—his current hometown—to further his work. Randi's tireless efforts to expose deception and open people's eyes to misguided beliefs keep him busy year-round, and at age 69 he shows no sign of slowing down.*

In his younger days as a performing magician, *opposite page,* Randi's objective was to mystify people. Later in life, he became more concerned with helping people think more rationally so they could avoid being misled.

Science Year: For some 25 years now, you have been engaged in a personal campaign to combat irrational beliefs, test pseudoscientific and paranormal claims, and unmask individuals you suspect of hoodwinking the public—work that amounts to a personal crusade. How did you ever become so impassioned about these things?

Randi: My passion for my work stems from anger. I'm angry that people are being misinformed and that it's become politically correct to accept everything—to believe anything that anyone tells you, regardless of their credentials, or lack of them. And I'm in a good position to help set things right. As a magician, I know how people are fooled and how they often fool themselves.

Science Year: It is your stated belief that this growing tendency among the general public to accept unproven claims stems in large part from a lack of scientific literacy. Do you think this is a growing problem?

Randi: I definitely do. And not only has scientific understanding and education declined dramatically in the past 10 years or so, but now it's considered cool to know nothing about science. I talk to college kids who don't know the name Charles Darwin. They think he's a football player or someone on a quiz show. They don't have a clue that he was the great naturalist who developed the theory of evolution.

We have kids that come in here to the foundation and ask me about the lost continent of Atlantis or the mysteries of the Bermuda Triangle, and they're surprised when I say these things aren't real. And they'll argue that sure they're real, they read a book about Atlantis, or they saw a program about the Bermuda Triangle on TV. That's all the proof they need. We had a young woman in here the other day who said she believed in all these things, and when I asked her why, she said, "Because it's like, you know, energy." I said, "What do you mean by energy?" She said, "You know—energy. There's like a force, a power, and it's out there." This woman was an educated person—she had a graduate degree in pharmacology—and this was all she could summon up to explain these things to herself and to accept them.

Science Year: You indicated that your devotion to exposing pseudoscience, tricksters, and the like was a natural outgrowth of your career as a magician. How did you first get involved with magic?

Randi: Well, I was the child prodigy kind, and the school system in Toronto, Canada, where I grew up, didn't have any way of accommodating me. So they gave me special cards and permits so that I could spend my time at the Toronto Public Library and the Royal Ontario Museum and basically educate myself. My time was pretty much my own.

"As a magician, I know how people are fooled and how they often fool themselves."

The author:
David Dreier is the managing editor of *Science Year.*

When I wasn't at the museum or the library, I often frequented the Toronto theaters. And one day Harry Blackstone, Sr., one of the most famous magicians of the time, came to town. I'd never seen a magician before, and I was pretty amazed when he made a woman float in the air and passed a hoop around her. I decided right then that I had to learn how tricks like that were done. And that led to a lifelong interest in magic. I fell into the clutches of a few magicians—older fellows in Toronto who took me under their wing and taught me. I eventually got to be a pupil of Harry Blackstone, Sr., himself.

Science Year: Once you had been initiated into the mysteries of magic, did it change your outlook on life?

Randi: Yes, it did. I found out that "reality" is not necessarily what your senses tell you it is—that often the actual reality is very different from what you see, what you hear, and what you touch. Those sensory impressions are just an approximation of the true situation, and they may simply be what someone wants you to believe. Magicians make no bones about the fact that they are deceiving you in this way. But there are other people who pretend that the surface reality they're showing you is all there is. They want you to think that they're concealing nothing from you, when in fact they're concealing plenty.

Science Year: And seeing this sort of deception was what prompted you to go from being a magician to being a professional debunker?

Randi: Yes, but let me emphasize that I'm not a debunker. I've nev-

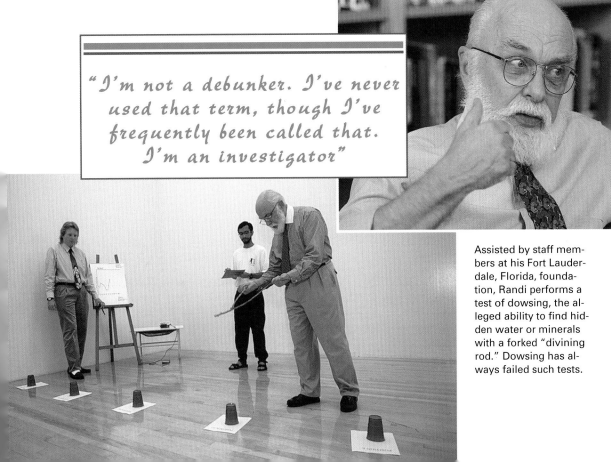

"I'm not a debunker. I've never used that term, though I've frequently been called that. I'm an investigator"

Assisted by staff members at his Fort Lauderdale, Florida, foundation, Randi performs a test of dowsing, the alleged ability to find hidden water or minerals with a forked "divining rod." Dowsing has always failed such tests.

An Amazing Life

James Randi never misses an opportunity to sound the alarm about what he sees as a growing problem of illogical thinking and scientific illiteracy in our society. To his listing in *Who's Who in America* is appended this message: "Irrationalism and the antiscience movement continue to grow, fed by the irresponsible media. Quack medicine, creation 'science,' TV psychics, and other pseudo-scientific matters are heedlessly and increasingly embraced by the public. This flight into superstition must be checked; that can be done if legislators accept their responsibility to look into the activities of those who publish wild claims with no foundation in fact. We are facing a crisis."

Randi, however, has never waited for elected officials to do their duty when there were charlatans or mistaken beliefs to expose. He unmasked his first fraud at the age of 15 in his hometown of Toronto, Canada. Dropping in at a spiritualist church to watch an evangelist who claimed to be reading and answering sealed questions from the congregation through "spirit communication," Randi quickly sized it up as a scam. He deduced that the minister was using an old stage technique known as the "one-ahead" method: The preacher would answer the previously opened question rather than the one in the sealed envelope he was holding. The outraged teen charged to the pulpit and exposed the deception. Expecting to be applauded, he was instead booed and then arrested for disturbing a religious meeting.

By that time, Randi was used to being an outsider. The lad—born Randall James Hamilton Zwinge in Toronto on Aug. 7, 1928—had been wandering the city alone since the age of 12, when the school system gave him permission to study independently. A frequent visitor to the public library and the Royal Ontario Museum, he taught himself trigonometry and calculus and learned to read Egyptian hieroglyphics. He also studied the performance of magic, tutored by some of the masters of the day, including Harry Blackstone, Sr.

At the age of 17, Randi dropped out of high school and joined a traveling carnival, billing himself as Prince Ibis the mind reader. Later, he became The Great Randall and appeared in Canadian nightclubs, where he performed sleight-of-hand magic and began honing his skills as an escape artist. While he was touring in Quebec, a police officer challenged him to escape from a prison cell, which he did—with little difficulty. The next day, a newspaper carried an account of the feat, referring to the young performer as "the amazing Randi." From then on, he was The Amazing Randi, escape artist extraordinaire, and he later legally changed his name to James Randi.

At the age of 27, with a growing reputation as a modern Houdini, Randi was invited to New York City to appear on a CBS television program called "It's Magic." As viewers watched live, Randi wriggled out of a straitjacket while suspended upside down from a cable high above Broadway. That feat led to many other TV appearances, including more than 30 on NBC's "Tonight Show."

Randi began making the switch from performer to investigator in 1973 when he learned that scientists at the Stanford Research Institute in California had allegedly confirmed the paranormal powers of a young Israeli man named Uri Geller, who claimed to have psychic abilities. The researchers said they could offer "no scientific explanation" for several effects Geller had demonstrated. Randi scoffed at that statement. In his opinion, he said, the testers had been duped by tricks of the sort "that used to be on the back of

Bound in a straitjacket and suspended above a New York City street in 1956, Randi struggles to free himself—and succeeds in 100 seconds.

Late in his performing career, Randi prepares to escape from a safe on *The Mike Douglas Show*, as guest Jackie Gleason assists him.

cereal boxes when I was a kid. Apparently, scientists don't eat cornflakes anymore."

In 1976, Randi joined with a few dozen kindred spirits, most of them scientists and writers, to establish the Committee for the Scientific Investigation of Claims of the Paranormal (CSICOP). The organization, now based in Buffalo, New York, assumed a leading role in the battle against irrationalism, looking into supposed psychic phenomena and reporting its findings in the organization's own publication, *The Skeptical Inquirer*.

By the time of CSICOP's founding, Randi had already become Geller's nemesis, speaking out against his alleged trickery at every opportunity and giving his explanations of Geller's methods in a 1975 book, *The Magic of Uri Geller* (renamed *The Truth About Uri Geller* when reissued in 1982). This ongoing battle culminated in a $15-million lawsuit that Geller filed against Randi and CSICOP in 1991. The beleaguered Geller claimed that Randi's relentless assault had defamed him and ruined his career. In 1994, the U.S. Court of Appeals ruled against Geller and ordered him to pay CSICOP $150,000 in penalties (later adjusted downward). Despite the victory, Randi was forced out of CSICOP, which wanted no further trouble with Geller. "They got wimpy on me," Randi says.

Geller hasn't been the only person on whose activities Randi has focused an unwelcome spotlight. One of Randi's best-remembered appearances on the "Tonight Show" was his 1986 exposure of a California TV evangelist, Peter Popoff. Randi had attended several of Popoff's services accompanied by volunteer helpers, capturing the minister on videotape and intercepting secret radio transmissions from the preacher's wife with tape recording equipment. Mrs. Popoff, Randi said, had been concealed backstage feeding her husband previously obtained information about members of the audience through a small concealed earphone.

Randi's tape showed the reverend striding up to individuals he had never met, greeting them by name, identifying their illnesses, and declaring them cured. He claimed to be listening to the voice of God, but the voice that the "Tonight Show" audience heard was that of Mrs. Popoff. After the program aired, the minister's credibility was ruined, and he was forced into bankruptcy.

Randi himself has flirted with bankruptcy. Defending himself in court against Geller and other self-styled psychics and parapsychologists had wiped him out financially by the mid-1990's. The money he paid to lawyers included most of a $272,000 "genius grant" that he received from the MacArthur Foundation in 1986.

Down virtually to pocket change, Randi was afraid he would have to give up his investigative work when suddenly his fortunes took a considerable turn for the better. In 1996, the head of a company in the computer field who admired Randi's work offered to finance the establishment of an organization devoted to public education and investigations of paranormal claims. The result was the James Randi Educational Foundation, which began operations in June 1996 in a converted house in Fort Lauderdale, Florida. Randi is president of the foundation, overseeing a staff of six people.

Randi says his benefactor, who requested anonymity, has not attempted to influence the foundation's activities in any way. Although Randi hopes the foundation will soon become self-supporting through grants and memberships, he is glad to know that he has a supportive patron.

The Randi Foundation is equally committed to both research and education. Besides conducting tests of alleged paranormal phenomena, it is compiling a collection of videotaped lectures on parapsychology, the occult, and related topics by Randi and other speakers that are available to researchers and schools. The foundation also hosts school groups for two- or three-day courses in critical thinking.

Randi has been a Florida resident since 1985 and an American citizen since 1987. When he isn't working at the foundation or wandering the globe giving lectures, he is at home with "several untalented parrots and numerous other creatures." He has never been married. "I was too good an escape artist," he says.   [D. D.]

er used that term, though I've frequently been called that. I'm an investigator. When I look into an alleged phenomenon, or a claim of paranormal abilities, or whatever, I don't set out with the attitude that "this is not so, and I'm going to show it to be not so." I can't afford that sort of attitude about a subject of investigation, because that would mean I've already made up my mind about what I'd like to discover about it.

Now mind you, I will not sit by my chimney for a long period on the evening of December 24th waiting for Santa Claus. My past experience and my common sense tell me that I'm not likely to obtain any fruitful results from that activity. Similarly, when I go into an investigation I naturally have a prejudice based upon experience and, as I say, common sense. I may tend to doubt the claims that are being made. But doubt is not denial. I have to be prepared to accept a genuine phenomenon if and when it presents itself.

Science Year: So there are, in fact, instances where you're not certain to begin with what's going on and you're willing to give the person the benefit of a doubt?

Randi: Oh, sure, particularly if it's something I've never seen or heard about before. In that case, I may have to see the alleged ability or phenomenon a couple times before I can conclude that it's a trick or a delusion and then proceed to explain it.

Science Year: You have examined the methods of a number of people claiming to have paranormal powers. The most prominent of them was the self-proclaimed Israeli psychic Uri Geller, who asserts that he can bend spoons and accomplish other extraordinary feats using only the power of his mind. In the early 1990's, after you had spoken out many times about Geller and written a book about him, he sued you unsuccessfully for allegedly defaming him. How did your ongoing battle with him get started?

Randi: It began back in the early 1970's when I heard that Mister Geller had been tested at the Stanford Research Institute in California. He did some demonstrations for them that were written up in the scientific literature as though they were carefully controlled experiments. And the Stanford people had accepted his "powers." That was like saying, "We challenged the magician David Copperfield to take a big box and a saw and cut a girl in two. And by golly, he did it right there in front of a huge audience of people all watching very carefully. He cut her into two and then put her back together again, and she's alive and well today. Thus, sawing a woman in half and putting her back together is possible."

Science Year: So in your opinion, all the supposedly mystifying things that Geller does are just tricks?

Randi: Well, speaking as a recognized expert in the field, I will say that I can see no difference between what he does and common tricks, all of which I can duplicate and teach a 12-year-old child to perform. Mister Geller says he does these things by divine power. All I can say is, if he does them by divine power, he's doing them the hard way.

Science Year: Didn't you serve as an adviser to the "Tonight Show" once when Geller was scheduled to appear on the program?

Randi: Yes. I told the "Tonight Show" people how to prepare for him, and they followed all my recommendations. As a result, Mister Geller was unable to exhibit any of his alleged powers. One of his demonstrations involved these little aluminum cans that 35-millimeter film used to come in. He would have 10 of these film cans on a tray in front of him, and one of them would be filled with water, or nuts and bolts, or whatever substance anyone wanted to secretly put inside it. Then Mister Geller would point to the cans one at a time without touching them, saying, "That one's empty, that one's empty," and each time he said that, the can he was pointing to would be taken off the tray. Finally, the one that was left was the one that had something inside of it.

Science Year: And so how did you thwart this particular demonstration?

Randi: Well, I had observed Mister Geller doing it before and—in my professional opinion as a magician—it usually had to do with the movement of the tray. When the tray was moved in any sudden way, the one filled can would move differently from the other ones because it was heavier, and that difference in movement was quite easy to see. So I told the "Tonight Show" people to coat the bottoms of the cans with rubber cement and then let it dry. Now the cans had a layer of slightly tacky rubber on the bottom. They wouldn't stick to a surface when you picked them up, but they wouldn't skid on it either.

On the show, the cans were arranged on a low table on the set. Mister Geller pointed to a couple of cans or so before they cut to a commercial, and when they resumed the demonstration a couple of minutes later, he suddenly gave up on it. He said he just didn't have a "feel" for it that night. ["Tonight Show" host] Johnny Carson told me later, "Boy, you should've seen him during the break." Carson said that while the band was playing, Mister Geller was sitting there kicking the table in time to the music, trying to get those cans to move—or at least that's my opinion of why he was doing that. Everyone on the show who knew what was going on got a good laugh out of it.

> "I can see no difference between what Uri Geller does and common tricks, all of which I can duplicate and teach a 12-year-old child to perform."

Science Year: Whatever may be the truth about Uri Geller's supposed powers, the field of parapsychology has gained a certain legitimacy by being explored at some of the top universities in the country. And researchers have claimed to find evidence of paranormal abilities in some people. Do you think any of these findings have any validity?

Randi: None of the results that you refer to have ever stood the test of time. Whenever you take a close look at any of these studies, you find that it's full of holes. The test of a valid scientific finding is that it can be reproduced independently by other researchers, but the parapsychologists haven't come up with one repeatable case, not one.

Science Year: And it's your feeling that they never will?

Randi: No, I can't say that. I can only say that it's not very likely. It's like that business of sitting by the chimney on December 24th. Your expectation has to be colored by your past experience. The history of these experiments indicates that there are no real phenomena there.

Science Year: What would you say was your most satisfying experience as an investigator?

Randi: Well, I think the investigation I'm proudest of falls in the category of pseudoscience. In the late 1980's, I went with a couple of other researchers to Clamart, France, outside Paris, to investigate the experiments of a very respectable scientist who unfortunately was, I believe, fooling himself about homeopathy. He said that he and his associates had proved that it works.

Science Year: Many people seem unsure of what homeopathy is. They seem to think it is some form of "natural" medicine.

Randi: Homeopathy is the treatment of illness with various solutions that have been diluted by a factor of millions, so they are essentially just water or alcohol. But supposedly the liquid retains a "memory" of the active substance. Homeopathy, in my opinion, is just quackery. There's no question about it. It doesn't work; it never has worked. It's been tested endlessly, and it's failed every test.

> *"The test of a valid scientific finding is that it can be reproduced independently by other researchers, but the parapsychologists haven't come up with one repeatable case, not one."*

Randi and James Gardner, executive director of the Randi Foundation, sort through claims of paranormal abilities from people seeking to win a $1-million prize that Randi has offered to anyone who can demonstrate such an ability under controlled conditions. As of 1997, no one had come close to winning the prize.

Science Year: Yet the French scientist thought he had proof that homeopathy is valid?

Randi: Yes. He had published a report in *Nature* magazine in the form of a scientific paper in which he said there were no negative results with his tests of homeopathic solutions, based on their effects on human blood samples—that is, there was always a measurable effect. He also claimed that his trials were double-blinded. In clinical trials with patients, double-blinding means that neither the researchers nor the patients know which patients are receiving the drug being tested and which are getting a placebo—an inactive substance. In the French study, the double-blinding involved an elaborate system of coding the blood samples.

When we examined the French team's lab books, though, we saw that none of the things that had been claimed about the experiments were true. We found that they hadn't blinded the experiments properly. And there were lots of negative results. But the researchers had made up all kinds of excuses to explain them away: bad water or bad reagents [reactive chemicals], or allergic blood, or what have you. Whenever it appeared that they had gotten positive results, however, they accepted them. That is not science and it's not the scientific method. When we repeated their experiments using a true double-blind approach, we found that the homeopathic solutions had no effect whatsoever.

Science Year: You also investigated the so-called psychic surgeons in the Philippines, who seem to plunge their hands into patients' bodies, with no surgical incision or instruments, and pull out "diseased tissue." Did you go into that inquiry with an open mind thinking that maybe those fellows were really curing people?

Randi: No, because what I saw was obviously sleight of hand. I could see exactly how it was being done. These guys were just pretending to thrust their hands into patients' bodies. And the "diseased tissue" looked a lot more like chicken guts than human organs, which is exactly what it was. I've duplicated this technique on television and in my lectures.

Science Year: Today, many people seeking health and well-being have accepted so-called New Age notions, such as healing with crystals. What is your opinion of these kinds of practices?

Randi: It's a very low opinion. I'll tell you, some of the things that get palmed off on gullible people these days are criminal. We have a hospital just down the way that offers "therapeutic touch." The practitioners of therapeutic touch call it medicine, but it's a song and dance. The nurse comes into the room and makes stroking motions above the patient's body to remove "evil vibrations," which she then throws out the window. Then she takes "positive emanations" from her own body and transfers them to the patient. Some of the people in that hospital are being charged $60 a day for that treatment. I recently conducted tests on therapeutic touch in Philadelphia and found it to be worthless. And I've invited nurses from the nearby hospital to come to the foundation for testing, but they've ignored me. They won't come anywhere near this place.

Science Year: You've singled out the media as a major cause of scientific ignorance among the public. How are they at fault?

Randi: The media have been singularly damaging in the respect that they present things that people would like to believe to be true, and they—the media—don't care whether they're true or not. I was interviewed right here for four-and-a-half hours for the "Biography" show on A&E [Arts & Entertainment], one of the cable networks, for a program on Nostradamus, the French seer of the 1500's. We talked about my book *The Mask of Nostradamus,* in which I argued that Nostradamus was not the great prophet that many people think he was. And how did the program turn out? They used me for a total of 40 seconds in a one-hour program—just showed me answering a couple of simple biographical questions, like when Nostradamus was born and where he lived. Most of the show was devoted to comments by true believers: "He was the greatest prophet of all time," "He foretold World Wars I, II, and III," and so on. Not one negative word about Nostradamus appeared in that entire program, because that's not what people want to hear. In the media world, the buck is the bottom line; truth is secondary.

Science Year: Do you think scientists bear some responsibility for the problem of scientific illiteracy by often remaining aloof from the public instead of trying to explain what they're doing?

Randi: Yes, I think there's some validity to that view. One of our greatest explainers, [Cornell University astronomer] Carl Sagan, died last year. It's a terrible thing that this man had to go at the age of 62. But he did a wonderful job while he was here, and we can all be grateful for that. Nonetheless, he was censured by his colleagues, who kept telling him, "Get back to astronomy, Carl. You're supposed to be an astronomer; what are you doing?" But his calling was much wider than that. The "Cosmos" series that he hosted on TV—and pretty much created and wrote as well—was seen by 400 million people all over the world. And many people said that was the first exposure they'd had to real scientific thinking and to the beauty of what science really can be. We need more of that.

Science Year: One reason that so many people have turned their backs on real science seems to be a distrust of science, a feeling that science and technology have made our world worse by giving it nuclear weapons, toxins that poison the environment, and assorted other evils. What's your comment on that?

Randi: I would tell those people that I can also point out that hundreds of thousands of diabetics in the world today are alive because of medical science, also hundreds of thousands of people who would be dead from smallpox and cholera and other illnesses. And the conquest of many diseases is just one of numerous benefits humanity has derived from science and technology. So you have to balance that against the horrors of World War II, for example. You have to consider both sides of the situation.

Science Year: Do you think there are any questions that science will never be able to explain?

Randi: Well, if you mean metaphysical questions like "Why are we here?," probably not. But that may be a meaningless question, like "Why is my beard green?"

Science Year: Your beard isn't green.

Randi: Exactly. And maybe there's no "reason" why we're here, I don't know. But as far as questions about the physical universe are concerned, I have faith in science. Whenever there's been a question that science can get its teeth into—when there's been solid evidence to examine—it's come up with a good, rational answer. It's the same with my investigations of all these so-called psychics. Whenever I've been able to get close enough to these people to examine their methods, I've been able to offer a rational explanation for what they're doing.

Science Year: Can you give an example of an investigation in which you were actually a little bit mystified about what

"The media have been singularly damaging in the respect that they present things that people would like to believe to be true, and they—the media—don't care whether they're true or not."

was going on and had to do some serious thinking before you could solve the puzzle?

Randi: Well, I was mystified years ago when I got a call from an editor at *Time* magazine asking me to investigate the abilities of a certain gentleman who claimed that he could take an LP record and, by just looking at the grooves on it with the label covered over or stripped off, tell you who the composer was and what the music was. And I thought that was quite remarkable.

But as soon as I started looking into it, the miracle began to shrink. The fellow was able to accomplish this feat only with classical composers from Beethoven to the present and then only with their complete works—it couldn't be selections from symphonies or other abbreviated pieces. It turned out that beginning with Beethoven, classical music took on varied forms that, for someone with sharp eyes, could be discerned as variations in the grooves of a record. This man was an ardent devotee of classical music, and he had simply familiarized himself with the groove patterns of various symphonies, concertos, and what not. And he showed me how he did it. He never claimed to have any psychic powers.

Science Year: Of course, the great majority of the people you have investigated insist that they do have such powers. And for almost 30 years now, you've been offering a reward to anyone who can demonstrate a true paranormal ability under controlled observing conditions.

Randi: Yes. It was $10,000 to begin with and stayed $10,000 for many years. Then a couple of years ago, a friend of mine in Canada, a retired magician, suggested that I ask for pledges from interested people around the world to increase the reward to $100,000 so it would make more of a news bite. So I floated that idea on the Internet, and within a few days I was up over $100,000. And now we have more than 300 pledges from fifteen countries totaling more than $1 million.

Science Year: How many people claiming paranormal powers have accepted the challenge over the years?

Randi: About 75 [as of early 1997], including both individuals and groups of people, but no one has

"I've always got to be prepared for the possibility that someone's going to come along with a paranormal phenomenon that really is genuine. It could happen. And if it did, it would turn science on its head."

come close to winning it. Only about 15 of the challengers have been frauds, however; most have simply been self-deluded, like this one fellow who said he could find diamonds all over the place. It turned out that he was just finding pieces of quartz and couldn't tell the difference. Quartz is just sand—we've got a whole beach of it here in Fort Lauderdale.

Science Year: Do you see any possibility of ever having to pay up on your challenge?

Randi: I think it's highly unlikely. One thing that concerns me, though, is that someday I'll be fooled by a simple trick. Or perhaps more likely by a complex trick, because there is technology out there now that I can see being used in mentalism and magic tricks—very impressive stuff.

But then again, I've always got to be prepared for the possibility that someone's going to come along with a paranormal phenomenon that really is genuine. It could happen. And if it did, it would turn science on its head.

Science Year: If that occurred, would you be upset?

Randi: No, I couldn't be upset, because it would mean that the world is an even more exciting place than I had supposed. It's exciting enough right now, but if there were a supernatural world, too, you would have to say, wow, we were wrong all that time. Many of the people who have made pledges to the reward fund have said exactly the same thing. They say it's worth it to them to find out that maybe there is such a thing as the paranormal. So these 300-plus people didn't necessarily pledge money in order to defy the phony psychics. At least some of them, I feel certain, made their pledges in the hope that maybe a real psychic will try for the prize and win it. And if that ever happens, they'll have made an investment in this wonderful, unexpected discovery.

Additional resources:

The James Randi Educational Foundation maintains a site on the World Wide Web. The address is http://www.randi.org

For further reading:

Randi, James. *An Encyclopedia of the Claims, Frauds, and Hoaxes of the Occult and Supernatural.* St. Martin's Press, 1995
Randi, James. *Flim-Flam: The Truth About Unicorns, Parapsychology & Other Delusions.* Harper & Row, 1980.
Randi, James. *The Mask of Nostradamus.* Scribner's, 1990.
Randi, James. *The Truth About Uri Geller.* Prometheus Books, 1982.

SCIENCE STUDIES

The Population Explosion

We are witnessing a world that is being stretched to its limits by population growth. With population pressures expected to continue—and to worsen—many scientists are sounding the alarm.

Introduction

With each passing day, some 220,000 people are added to the world's population. Scientists concerned with the Earth's rapidly growing population and its effects on nature have sounded the alarm and are urging international cooperation to search for solutions.

The global population is indeed worrisome. There were about 5.8 billion people living on Earth in 1997, and according to some experts, that number could reach 9.4 billion to 11 billion by the year 2050. The rapidly expanding population has dumped a raft of problems on a world already bursting at its seams.

Among those ills are a decline in the quality of people's lives, especially in the increasingly congested nations of the developing world. Rapid population growth has also degraded the quality of our air, water, and land.

Another negative effect of rampant increases in population is the rising demand for non-renewable resources such as fossil fuels—coal, oil, and natural gas. Some scientists also warn that unless population growth is checked, medical advances will not be able to keep pace with the startling number of diseases that are ravaging human communities.

In spite of the rising concern about population growth in the scientific community, some observers, including a number of conservative economists, contend that the world is far from being in a crisis. In support of their position, they cite a 1997 report by the United States Bureau of the Census that claimed that world population growth has begun to slow dramatically.

In spite of those findings, many scientists have come out in opposition to what they call a "don't worry, be happy" point of view. Two such scientists, biologists Paul R. Ehrlich and Anne H. Ehrlich of Stanford University in California, wrote in their 1996 book *Betrayal of Science and Reason* that some experts have "sowed the seeds of doubt" among policymakers and the public about the reality of overpopulation.

Predicting future growth is a tricky task. The question, though, is not whether global population will continue to rise, but by how much. In the meantime, scientists face an even tougher chore in trying to figure out how to squeeze more resources from an overworked planet.

The authors:

Dan Chiras is an adjunct professor in the Environmental Policy and Management Program at the University of Denver.

Scott C. Reuman is a free-lance writer.

The Surging Global Population

Every second that ticks away, four babies are born somewhere in the world. These births produce a net increase in the global population (births minus deaths) of about 220,000 people every day. When a year ends, there are almost 80 million more people on Earth than there were when the year began. In 1997, some 5.8 billion people inhabited the planet.

This rapid growth of an already large population has far-reaching social, economic, and environmental impacts. Not all of the impacts on the planet are immediately obvious, however, and many of the predicted effects are hotly debated among experts. The issues involved are very complex, and to begin addressing them we need to take a glimpse back in time to understand how and why the human population has become so large.

A problem of our times

The growth of the world's population is a relatively recent phenomenon. Anthropologists believe that *Homo sapiens*, the modern human species, appeared between about 400,000 and 300,000 years ago. Those early human beings were hunters and gatherers, moving from place to place in search of food. Life spans were short. High death rates kept the population stable.

About 10,000 to 12,000 years ago, people began to grow their own food. They planted crops and used simple wooden tools and irrigation systems. The development of agriculture made it possible for more people to live off the land. And so the human population began to grow.

Scientists estimate that 2,000 years ago there were about 138 million people in the world. A thousand years later that population doubled to 275 million. By 1650, the population had doubled again, and 200 years later, it had again doubled. At that point, around 1850, a phenomenal rise in the human population began, and population continued to soar through the 1900's. One United Nations (UN) report predicted that global population would reach 9.4 billion by the year 2050.

The Industrial Revolution

The major factor in this explosive growth, far surpassing the early influence of agriculture, was the Industrial Revolution. The Industrial Revolution began in Great Britain

in the 1700's, then spread to Europe and reached North America in the 1800's. During that time, many new developments spurred population growth. Metal plows manufactured in factories of the industrializing nations made it possible for farmers to cultivate more land and grow far more food than ever before. Gas-powered tractors, combines, and other farm machines greatly expanded the world's grain production and gave the human population the fuel it needed—a virtually unlimited supply of food—for unprecedented growth.

The Industrial Revolution also ushered in the age of chemistry. With it came new drugs to combat disease and illness. These medicines helped reduce the devastating epidemics of infectious disease that had killed millions of people.

Yet another advance that allowed people to live longer was the installation of municipal sanitation and water treatment systems. Treating sewage with chemicals before it was released into rivers and lakes killed harmful microorganisms and reduced the risk of infectious disease spread through drink-

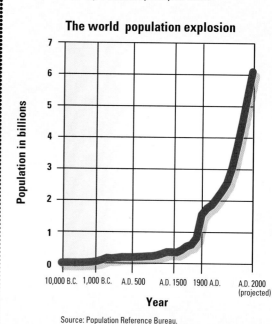

The population explosion is a relatively new phenomenon. Only since about 1850 has the world's population soared. Global population was expected to top 6 billion by the year 2000.

The world population explosion

Population in billions

Year

10,000 B.C. 1,000 B.C. A.D. 500 A.D. 1500 1900 A.D. A.D. 2000 (projected)

Source: Population Reference Bureau.

Factors producing the population boom

Ironically, although the population explosion is reducing living standards around the world, it was improvements in human society that brought about the population problem. Tremendous increases in food production, such as mechanized rice production in Malaysia, *right*, have made it possible to feed ever larger numbers of people. Another factor contributing to rapid population growth has been reductions in death rates brought about by better public health, such as immunizations provided at a mobile health clinic in Sierre Leone, *below*. Populations double rapidly in areas where birth rates are high, *below right*.

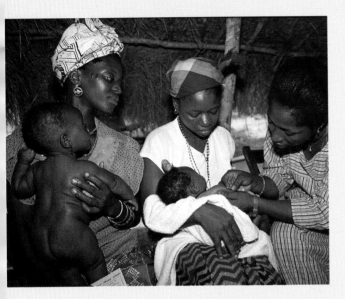

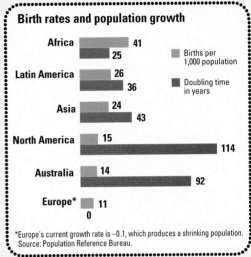

Birth rates and population growth

Region	Births per 1,000 population	Doubling time in years
Africa	41	25
Latin America	26	36
Asia	24	43
North America	15	114
Australia	14	92
Europe*	11	0

*Europe's current growth rate is −0.1, which produces a shrinking population.
Source: Population Reference Bureau.

ing water. Treating drinking water had similar benefits. As a result of these advances, the death rate plummeted. More children than ever survived into adulthood, married, and had children of their own, spurring population growth.

Although global population has grown largely unabated since the mid-1800's, growth rates in the industrial nations of Europe and North America eventually slowed as couples began voluntarily to have fewer children. By the 1990's, the more industrialized countries contained some 1.2 billion people—about 20 percent of the world's population—and had a relatively slow population growth rate of 0.2 percent per year. At that rate it would take 432 years for the industrialized world's population to double.

In contrast, population growth in the poor countries of Asia, Africa, and Latin America continued at a very rapid pace. By 1997, approximately 4.6 billion people—about 80 percent of the world's population—lived in developing countries. The populations of those countries were increasing by almost 2 percent a year, nearly 10

times faster than the population of the industrialized world. If this rate continues, the developing world's population could reach 9.2 billion by the year 2030.

Dire consequences

Their surging populations make it difficult for the less-developed countries to meet many basic human needs—food, clothing, and shelter. The UN Food and Agriculture Association has estimated that more than 800 million people around the world go to bed hungry each night. By various estimates, 12 million people die each year because of starvation or malnutrition or from diseases made worse by a lack of food.

Access to clean water is another problem for people in poorer nations. In 1994, the World Health Organization (WHO), a UN agency, estimated that 940 million people worldwide lacked access to safe water and more than 1.7 billion people lived in areas without adequate sanitation facilities. WHO further noted that most urban centers in Africa and

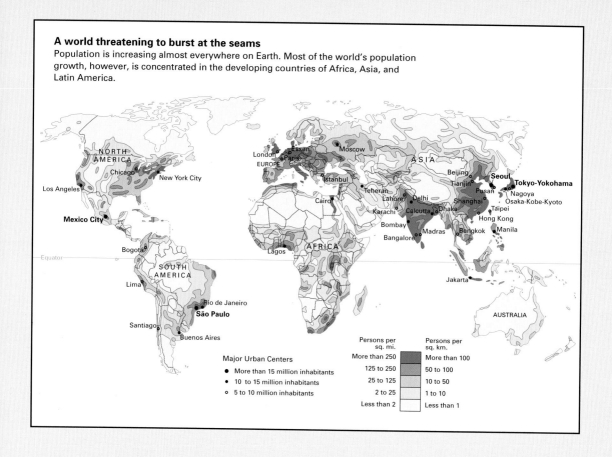

A world threatening to burst at the seams
Population is increasing almost everywhere on Earth. Most of the world's population growth, however, is concentrated in the developing countries of Africa, Asia, and Latin America.

Major Urban Centers
● More than 15 million inhabitants
● 10 to 15 million inhabitants
○ 5 to 10 million inhabitants

Persons per sq. mi.	Persons per sq. km.
More than 250	More than 100
125 to 250	50 to 100
25 to 125	10 to 50
2 to 25	1 to 10
Less than 2	Less than 1

Asia, including many cities with populations of more than 1 million, had no sewage systems at all. Water supplies contaminated with microorganisms that cause cholera and other diseases were responsible for the death of an estimated 25 million people annually in the 1990's, according to a report by the Natural Resources Defense Council, a nonprofit organization based in the United States.

Shelter has also become a severe problem in many less-developed nations. Housing shortages have arisen as people in rural areas migrated to urban centers in the hope of finding greater economic opportunity. Most of those people, however, have been unable to find work, nor have the cities to which they moved been able to house them. In Cairo, Egypt, poverty and housing shortages had become so severe by the late 1990's that more than 300,000 people were living in shelters of cardboard and other materials in a large cemetery on the outskirts of the city. Even people who can afford and find housing in Cairo have been forced to live in tiny, dirty apartments, many without toilets.

In Calcutta, India, conditions are even worse. An estimated 70 percent of the people live in poverty, and many of the poor occupy slum housing without running water. Often, as many as 25 families share a single outdoor tap to get water for drinking and bathing. About half of the dwellings in Calcutta's slums also lack indoor toilets. An estimated 600,000 homeless people roam the city's streets, begging and stealing. Many sleep in alleyways strewn with garbage and human waste.

Even in the more well-to-do cities of developing nations, such as Shanghai, China, population growth has severely limited the available living space. In this city of more than 12 million people, the average resident has living space about equal in size to an average American bathroom.

Escalating social problems

Population growth and crowding in cities spawn a host of social problems, such as crime and civil unrest. In several nations of Africa by the mid-1990's, rapidly growing cities had sunk into anarchy that threatened to spread throughout the continent. In the region south of the Sahara, called the Sahel, police and the military have had only a tenuous hold on cities during the day. At night, the streets belong to rival gangs.

Crime, social strife, food shortages, and poverty triggered massive movements of refugees in Africa during the 1990's. People from Burundi, Rwanda,

Somalia, and Zaire fled into neighboring lands seeking safety from intolerable living conditions and swamped refugee camps while war raged between rival groups in their homeland. The best estimates in 1997 put the number of African refugees at 19 million.

The industrialized nations

It would be easy to assume that these statistics mean that the world population crisis is largely a problem of the less-developed nations of the world. Experts do agree that the developing world's population growth represents an enormous challenge with potentially grave consequences for the planet.

But population growth is also an important problem among the wealthier nations of the world—perhaps even more so because of one factor: their level of affluence.

To maintain the higher living standards that they have achieved, the industrialized nations consume extraordinary amounts of resources. This demand for resources, in turn, places incredible pressure on the Earth's natural systems.

According to several estimates, the average American consumer uses 20 to 40 times more resources in a given day than, say, a resident of In-

dia. Driving one's car a mile to a convenience store, for example, uses as much energy as an average resident of a developing nation uses in a single day.

Because of these high levels of consumption, each child born into a more developed nation will have a far greater impact on the planet than a child born into a family in Bangladesh or China. The 8 million children born in the industrialized nations in 1996 actually have about the same environmental impact as 160 million to 320 million children born in the less-developed nations of the world.

Given the fast pace of growth of the world population and the inadequate state of many services worldwide, population experts believe that the already intolerable conditions in crowded urban areas in both the industrialized and developing nations are bound to worsen as the number of people continues to grow.

High population levels can sometimes be a contributing factor to a low standard of living, but that is not always the case. For example, while Africa and Europe have comparable population totals, their per-capita gross domestic product—an important measure of people's economic well-being—varies wildly, *right*.

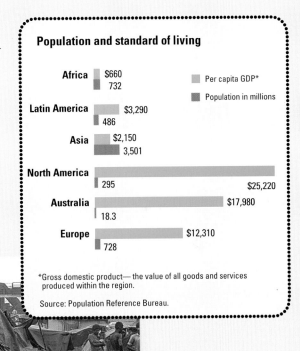

Population and standard of living

Region	Per capita GDP*	Population in millions
Africa	$660	732
Latin America	$3,290	486
Asia	$2,150	3,501
North America	$25,220	295
Australia	$17,980	18.3
Europe	$12,310	728

*Gross domestic product— the value of all goods and services produced within the region.

Source: Population Reference Bureau.

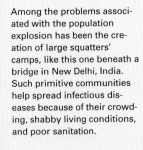

Among the problems associated with the population explosion has been the creation of large squatters' camps, like this one beneath a bridge in New Delhi, India. Such primitive communities help spread infectious diseases because of their crowding, shabby living conditions, and poor sanitation.

Environmental Impact

The population explosion has profound effects on the quality of Earth's environment—its air, water, and land. The impact can be felt locally, regionally, and, with growing frequency, globally in ways that are cause for grave concern.

Natural systems, or ecosystems, are vital to our lives. An ecosystem is a community of plants, animals, fungi, and microbes, together with the soil, water, and other nonliving components of the environment. Wetlands, forests, rivers, lakes, and the ocean are all different types of ecosystems.

Ecosystems are quite literally the life support systems of the planet, and they are essential to our welfare—indeed, to our very survival. They provide the air we breathe, the water we drink, and the food we eat. Some natural systems also absorb waste products, even toxic ones, and render them harmless.

Ecosystems provide many other benefits as well. Wetlands, or swamps, along rivers, for example, absorb rainwater and thus reduce flooding. Wetlands also help filter impurities from water and replenish *aquifers*, underground layers of soil or porous rock that contain fresh water. Coastal wetlands are a vital habitat for many commercially important fish and shellfish. In fact, most of the oceanic fish we eat spend some part of their life cycle in a coastal wetland.

Forest ecosystems also provide important environmental functions. Tree roots help hold soil in place, which reduces soil erosion. Trees' leaves remove carbon dioxide from the air and give off oxygen, which is required by humans and animals. Forests are therefore essential for the global cycling of oxygen and carbon dioxide and for maintaining a proper balance of these vital gases. An increase in atmospheric carbon dioxide could increase the global temperature.

In recognition of the importance of ecosystems to our well-being, some economists and ecologists have begun to refer to the natural world as the biological infrastructure, or support system, of human society. But just as the importance of this infrastructure is being more widely recognized, growing evidence shows that many elements of it are being jeopardized by the growth of the human population.

Vanishing species

Species extinction is a major sign that the environmental infrastructure is in danger. The loss of *biodiversity*, the great variety of plant and animal species that exist in the natural world, could have far-reaching consequences. Most species are lost as a result of habitat destruction—for example, when forest land is cleared or wetlands are drained for agriculture, housing, and other uses.

Virtually every habitat on Earth is under pressure from the expanding human population. As of 1997, according to most estimates, about 880 square kilometers (340 square miles) of tropical rain forest were being cut down each day. Tropical rain forests are cleared to harvest valuable hardwoods and to make room for cattle ranches and mines. In addition, many large areas of forest are cut to plant cash crops such as bananas, tea, oranges, and coffee.

Part of a rain forest in Malaysia is obliterated to create a construction site for an apartment complex and shopping center. Each year, huge tracts of tropical rain forests are cleared to harvest valuable hardwoods, make room for mines and cattle ranches, and plant cash crops such as bananas, tea, and coffee.

Outside the tropics, damage has also been extensive. Much of the temperate rain forest of the U.S. Pacific Northwest has been cut down for lumber. Deciduous forests of the eastern United States have also been heavily cut, and only a tiny fraction of the original forested land remains. Grasslands the world over have been plowed under to plant crops. Swamps, bogs, coastal marshes, and other similar lands that are wet for at least some part of the year are fast disappearing throughout the world.

Birds are a good indicator of the impact of population growth on habitats and species. Earth is home to approximately 9,600 bird species, but 70 percent of those species are declining in numbers. Approximately 1 of every 10 bird species is threatened with extinction.

The decline in bird populations can have considerable environmental impact, because birds are key ecological players. Predatory birds such as hawks and owls help control rodent and rabbit populations. Other bird species, such as flickers, flycatchers, and nighthawks, help limit insect populations. Nectar-feeding birds such as hummingbirds spread pollen and fertilize a variety of useful and beautiful plants. Fruit-eating birds help disperse the seeds of plants, thereby ensuring that the plants will continue to flourish.

But birds are not the only animals affected by habitat destruction. Each year, an estimated 27,000 species, from plants to insects, vanish forever. More alarming than the actual number of species that are now endangered or extinct, however, is the rate at which species are vanishing. Throughout geological time, species have become extinct because of natural causes. But today, species are vanishing at a rate 100 to 1,000 times greater than normal.

The loss of natural habitat and wild species is not just an ecological or aesthetic deduction from our planet's once-vast biological assets. It is an economic loss as well. Each acre of coastal marshes, for example, provides the equivalent of $85,000 per year in water purification. Wetlands also help prevent floods. The water storage capacity provided by a 223,000-hectare (550,000-acre) swamp in Florida provides flood protection and aquifer replenishment valued at $25 million per year.

Water woes

Human population growth has also had a tremendous impact on surface fresh waters—streams, rivers, lakes, and ponds. For example, farming and timber harvesting to meet needs of the burgeoning human population have reduced vegetative cover and increased soil erosion—often dramatically. Soil washed from these lands enters surface waters, making the water cloudy and reducing the amount of sunlight reaching aquatic plants. This, in turn, decreases *pho-*

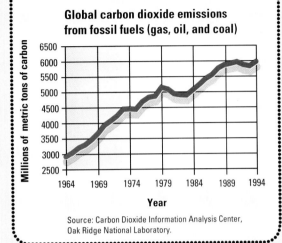

The continued use of fossil fuels (coal, natural gas, and oil) releases tremendous amounts of carbon dioxide into the atmosphere. Increasing levels of carbon dioxide in the atmosphere may be contributing to global warming.

Source: Carbon Dioxide Information Analysis Center, Oak Ridge National Laboratory.

tosynthesis, the process by which plants convert carbon dioxide and water into sugars and other molecules with energy provided by the sun. Photosynthesis also produces oxygen needed by animals. Reduced photosynthesis by aquatic plants results in lower levels of dissolved oxygen in water, which can kill sensitive fish and other water-dwelling species.

Industrial pollution also poses a threat to the world's supply of fresh water. Manufacturing facilities produce wastes that are often dumped into nearby lakes and rivers. Such pollution changes the chemistry of the water and can harm or kill aquatic plant and animal species.

Polluted air and acid rain

Yet another environmental problem that stems from population growth is air pollution. All nations of the world suffer from air pollution, sometimes at choking levels. Air pollution is released from factories and power plants and ever-growing fleets of motor vehicles. Huge amounts of air pollutants are also produced by many small sources, such as the millions of coal-burning stoves used by China's peasant farmers to cook their food.

Two air pollutants of special concern are the acid-forming gases nitrogen dioxide and sulfur dioxide. These pollutants are produced by the combustion of fossil fuels in power plants and factories as well as by motor vehicles. Harmful in their own right, these pollutants also combine with water in the atmosphere to produce two of the strongest acids known to science—nitric acid and sulfuric acid. These acids can be transported hundreds of kilometers in the atmosphere, but they eventually fall to the ground in rain or snow, a problem known as acid rain or acid precipitation.

Acid precipitation causes incredible damage. It degrades the surfaces of statues and buildings and changes the chemistry of streams and lakes in dramatic ways. Fish and other organisms may die when acid rain deposited in a lake, river, or stream makes the water too acidic for the species to survive.

Acid precipitation is found downwind of virtually all major industrial or population centers in the world. The most severe damage in North America occurs in the Northeastern United States and Southeastern Canada, where hundreds of lakes have been rendered virtually lifeless. Acid precipitation also kills trees in forests and damages crops the world over.

Greenhouse gases

Of far greater impact, however, are the effects of air pollution on the global climate. One of the key players in this unfolding drama is the gas carbon dioxide. Carbon dioxide makes up about 1 percent of Earth's atmosphere. It is given off by animals during respiration. It is also released in large amounts by the burning of fossil fuels, such as coal and oil, and of wood and other organic matter.

For thousands of years, the level of carbon dioxide in Earth's atmosphere was kept relatively constant by the carbon cycle. In this cycle, plants remove carbon dioxide from the atmosphere, which they use to produce or-

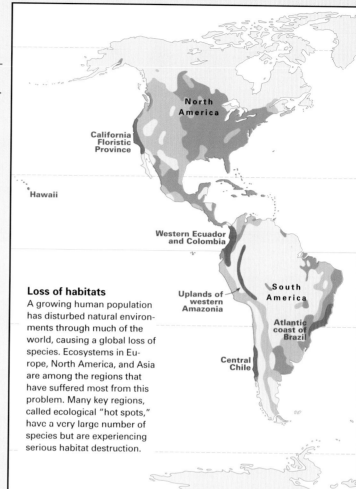

Loss of habitats

A growing human population has disturbed natural environments through much of the world, causing a global loss of species. Ecosystems in Europe, North America, and Asia are among the regions that have suffered most from this problem. Many key regions, called ecological "hot spots," have a very large number of species but are experiencing serious habitat destruction.

Garbage and other wastes from a shantytown in Manaus, Brazil, blight a stretch of the Amazon River. Waterways in many parts of the world are being polluted by masses of people living in areas lacking garbage removal, sewage facilities, and other services.

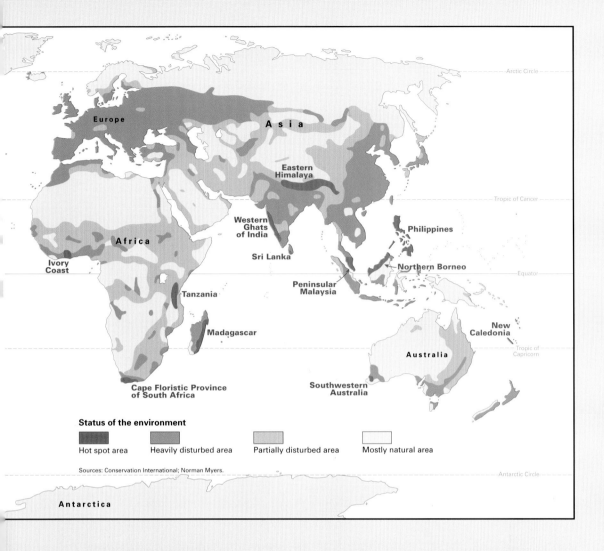

Status of the environment

Hot spot area	Heavily disturbed area	Partially disturbed area	Mostly natural area

Sources: Conservation International; Norman Myers.

ganic molecules. Animals that eat plants break down the molecules and release carbon dioxide back into the atmosphere. However, as the human population has grown—and with it the use of fossil fuels—atmospheric carbon dioxide levels have increased. Scientists monitoring carbon dioxide have found that since 1880, carbon dioxide levels in the atmosphere have risen 25 percent.

Carbon dioxide is known as a greenhouse gas because, like the glass of a greenhouse, it traps heat. Sunlight striking the Earth turns into heat and is reflected back toward space. But carbon dioxide prevents some of the reflected heat from escaping. Carbon dioxide therefore helps keep the atmosphere warm and permits life to flourish on Earth. In fact, scientists believe that without carbon dioxide, Earth would be too cold to support life.

Like many things, a little carbon dioxide is good, but too much can be dangerous. Several studies have shown that excess levels of carbon dioxide and other greenhouse gases such as methane increase the amount of heat retained in the atmosphere and could be responsible for the slow but steady increase in the planet's temperature that has occurred since the early 1900's, a phenomenon known as global warming.

Many scientists believe that even slight temperature increases could have profound effects on Earth's climate. One possible result of global warming could be the melting of the polar ice caps and glaciers. Atmospheric scientists predict that global warming could also cause more frequent droughts in some regions, costing billions of dollars in lost crop production each year and leading to widespread hunger and starvation. Changes in rainfall and temperatures could also cause a massive loss of species.

Scientists are concerned about the many environmental impacts of human population growth. Air and water pollution, together with habitat destruction, have the potential to wreak havoc with the biological infrastructure that supports all life on Earth, including human life.

Diriminishing Resources

Scientists recognize the exhaustion of both renewable and nonrenewable resources as a troubling consequence of explosive population growth. Renewable resources—such as topsoil, ocean fisheries, and forests—along with nonrenewable resources—such as oil, natural gas, and coal—are vital to the welfare of people throughout the world.

Farmlands and forests

Good farmland is necessary to grow food to support the world's population. Yet, each year, tens of millions of metric tons of topsoil are eroded from the world's croplands by wind or rain. Rainwater carries soil into streams, rivers, lakes, and ponds. Wind blows soils many kilometers away. Scientists estimate that at the current rate of soil erosion—24 billion metric tons (26 billion tons) per year—the world's croplands could lose the equivalent of half of the topsoil on all U.S. farms by the year 2010. This trend is all the more serious because the very force contributing to soil loss and farmland destruction—population growth—relies on ever-increasing amounts of food.

Soil erosion can be prevented or greatly reduced by proper farming techniques such as terracing and crop rotation. For this reason, some experts argue that erosion is not the direct result of population growth but rather a consequence of poor land management. But population growth often requires that resources be used to fulfill immediate needs. The need for food frequently overrides the need to protect agricultural lands for future generations. For example, grasslands in many parts of the developing world are commonly overgrazed because the people in those areas have an immediate need for the milk, meat, and wool provided by livestock.

Farmland is also lost to construction. Shopping centers, housing developments, new airports, and highways all have one thing in common: They are often built on valuable pasture, rangeland, or cropland. In the United States, it has been estimated that 1,400 hectares (3,500 acres) of rural land are lost every day due to construction. That adds up to 510,000 hectares (1.3 million acres) per year.

Another resource that is rapidly diminishing is forest land. As population grows in the developing world, huge tracts of tropical forest are being cut or burned to make way for crops such as bananas, tea, and coffee. Forests are also cleared to make room for cattle ranches and mines. Both are valuable assets needed to improve the economies of developing nations, but at great cost to this vital natural forest ecosystem.

Fossil fuel usage on the rise

The world's rising population has an ever-increasing need for fuel supplies, especially fossil fuels—like coal, natural gas, and oil. The U.S. Energy Information Administration reported that coal consumption leveled off during the 1990's, but the use of natural gas and oil increased in both industrialized and developing nations.

● World total
● Industrialized nations
● Developing nations

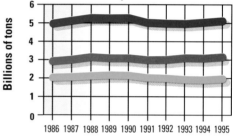

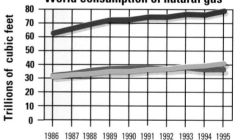

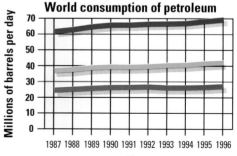

Source: U.S. Energy Information Administration.

Catches in 13 of the world's 15 major fishing regions have fallen since 1989, the United Nations' Food and Agriculture Organization (FAO) reported. According to the FAO, 70 percent of the world's commercial fish species were at risk of decline or were already declining as a result of overfishing. Most experts predict that as the world population grows and the demand for food increases, further declines in fish species will follow.

Disappearing fresh-water supplies

Making matters worse for agricultural production is a growing scarcity of fresh water for irrigation. Irrigated land produces a huge share of the world's food supply. In many regions, however, groundwater for irrigating cropland is rapidly being depleted. Rain and melting snow replenish groundwater near the surface, but in some major agricultural regions, groundwater is pumped from deep aquifers that took many thousands of years to fill.

Water levels in the Ogallala aquifer underlying large portions of Colorado, Kansas, Nebraska, New Mexico, Oklahoma, Texas, and Wyoming, fell at the astounding rate of 1 meter (3 feet) per year in the 1990's. Nature can replenish water in the Ogallala at only about 0.1 millimeter (0.025 inch) a year—10,000 times slower than that rate at which water is being extracted.

The use of groundwater in parts of Africa spawned disaster in recent years. Vast amounts of water lie beneath the Sahel and the Sahara, in most places at a depth of more than 2,000 meters (6,550 feet). Beginning in the 1940's, people of the Sahel drilled deep wells to obtain the water for their herds and to irrigate crops.

The new sources of water meant more land could be cultivated. More food caused a dramatic rise in human and animal populations, more than the land could support before the wells were drilled. Then, drought in the early 1970's and again in the mid-1980's led to massive destruction of the land cleared for agriculture, and hundreds of thousands of people and animals died of starvation. Some scientists say the damage to parts of the Sahel is irreversible.

Fewer fish in the sea

Just as the ability of the land to produce food is being endangered, the food-producing capacity of the oceans is also threatened. The sea provides people with an enormous amount of food. Fish, clams, and oysters are the primary sources of protein for more than 1 billion people around the world. But years of habitat destruction, pollution, and overfishing have compromised the health of the oceans. Overfishing also threatens the livelihood of many of the 15 million to 21 million people whose occupation is catching fish.

The United Nations' Food and Agriculture Organization (FAO), which tracks global fishing catches, issued a disturbing report in 1995. The FAO reported that catches in 13 of the world's 15 major oceanic fishing regions had fallen since 1989. In four regions, catches had fallen by 30 percent. According to the FAO, 70 percent of the world's commercial fish species were at risk of decline or were already in decline as a result of overfishing. In the 1950's and 1960's, the oceans abounded with cod, halibut, snapper, and other large, commercially valuable fish. By the mid-1990's, most of the world's fish catch consisted of smaller, less valuable species and squid. Most experts predict that as global population continues to rise, placing increasing demands on the world's fisheries, further declines in fish species will occur.

Fossil fuel usage

In addition to using renewable resources, the world relies on nonrenewable resources, such as *fossil fuels* (coal, oil, and natural gas) for energy. The main advantages of fossil fuels are their accessibility, ease of storage, and low price. Coal, oil, and natural gas deposits can be found in many parts of the world.

Fossil fuels come from the remains of plants that died millions of years ago. While living, the plants harnessed energy from sunlight during *photosynthesis*, the process by which plants convert carbon dioxide and water into food. Burning fossil fuel releases the energy captured by the plants millions of years ago.

Much of the world's coal formed between about 360 million and 290 million years ago, though most coal deposits in the United States are just 50 million to 75 million years old. Coal was made from the compressed remains of vegetation, most likely in swamps. As those remains became buried under sediment, they were transformed into coal.

Oil and gas deposits were created in a similar process that began when tiny plantlike organisms in the seas that covered Earth millions of years ago died and settled to the sea floor. As sediment compressed these organisms, they turned into a waxy substance called kerogen. The extreme pressures and high temperatures far underground eventually caused the kerogen to separate into liquid (oil) and gas (natural gas).

Power plants burn coal, natural gas, or oil to produce electricity. Homeowners use fossil fuels to heat their homes. Motor vehicles also consume huge quantities of petroleum products. Trucks burn diesel fuel, airplanes use jet fuel, and automobiles use gasoline.

In 1996, worldwide consumption of petroleum rose for the third straight year as the demand for oil continued to increase. Petroleum products were consumed at a rate of about 72 million barrels a day—a 2.5 percent increase over 1995. (There are 159 liters [42 gallons] of oil in a barrel.)

Of these three fossil fuels, experts predict, natural gas, a clean-burning fuel, will increase in use at the most rapid rate through the year 2015. The use of natural gas rose throughout the world in 1996,

with consumption in the United States exceeding 453 billion cubic meters (16 trillion cubic feet) in the first nine months of the year. Experts say the use of natural gas will grow most rapidly in the developing nations of Asia, Central America, and South America.

Limited supplies

But the world contains only a limited amount of fossil fuels, and scientists agree that someday the supplies will run out. The amount of fossil

Deforestation in Mexico's Chiapas State has led to severe erosion of the land, *above*. Erosion, including of valuable croplands, is a problem in much of the world. Although most farmland erosion is due to improper land management, population pressures also contribute, as the need to grow ever-larger amounts of food often causes proper growing methods to be ignored.

fuel burned by people to produce energy has nearly doubled every 20 years since 1900. Moreover, the world is consuming fossil fuels 100,000 times faster than geological processes can replace them.

Estimates of the amount of fuel remaining in the Earth vary considerably, but some experts believe that at the usage levels of the 1990's there may not be enough oil to last beyond the year 2100. Natural-gas reserves may be depleted at about the same time. Without new discoveries, coal reserves may not last beyond the year 2300. But increased demands by a growing population could deplete the supplies of all these fuels in a much shorter amount of time.

The Threat of Infectious Diseases

From the late 1800's and well into the 1900's, citizens and health officials alike were optimistic about the prospect of conquering infectious diseases caused by viruses, bacteria, and a host of other microorganisms. First came improvements in sanitation, then the discoveries of antibiotics and vaccines to ward off infectious diseases. By the late 1900's, however, optimism had changed to concern. Rather than being eliminated, infectious diseases were claiming the lives of 17 million people a year worldwide.

Population growth was a key element in this lethal resurgence. Scientists found that as the world population grew and as the density of populations increased in urban areas, humanity was creating ideal conditions for the spread of disease. Experts warned of the possibility of devastating global epidemics.

Making it easy for microbes

Infectious diseases are spread in a variety of ways. Some are transmitted in water or through the air, some are carried by insects, such as mosquitoes, and others contaminate foods. Still others are spread through person-to-person contact.

Our crowded world, with its mobile and often impoverished masses, has set the stage for the spread of disease. With the crowding of millions of people into urban slums sadly lacking in sanitary facilities; increased international travel by plane; and the encroachment of humans into once-wild areas, where they run the risk of exposure to new and deadly disease-causing organisms, humanity is lending a helping hand to deadly microbes.

The problem is most severe in developing nations, where large numbers of people have migrated from rural areas to cities in search of work and a better life. By the mid-1990's, about 2.7 billion people, nearly half of the world's population, were living in urban areas, and all trends indicated that this number would increase. *Demographers* (population scientists) predicted that the number of cities containing more than 1 million people would increase from 280 in 1990 to more than 500 by 2015. Moreover, the world's urban population has been growing three times faster than rural populations, meaning that more and more of humanity would be restricted to close quarters.

Many immigrants to urban areas in developing nations have settled in squatters' camps on the outskirts of cities. These camps often have no clean water, sanitation facilities, or provisions for garbage removal. People living close together, especially in impoverished conditions, create breeding grounds for infectious disease. Poor nutrition and lack of sanitation foster illness, and crowding enhances the spread of disease from one person to another.

Scientists have reported that infectious diseases occur at higher rates in the poorest sections of many major cities, such as São Paulo, Brazil, the third-largest city in the world. For example, tuberculosis, a disease once thought to be under control, has become a growing problem there and in the crowded urban areas of other less-developed nations. Tuberculosis is an infectious disease caused by a bacterium that invades the lungs. It is spread from one person to another through the air. Untreated, tuberculosis kills its victims in one to two years. In 1996, tuberculosis was responsible for an estimated 3 million deaths worldwide.

Another potential breeding ground for disease is garbage, which urban populations produce in enormous amounts and—especially in less-developed nations—often dump carelessly. Mountains of garbage make an ideal home for disease-carrying pests, such as insects or rats.

More people also means more sewage. In many crowded cities, streams and rivers are severely polluted with human wastes carrying disease-causing microorganisms. Fortunately, drinking water can be filtered or boiled to make it safe, but often people don't bother.

Air pollution from industrial emissions and auto exhaust can also contribute to disease. Breathing dirty air can weaken people's immune systems, making them more susceptible to airborne germs.

Ferrying germs to new lands

International travel and trade is a major factor in the spread of disease from one region to another— or from one continent to another. Air travel is of particular concern. International air traffic increased from 163 million passengers in 1980 to more than 321 million passengers in 1993, the latest year for which data were available.

The U.S. Centers for Disease Control and Prevention in Atlanta, Georgia, warns that infected travelers can spread viruses worldwide in a very short amount of time. Every city in the United States is accessible from anywhere in the world within 36 hours—well within the incubation period of all infectious diseases. What this means is that an infected person can travel abroad carrying a disease before he or she is aware of it. In fact, public-health officials estimate that within two years of the emergence of a new influenza virus, 50 percent of the world's population will have been exposed to it.

International trade carries useful products worldwide, but disease-causing organisms may occasionally go along for the ride, attached to those products or to their containers. For example, shipments of used tires carried the tiger mosquito from Asia into the United States, South Africa, New Zealand, and southern Europe. Although this mosquito is a tropical species, scientists have found that it is able to survive cold winters and has recently spread northward in the United States.

The tiger mosquito carries dengue fever, a viral disease common in the tropics. Infected people suffer intense headaches, diarrhea, and, with the most serious form of the disease, internal hemorrhaging. Each year up to 100 million people worldwide, mostly city dwellers, are infected with dengue fever.

Cholera is another threat. This bacterial illness once caused epidemics in Europe and the United States, but since the late 1800's it had been largely confined to Asia and Africa. Cholera is transmitted in contaminated water or food and results in diarrhea, vomiting, rapid dehydration, and kidney failure. If untreated, it is usually fatal. But even with proper treatment, 5 to 10 percent of cholera victims die of the disease.

In the 1960's and 1970's, cholera cases began to appear in Europe and the South Pacific, even in Texas and Louisiana. In 1991, a major outbreak occurred in a Peruvian port. The cholera bacterium was carried to Peru in the *ballast water* (water used to help balance an empty ship) of a Chinese freighter. The freighter dumped some of this contaminated ballast water into the waters of the port. From there, cholera spread quickly and relentlessly, and by 1995 it had infected more than 1 million people in Latin America.

Newly emerging diseases

In addition to the reappearance of diseases that public-health officials once thought were conquered, new diseases have emerged. These previously unknown illnesses have usually resulted from human encroachment on isolated habitats, particularly tropical rain forests. In these wilderness areas, people have encountered new viruses—often with deadly consequences.

One of the best known and most horrifying of these recently emerging organisms is the Ebola virus. This virus causes a severe hemorrhagic fever, an illness characterized by intense and often fatal internal bleeding. There is no effective cure for Ebola, and up to 90 percent of those infected die. A major outbreak of Ebola in the African nation of Zaire killed about 250 people in 1995.

Habitat disturbances around growing urban areas in North America have also led to problems with disease-causing microorganisms. People looking for an escape from crowded U.S. cities create a demand for housing in the surrounding countryside. Subdivisions destroy the habitats of animals that prey on deer, raccoons, and various other mammals that can carry disease. In regions such as suburban New England, the deer, raccoon, and mouse populations have soared as the population of predators declined. Grassy lawns, decorative shrubs, and garbage cans provide these species with ready food sources, which further boosts their population.

In many places, the close contact that people now have with deer has resulted in a dramatic increase in the incidence of Lyme disease. This malady, which was first seen in Lyme, Connecticut in 1975, is caused by a bacterium carried by ticks that infest deer and various other wild animals. The symptoms of Lyme disease include skin rash, fever, fatigue, headaches, and swollen lymph nodes. If untreated, this infection leads to severe joint pain, arthritis, and damage to the heart and nervous system. Public-health authorities in the 1990's recognized Lyme disease as a danger in 47 states and Canada. There were more than 13,000 cases reported in 1994.

Public-health workers in Zaire bury 1 of about 250 people killed by Ebola hemorrhagic fever in 1995. Ebola is just one of several new diseases that have emerged in the world as a result of human encroachment on wild areas.

Some modern-day plagues

Disease	Cause and mode of transmission	Symptoms
AIDS (worldwide)	HIV virus; transmitted by sexual contact, direct contact with infected blood or tissue, from an infected woman to her fetus or baby, or by sharing contaminated needles or syringes.	Severe multiple infections from opportunistic microorganisms, and the development of rare cancers—both resulting from a weakened immune system.
Cholera (mostly in Asia, Africa South Pacific)	Cholera bacterium; transmitted in contaminated food and water.	Diarrhea and vomiting, causing severe loss of body fluids; circulatory collapse, kidney and failure, and muscle cramps.
Dengue fever (Tropical areas)	Dengue virus; carried by mosquitoes.	Intense headaches, diarrhea, gastrointestinal disturbances, fever, and muscle and joint aches.
Ebola hemorrhagic fever (Africa)	Ebola virus; transmitted through contact with infected blood, secretions, tissues, or semen.	High fever, formation of clots in blood vessels, massive internal bleeding, headache, vomiting, and diarrhea.
Four Corners disease (United States and Canada)	Hantavirus; transmitted in airborne particles of urine, saliva, and feces from infected deer mice and other rodents.	Fever, abdominal pain, muscle aches, and severe lung congestion and cardiac shock.
Venezuelan hemorrhagic fever (South America)	Guanarito virus; carried by rats and transmitted in dust contaminated with their feces.	High fever, bleeding, diarrhea, fatigue, and headache.
Lassa fever (Africa)	Arenavirus; carried by mice and rats, and transmitted in their urine, or by dust contaminated with feces.	High fever, massive internal bleeding and convulsions.
Rift Valley fever (Africa)	Rift Valley virus; carried by mosquitoes and flies.	Influenza-like symptoms progressing to hemorrhage and swelling of retinas and brain.
Tuberculosis (worldwide)	Mycobacterium; carried in tiny droplets of moisture from coughing or sneezing.	Coughing, chest pain, fever, fatigue, weight loss, and loss of appetite.
Lyme disease (United States and Canada)	Lyme disease bacterium; carried by ticks.	Skin rash, fatigue, chills, fever, muscle aches, pain in joints, and some cardiac and neural abnormalities.
Yellow fever (Africa and South America)	Yellow fever virus; carried by mosquitoes.	Fever, chills, backaches, nausea, vomiting, jaundice, and internal bleeding.

Unexpected outbreaks, resistant strains

As the world population grows and resource demand increases, efforts are made to increase the productivity of existing lands. These efforts sometimes lead to surprising outbreaks of disease. Dams, irrigation canals, and other water projects create new farmlands and fisheries, but they also create new breeding grounds for water-borne organisms that cause diseases such as schistosomiasis, malaria, cholera, and typhoid. An irrigation canal excavated in India for a project aimed at turning a desert into farmland also provided water in which malaria-carrying mosquitoes could breed. Deadly strains of the disease infected farmers and field workers who moved to the area in search of food and prosperity.

Another factor of grave concern is the emergence of genetically resistant strains of microorganisms and of the insects that transmit them. Resistance arises when some organisms survive efforts to destroy them. Antibiotic treatment of a bacterial infection, for example, may kill 99.9 percent of the microbes, but the remaining 0.01 percent survive because of naturally occurring resistance to the drug. The remaining bacteria can multiply, producing huge numbers of drug-resistant organisms.

Insects that transmit some infectious organisms can also become resistant to insecticides in a similar way. The worldwide threat of malaria has increased because the parasite that causes it has become drug resistant. In addition, the mosquito that carries the malaria parasite to humans has become resistant to the insecticides once used to control it.

As people push farther into new environments to meet the food and shelter needs of an ever-growing population, they are upsetting an intricate set of checks and balances that once kept microbes under control. Some experts warn that if humanity continues to encroach heedlessly on nature, there could be a terrible price to pay. Some worry that we may encounter a microorganism as deadly as the Ebola virus that is transmitted through the air. Such a microbe could cause a catastrophic epidemic. Meanwhile, scientists are working on new drugs to combat such microbes in the hope that a public-health calamity from an as-yet-unknown disease can be averted.

Population and the Future

Scientists are working on strategies for coping with the overpopulated world of the future. To do this, they must first estimate how large the population will become. Then they must find ways of providing for the needs of so many people.

But determining the future growth of the world's population is a difficult task for *demographers* (population experts). Demographers base growth rates and projections on at least three factors: fertility—the number of children women bear; mortality—the number of expected deaths; and migration—the movement of people from one country to another. Migration is an important

Population experts say São Paulo, Brazil, *above,* home to some 22 million people in 1997, is a glimpse of the world's future. Eighteen megacities—cities with a population of more than 10 million—dotted the globe in the late 1990's, and their number was certain to increase as the population explosion continues. Providing decent living conditions in these huge urban areas will be a major challenge.

factor for individual countries but not for the world as a whole. All three variables can change rapidly, which in turn can alter predictions. Like weather forecasts, today's population predictions may turn out to be tomorrow's mistakes.

Scientists have been able to draw two conclusions. First, continued world population growth is inevitable. Second, the size of the human population is likely to increase quickly and substantially.

Working on the numbers

In 1997, demographers at the United Nations (UN) predicted that the world population would climb to 9.4 billion by 2050—up "only" about 3.5 billion from the number of people in 1997. Estimates by other organizations ranged from about 8 billion to 11 billion people by 2050. The latter figure is almost twice the population of the world in 1997.

Demographers use past population trends to help them make their predictions. For example, the U.S. Bureau of the Census reported that the world's population grew by about 80 million people in 1996. The figure, which was also confirmed by the UN Population Division, was 6 million people fewer than the 86 million people by which the global population grew in 1994. It was also significantly less than the estimated 90 million to 100 million that were added each year to the world's population in the 1980's.

The U.S. Census Bureau reported that shrinking family size had much to do with the population decrease. The bureau said that the world's total *fertility rate*—the number of children born per woman during her lifetime—declined to 2.9, the lowest level ever recorded.

In 1985, the worldwide total fertility rate was 4.2. A study released by the UN in 1997 also found that fertility rates were dropping faster than experts had predicted. Another factor contributing to the decline in population growth was an increase in death rates and declining life-expectancy in Africa, Eastern Europe, and the former Soviet Union. Scientists attributed the increase in death rates to AIDS, other infectious diseases, and war.

Some scientists were encouraged by the statistics indicating a slowing in the rate of population growth. The Washington, D.C.-based Population Institute, in fact, speculated that this decline could result in a stabilization of world population at 8 billion by the year 2025. That projection, however, still represented a major increase in population over the 5.8 billion people in the world in 1997. Furthermore, some scientists warned that conditions could change, rendering current projections obsolete.

For example, they said, reversals in the decline in life expectancy in the regions where that has been occurring, together with increases in fertility in some countries, could increase the rate of world population growth. Or fertility could continue to fall and death rates to rise, resulting in a further decline in growth. In either case, however, the world's population would continue to increase—whether at a fast or slow pace.

A growing population in the United States will add to that increase, though by how much was still a matter of debate. In 1997, the population of the United States was about 265 million. In 1988, the U.S. Bureau of the Census had estimated that by 2050 the population of the United States would stabilize at 290 million to 300 million. In 1993, however, the Census Bureau revised its projections upward, based on rising fertility, continuing high levels of immigration, and increasing life spans.

The bureau predicted that by the year 2050 the U.S. population would reach 392 million. The bureau saw no signs of the population's stabilizing in the near future. An addition of almost 130 million people in the United States in a little over 50 years could place a significant strain on already limited resources, including land, food, and water.

Because all population experts agree that the world's population will continue to increase, they are calling for plans to deal with the situation. According to the experts, strategies for addressing population growth fall into two main categories: measures to produce more food and to reduce pollution, waste, and resource depletion brought on by more people; and measures to slow population growth itself.

In search of ways to produce more food

Efforts are underway today to boost the per-acre yield of crops, mainly through more intensive use of irrigation and fertilizers. Scientists are also investigating the use of genetic engineering to increase crop yield. They had already been successful in genetically altering some crop plants, enabling them to resist disease and insects. But some agricultural experts questioned whether future food production increases can match those achieved since the 1960's, when higher-yielding varieties of food plants, especially rice, were introduced.

Another strategy for increasing food produc-

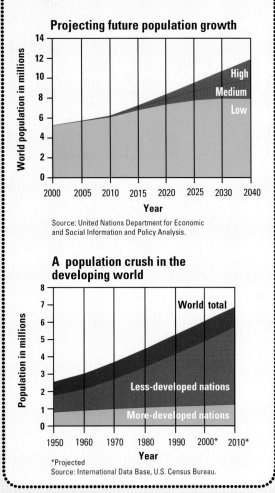

Scientists use various information to predict trends in future population growth. Weighing factors such as fertility, mortality, and migration, they then make low, medium, and high population projections. Experts predict that most population growth in the future will continue to occur in less-developed nations.

Projecting future population growth

Source: United Nations Department for Economic and Social Information and Policy Analysis.

A population crush in the developing world

*Projected
Source: International Data Base, U.S. Census Bureau.

tion involves the conversion of nonagricultural land to farm production. This usually means cutting down forests and plowing grasslands to make room for crops. In many parts of the world, including Asia, however, all *arable land* (land that can be used for farming) is already being cultivated. In regions with substantial reserves of unused land—notably Africa and South America—much of the land is of marginal value or is vital wildlife habitat. The soils of tropical rain forests, for example, are very thin and infertile. Moreover, cutting down tropical forests to make room for farms hastens the loss of species.

A public-health field worker in Bangladesh lectures village women on birth control. The majority of the world's nations had some kind of family planning program in place in the 1990's. Most scientists and governments view efforts aimed at encouraging people to make greater use of birth control measures—such as condoms, birth control pills, diaphragms, and sterilizations— as essential to achieving the goal of lowering birth rates.

Protecting the environment

Lessening the impact of human beings on the environment is a major concern as the world's population grows. Some nations are pursuing a variety of strategies to accomplish this goal. One approach has been to improve the efficiency with which resources such as fossil fuels are used. Some nations have also promoted the use of renewable energy sources.

Renewable sources of energy are significant alternatives to fossil fuels, which are responsible for many major environmental problems, such as global warming and acid precipitation. Renewable energy sources include wind power, solar energy, hydroelectric power, and geothermal energy. The use of most of these energy sources has very little impact on the environment.

Scientists have already created ways to capture and use the energy of the sun. For example, they have developed photovoltaic cells, thin silicon wafers that convert sunlight into electricity. These devices were still being perfected in the 1990's but were gaining in popularity.

Recycling industrial and municipal wastes offers another enormous opportunity to lower human impact on the planet. Recycling not only reduces the amount of garbage dumped into landfills, it also lowers the demand for raw materials. Every aluminum can that is recycled, for instance, reduces the need to mine more aluminum ore. Every ton of newspaper that is recycled saves 17 trees. What's more, producing goods from recycled materials can be cheaper than making them from raw materials, in part because it requires less energy. This in turn substantially reduces the amount of pollution emitted by factories—another plus for the environment.

Family planning

All of these actions, experts say, are essential for creating a sustainable future and for maintaining a healthy economy while protecting natural systems. But the most important action is to stabilize human population growth, which means reducing birth rates still further.

Because of the wide range of birth control options, most countries fashion strategies to reduce family size in ways that are socially and morally acceptable to their citizens. Most population control programs focus on family planning, education, and economic development.

The majority of the world's nations had some form of family planning program in force in the 1990's. Family planning enables couples to determine the spacing and number of their offspring. National programs in the less-developed nations often educate couples about the desirability of smaller families. China promotes the one-child family. Most nations throughout the world also provide free or low-cost birth control measures, such as condoms, birth control pills, diaphragms, and sterilizations. Many states in India have developed programs that encourage men to undergo voluntary sterilization the hope of reducing the birth rate.

Most people in industrialized nations have agreed that some form of family limitation, or at least more widely spaced births, is desirable for the good of both the family and society. But individuals and groups—especially some religious groups—differ sharply on the methods of birth control that they consider morally acceptable. The governments of many countries are striving to reach compromises with their citizenry on these issues.

The role of women and education

For several decades, population stabilization strategies focused almost entirely on family planning. In the 1990's, however, many people came to realize that the population dilemma could not be solved simply by family planning programs alone. They saw that other factors in a nation, such as the educational level and economic prosperity of its citizens, also had profound influences on family size.

For example, women who decide to pursue an education often choose to delay childbearing. Obtaining an education also provides women with an opportunity to pursue careers. As a result, they tend to have fewer children.

Efforts to improve education and enhance the economic opportunities of women can also bolster a woman's status in society, especially in developing nations. In many developing nations, a woman's value is based on the number of children, often male children, she bears. But, experts contend, educational and economic opportunities could create shifts in cultural beliefs and eventually change ways of thinking about women.

If women's self-esteem and perceived worth are no longer tied solely to childbearing, family size may decline.

Education and enhanced economic opportunities are also important for men in the developing countries. Male responsibility in family planning decisions could be enhanced by education. Furthermore, better education of men could serve as a springboard for broader social change aimed at rethinking the status of women in society. A better-educated society is also more likely to become economically successful. And a couple who are prosperous in their careers may decide to delay having children.

The threat of global overpopulation is probably the most important issue of our time. Scientists will continue to study this very serious problem and the many other problems, such as pollution and loss of species, that are directly linked to it. Their hope is that citizens and government leaders everywhere will acknowledge the seriousness of the situation and work with them to find creative solutions to the population explosion, solutions that can lead to a healthier—and roomier—society.

Reading and Study Guide

Questions for thought and discussion:

1. What do scientists consider to be the major factors causing the population explosion?

2. How does population growth in industrialized nations differ from that in developing nations? What are the reasons for this difference?

3. What kinds of social problems do some scientists attribute to overpopulation? What kinds of environmental problems?

4. Discuss the importance of an ecosystem and how overpopulation can affect it.

5. Explain the reasons why large areas of tropical rain forests are cleared each year. What are the potential effects of this destruction?

6. Discuss the problems that arise from the use of fossil fuels. What are alternatives to fossil fuels?

7. How is population growth connected to a resurgence in many infectious diseases?

8. Discuss the reasons why some scientists believe population growth is slowing.

9. Cite examples of how to create a livable future and maintain a healthy economy while protecting the natural systems of the planet.

10. Discuss how educational and economic opportunities for women can affect population growth.

For further reading:

Barron, Eric J. *Climatic Variation in Earth History.* University Science Books, 1996.

Brown, Lester R. *State of the World.* W.W. Norton & Company, Inc., 1992.

Chiras, D. D. *Environmental Science,* 5th edition. Wadsworth Publishing Co., 1998.

Ehrlich, Paul R. and Anne H. Ehrlich, *Betrayal of Science and Reason.* Island Press/Shearwater Books, 1996.

For additional information:

Centers for Disease Control and Prevention web page—www.cdc.gov

Oak Ridge National Laboratory web page—www.cdiac.esd.ornl.gov

Pan American Health Organization web page—www.paho.org

U.S. Energy Information Administration web page—www.eia.doe.gov

Contributors report on the year's most significant developments in their respective fields. The articles in this section are arranged alphabetically.

● ●

Page 176

Page 271

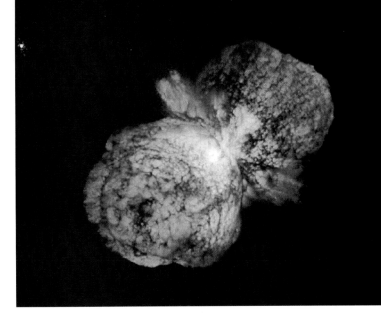

Page 184

Page 192

Imitation chicken breast made from soybeans was unveiled in December 1996 by scientists at the University of Missouri in Columbia, who claimed that the fabricated product tastes like chicken, looks exactly like breast meat, and has a meaty texture and mouth-feel. Made from a soybean protein, flour, and wheat starch, the imitation chicken meat could provide a new market for farmers who grow soybeans. Soy products are seen as potentially profitable because they tend to be low in calories and so appeal to diet-conscious consumers. In addition, substances called isoflavones that are found in soy protein seem to have anti-cancer properties.

To make the product, scientists led by food engineer Fu-hung Hsieh used a process called extrusion. Extrusion, which is commonly used in the cereal industry, combines heat and pressure to reshape and reconstruct food. To convert powdery soybean protein flour into the fibrous imitation chicken, the scientists melted the mixture and forced it into a cooling mold. Within the mold, the protein molecules realigned, trans-forming the mixture into a chunk.

After giving the soy protein the fibrous texture of chicken, it was a fairly simple matter to add the flavor and color of chicken with chicken broth and a browning agent. The imitation chicken breast could be on supermarket shelves in a couple of years, possibly sold as a dehydrated product that would require no refrigeration.

Disease-resistant wheat. Scientists at the University of Idaho in Moscow reported in October 1996 that they had used genetic engineering to develop wheat that can resist two devastating viruses, the barley yellow dwarf virus and wheat streak mosaic virus. These diseases ruin between 1 and 2 percent of the global wheat crop every year, causing the loss of hundreds of millions of dollars and many tons of a much-needed food.

Currently, farmers fight these viruses by delaying their fall planting of wheat until the aphids and mites that spread the diseases have been killed by frost or a lack of green plants to eat. But delayed planting causes other problems. Wheat

An orange-picking machine that shakes fruit from trees is towed behind a tractor during tests in West Virginia in late 1996. Two sets of rotating nylon rods loosen the fruit. The oranges land on a conveyor, which deposits them in a truck following behind. The tests showed that oranges picked by the machine were as clean and undamaged as ones picked by hand.

plants that are still small by the start of winter are likely to deliver small grain yields. They also make soil erosion more likely, because they are too small to cover the soil from rain and wind. Early-planted wheat that could resist these viruses, therefore, would help growers obtain higher yields and protect the soil from erosion.

The University of Idaho scientists, directed by wheat breeder Robert Zemetra, inserted genes from each virus into wheat embryos. The scientists knew that such genetic manipulation makes some plants resistant to the viruses, though they were not sure why. Through extensive testing, the researchers identified which plants had acquired a gene for resisting the viruses. Wheat kernels harvested from those plants were planted in a greenhouse. The resulting plants were used for further tests and to generate seeds.

Thornless blackberry bush. It took 17 years for horticulture professor Bob Skirvin of the University of Illinois at Urbana-Champaign to develop a thornless blackberry plant and another six years to patent it. But in October 1996, Skirvin and his colleague Ken McPheeters announced the development of a thornless bush, called Everthornless.

The new plant was genetically engineered from tiny pieces of tissue taken from the bark of a different blackberry bush, called Thornless Evergreen. In the past, growers could keep Thornless Evergreen bushes smooth-barked only through pruning, which takes a tremendous amount of labor.

The scientists planted 1,000 bushes, all of which turned out to be thornless. Only one of the plants, however, produced berries; the rest of them were sterile. The one fruitful bush became Everthornless.

Streamlining genetic engineering. A way to reduce the guesswork and errors in genetic engineering was announced in December 1996 by two scientists at Purdue University in West Lafayette, Indiana. Experts say the technique could speed federal approval of biotech-derived crops.

Thomas K. Hodges, professor of botany and plant physiology, and research scientist Leszek Lyznik invented a way to insert desired genes into plant chromosomes. (Chromosomes are tiny,

Double-duty alfalfa
Researchers at the University of Minnesota in summer 1996 compare a new type of alfalfa, *above,* at left, with smaller alfalfa plants. The new variety can be used both as a cattle feed and—when the stems are burned—to generate electricity. The new alfalfa yields more leaves and stems, *right,* center and right, than a variety grown only as a livestock feed, left.

threadlike structures in the cell nucleus that carry the genes.) The technique also allows scientists to remove genes that were introduced to carry out a temporary function in a plant after they have served their intended purpose.

In the past, scientists used a variety of methods to insert new genes into a plant's chromosomes. Insertions were random, with genes landing anywhere on the chromosomes and possibly interrupting important gene sequences, such as those coded for vital proteins. Such random insertions worry government regulators because they mean a gene insertion could have unforeseen consequences. Researchers say this new technique, by easing such fears, could hasten federal approval of genetically engineered crops.

The new technique enables scientists to remove an unwanted gene from a chromosome by bracketing the gene with two segments of DNA (deoxyribonucleic acid, the molecules genes are made of) called FRT. They then add a yeast gene called FLP to the mix. This produces an enzyme that causes the chromosome to break at the sites of the FRT segments. The chromosome rejoins, but without the unwanted gene, which is digested by the cell.

Alfalfa helps clean soil. Alfalfa may soon be used to clean up environmental spills of fertilizer, municipal sludge, and food-processing wastes, scientists at the U.S. Department of Agriculture (USDA) announced in January 1997.

Researchers at the USDA's Agricultural Research Service in St. Paul, Minnesota, developed a variety of alfalfa that extracts its nitrogen from the soil, rather than from the air. This alfalfa would be useful for absorbing excess nitrogen from soil or irrigation water.

The new alfalfa variety is a naturally occurring mutant first identified in the 1980's. In tests, the alfalfa absorbed up to 30 percent more nitrogen from the soil than standard alfalfa. Regular alfalfa gets its nitrogen from the air through a *symbiotic* (mutually beneficial) relationship with a bacterium living in the soil called *Rhizobium meliloti,* but the plant can also take some nitrogen from the soil. [Steve Cain]

Anthropology

The dramatic redating of *Homo erectus* fossils from Java, Indonesia, was reported in December 1996 by an international team of scientists led by *geochronologist* (geological-dating specialist) Carl C. Swisher III of the Berkeley Geochronology Center in California. The fossil skulls, from the villages of Ngandong and Sambungmacan, apparently date from 27,000 to 53,000 years ago. These ages mean that individuals of the species *H. erectus* were living about 250,000 years after the species is believed to have become extinct on mainland Asia and at the same time as Neanderthals and modern humans (*Homo sapiens*).

New dates for old specimens. *H. erectus* is an ancient type of *hominid* (human or prehuman species), first discovered in Java in 1891. The specimens in the 1996 study were skulls unearthed between 1931 and 1933, with additional specimens recovered between 1976 and 1980. *H. erectus* skulls differ from modern human skulls in that they tend to be longer and flatter, with a receding forehead and a smaller *cranial capacity* (braincase size).

A coauthor of the report, paleoanthropologist Susan Antón of the University of Florida in Gainesville, argued that although the braincase of each of the skulls is larger than that of classic Javan *H. erectus*, the skulls still belong to this species, and not *H. sapiens.*

The dates of the skulls have always been difficult to determine, and past tests of the specimens resulted in highly varied ages. Swisher and his colleagues used animal teeth from the same layer of sediment in which the skulls had been found to date the specimens. Geologist W. Jack Rink and geochemist Henry P. Schwarcz of McMaster University in Hamilton, Ontario, dated the teeth using two sophisticated techniques.

The first was a relatively new procedure known as electron spin resonance (ESR), which relies on measuring electric charges in tooth enamel acquired from radioactive material in the surrounding soil. The second technique, uranium series dating, measures the decay of radioactive uranium in the teeth.

The new dates for the skulls have important implications for two different

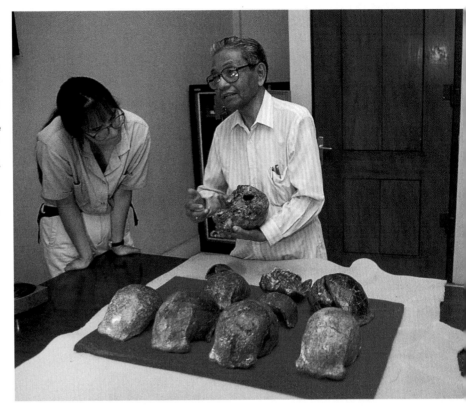

American paleoanthropologist Susan Antón and her Javanese colleague Teuku Jacob discuss skulls from Ngandong, Indonesia, that are believed to be of the species *Homo erectus*. The skulls had been thought to be about 300,000 years old, but in December 1996, an international team of scientists announced that they had redated the fossils to some time between 27,000 and 53,000 years ago. If the dates are correct, members of this species would have been living at the same time as early modern human beings, rather than being ancestors of modern humans.

theories about the origins of *H. sapiens* and were likely to be controversial. One theory, often called the "Out of Africa" theory, hypothesizes that modern people evolved only in Africa, sometime after about 200,000 years ago, and spread from there to the rest of the world. A second theory, often called the "multiregional evolution" theory, proposes that *H. sapiens* evolved from local populations of more primitive species in different parts of the world. In Southeast Asia, for instance, *H. erectus* is considered to be among the ancestors of modern *H. sapiens,* such as the people who colonized Australia about 40,000 years ago.

Some paleoanthropologists had seen the Javanese skulls as supporting the multiregional theory, representing a late type of *H. erectus* that was a probable ancestor for anatomically modern humans in the region. But the new dates challenged this interpretation. If the fossils are as young as the researchers claimed, then they may be younger than the first *H. sapiens* in the region and could not be their direct ancestors. Given these implications, it was likely that

the new dates would be hotly debated.

Earliest *Homo* jaw discovered. An international team of scientists reported the discovery of the oldest positively dated fossil belonging to the genus *Homo* in December 1996. The *Homo* fossil, an extremely well-preserved *maxilla* (upper jaw), was found at Hadar in northern Ethiopia. The scientists—led by William H. Kimbel, Donald C. Johanson, and Robert C. Walter of the Institute of Human Origins in Berkeley, California—dated the jaw at 2.33 million years old, plus or minus 70,000 years.

According to the international team, the newly found fossil looks quite different from the jawbones of the prehuman genus *Australopithecus,* an upright, small-brained hominid that lived between 3 million and 3.9 million years ago. For example, the Hadar maxilla has a relatively broad dental arch and a short, flat lower face, compared with *Australopithecus,* which had a narrow, projecting face. These characteristics as well as other details indicate that the jaw came from a member of the genus *Homo.*

Many scientists recognize three early

species of *Homo: H. habilis, H. rudolfensis,* and *H. erectus* (whose African form is called *H. ergaster* by some scientists). The Hadar fossil seems to resemble *H. habilis* most closely. Kimbel and his colleagues were cautious, however, and opted not to assign the jaw to a species until more fossils could be found.

On the other hand, the dating of the new Hadar jaw was very secure. Walters, the geochronologist on the team, used a technique known as the single-crystal argon laser microprobe method to date a layer of volcanic rock at the site. Animal bones from the area are sparse, but dating of the bones also agreed with the argon-determined age of the rock.

The new *Homo* find was important because it helped fill a critical gap in our knowledge of early human evolution. Most paleoanthropologists agree that the genus *Homo* arose in Africa sometime between 2 million and 3 million years ago, but until the Hadar find, the earliest well-dated *Homo* fossil was only 1.9 million years old. Scientists hoped that more discoveries of older fossils in the area would enable them to deter-

mine the species of the jaw, and thus investigate evolutionary relationships among early *Homo* species.

Several thousand stone tools found at sites in Gona, Ethiopia, were dated at 2.5 million years old, making them the oldest known tools. The finding was announced in January 1997 by a team of scientists, led by anthropologist Sileshi Semaw of Rutgers University in New Brunswick, New Jersey.

The tools were discovered between 1992 and 1994 in the Awash Valley, where the Hadar site is also located. They belong to what anthropologists call the Oldowan stone tool industry. The tools were made by what is known as the percussion method, which involved hitting one rock against another. If the angle at which it was struck was correct, a flake would detach, creating a sharp edge. More than one flake could be chipped off, producing several edges. Both the flakes and the rock from which they were struck, known as the *core,* could serve as tools. Although Oldowan tools were simple, the technique to produce such flakes was relatively sophisti-

A 2.5-million-year-old stone tool is one of the oldest tools ever discovered, according to a January 1997 report from a team of researchers working at a site in Gona, Ethiopia. The tool was made from a stone that was struck repeatedly with a second stone. Pieces of the first stone flaked off, creating a sharp cutting edge. Although the tool is primitive, a knowledge of the flaking quality of rocks was required to make it.

cated and required knowledge of the flaking properties of stone.

From other sites in Africa, paleoanthropologists know that the Oldowan industry lasted until about 1.6 million to 1.5 million years ago. Thus, the new dates showed that hominids were making Oldowan tools for about 1 million years, but the tools show relatively little change over that enormous time span.

One of the questions remaining about the tools is who made them. Most anthropologists have assumed that it was early *Homo* who made Oldowan tools. But paleoanthropologist Bernard Wood of the University of Liverpool in the United Kingdom disagreed. Wood argued that they were more likely made by at least one species of a prehuman genus called *Paranthropus*. The time range of this hominid, from about 2.5 million to 1.5 million years ago, is the same as for the Oldowan industry. Also, as with the tools, the appearance of *Paranthropus* changed little over that time. Although this was a powerful argument, scientists expected the debate to continue as new findings come to light.

A new *Homo* species? Human remains some 780,000 years old found between 1994 and 1996 in the Gran Dolina caves in northern Spain may be from a new species of *Homo* that was the common ancestor of Neanderthals and modern *H. sapiens* in Europe. That claim was announced in May 1997 by a team of paleontologists led by J. M. Bermúdez de Castro of the National Museum of Natural Sciences in Madrid.

The researchers based their conclusions mostly on the remains of a boy. The sunken cheekbones and projecting nose give the face a modern appearance, while other characteristics, such as a prominent brow ridge and certain dental features, appear more primitive.

The findings caused much debate among paleontologists. Some suggested that more research comparing the remains of children of other *Homo* species would be necessary to determine if the fossil did, indeed, represent a new species. Also, the claims altered the standard explanations of the lineage of *H. sapiens*.   [Kathryn Cruz-Uribe]

See also ARCHAEOLOGY.

Archaeology

The earliest rock art in the world may have been pecked and carved into sandstone outcrops in Australia's Northern Territory. In September 1996, archaeologist Richard Fullagar of the Australian Museum in Sydney announced that this artwork may be at least 75,000 years old—twice as ancient as the oldest of the famed cave paintings of Europe.

The petroglyphs, as the rock carvings are called, are precisely cut indented circles, or cupules, on a sandstone block 40 meters (130 feet) high and on surrounding boulders. The cupules, remarkably uniform in size, were about 3 centimeters (1.2 inches) in diameter. In one small area, over 6,000 of these indentations were counted.

Although the cupules create no recognizable images, the researchers noted that the uniformity of the carvings suggested a specific purpose. Carvings of kangaroos and other figures, believed to have been created much later, are carved over some of the cupules.

The excavations, begun in 1987, that uncovered the carved indentations also revealed stone tools and pieces of yellow and red ochre, minerals used in making primitive paints. Geologists from the University of Wollongong, near Sydney, Australia, found ochre that could be as much as 116,000 years old, suggesting some artistic activity may have begun even earlier than 75,000 years ago.

The researchers dated rocks, soil, and ochre from old campfire remains with a method called *thermoluminescence dating.* When objects that were heated in the past are reheated, they emit light. The longer the interval since the object was first heated, the stronger the light.

There is considerable discussion in the scientific community over the age and meaning of these Australian petroglyphs. Archaeologists agreed that further research was needed to verify the dates and to determine if the carvings are actually works of art or if they were created for some other purpose, such as to keep track of time or events.

New views on first Americans. The earliest known inhabitants of the Americas were dated in February 1997 to at least 12,500 years ago at the ancient village of Monte Verde in south-central

Chile. Anthropologist Thomas Dillehay of the University of Kentucky in Lexington announced a firm *radiocarbon* age of the site after specialists on the peopling of the Americas visited the site. (Radiocarbon dating involves measuring the amount of naturally occurring radioactive Carbon 14 remaining in substances that were once alive, such as wood, to determine how long ago they died and stopped absorbing the element.)

The preservation of the site in Chile is excellent, due to a layer of peat that covered Monte Verde shortly after its occupation. The peat preserved archaeological remains that usually do not survive for such a long time. The site included the remains of a wood-framed hut, tools, plant remnants, meat, and even three small footprints.

Although Dillehay began excavating Monte Verde in 1977, the accuracy of the dating had been contested because it challenged the standard theory of the first migration to the Americas. Many specialists of the ancient Americas had long believed that the so-called Clovis hunters, who lived in the present-day Southwestern United States about 11,200 years ago, had migrated from Asia across the Bering Land Bridge and down a corridor east of the Rocky Mountains not long before that time.

The presence of people at Monte Verde 12,500 years ago suggests that humans may have crossed the Bering Land Bridge between 15,000 and 20,000 years ago—as much as 9,000 years earlier than had been previously believed. Archaeologists think it would have taken about 9,000 years for humans to migrate from upper North America to central Chile, some 15,000 kilometers (9,300 miles) to the south. An alternative theory suggests that migration might also have been by water and land along the Pacific Coast.

"American" spearpoint in Siberia.
Discovery of a fluted stone spearpoint near the city of Uptar in eastern Siberia raised further questions about the peopling of the Americas. Archaeologist Maureen King of the University of Washington in Seattle and Russian archaeologist Sergei Slobodin reported their finding in August 1996.

The spearpoint has a groove chipped from the base of the stone toward the tip, most likely created to help attach the point to a wooden shaft. Scholars

had thought that the Clovis people had invented fluted points after reaching the Americas.

The Siberian discovery, buried under a layer of volcanic ash, was dated at 8,300 years old, and King speculated that the point could be as old as 12,000 years. If the latter age is correct, it could mean that the spearpoint technology had been developed in Eurasia before the people migrated to America, that it was invented independently on both continents, or that migration occurred back to Eurasia. Specialists concluded that more fluted points would need to be found in Siberia before they could determine the relevance of the artifacts and the dates to the migration theories.

Early humans along the Pacific.
Adding to the controversy surrounding the settlement of the Americas was the dating of a human skeleton found in 1996 on an island off the coast of Alaska. Archaeologist Thomas Stafford of the University of Colorado in Boulder reported in October 1996 that radiocarbon dating had shown the remains to be about 9,730 years old. Although the bones are younger than the Clovis culture or the Monte Verde site, scientists argued that the finding supported the theory that early immigrants may have traveled by boat along the Pacific Coast.

The dating of other human remains along the Columbia River near Kennewick, Washington, was announced in January 1997 by archaeologist Robson Bonnichsen of Oregon State University in Corvallis. The skeleton, called the Kennewick Man, was first thought to be of an early Anglo-European settler because it has Caucasian facial features, such as narrow cheekbones. Radiocarbon tests, however, showed the remains to be 9,300 years old.

Physical anthropologists who studied the skeleton concluded that the features of the Kennewick Man were clearly different than those of Western Native American tribes. They said that although the Kennewick Man may have been an early Native American, he apparently belonged to a native culture that has no living descendants.

Destruction of Iraqi antiquities. In 1997, archaeologists were very concerned about the alarming number of ancient Sumerian, Assyrian, and Babylonian artifacts from archaeological

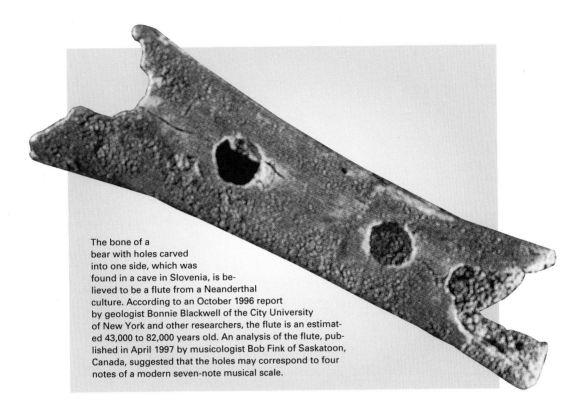

The bone of a bear with holes carved into one side, which was found in a cave in Slovenia, is believed to be a flute from a Neanderthal culture. According to an October 1996 report by geologist Bonnie Blackwell of the City University of New York and other researchers, the flute is an estimated 43,000 to 82,000 years old. An analysis of the flute, published in April 1997 by musicologist Bob Fink of Saskatoon, Canada, suggested that the holes may correspond to four notes of a modern seven-note musical scale.

sites in Iraq that had appeared in the world's art markets since the end of the Persian Gulf War in 1991.

According to archaeologist McGuire Gibson of the University of Chicago, the Iraqi government had carefully guarded its antiquities before the war. With more than 10,000 sites and only a few hundred poorly paid guards, however, the sites had fallen prey to looting and destruction. Most archaeologists believed the smuggling of the artifacts reflected the desperate economic situation in Iraq, which Iraq claimed was the result of sanctions imposed by the United Nations in 1991.

Particularly hard-hit by the looting was the well-known palace of Sennacherib, the king of Assyria in about 700 B.C. His palace in the ancient city of Nineveh had alabaster walls carved with detailed scenes of battles and royal life. John M. Russell, an art historian at Columbia University in New York City, reported in December 1996 that he had been shown photographs of 10 fragments of these walls that were for sale.

Most of the smuggled artifacts, some

dating back to 2500 B.C., were being stolen from royal graves. These treasures included small "cylinder seals" carved with military and ritual scenes. The cylinders, which identified the owners, were rolled across clay tablets and wax seals to create rectangular impressions. Since the cylinders are so small—usually no longer than 8 centimeters (3 inches)—they were easy to smuggle out of the country.

Another disturbing incident was reported in February 1997 by Muayad Demeriji, the head of the Iraq Antiquities Department. A colossal 4,000-year-old Assyrian statue of a winged bull with the head of a bearded man, which had served as a guardian to the throne room of a royal palace, was badly damaged at the site of the ancient city of Dur Sharrukin. Looters hacked off the head, apparently with the intent of selling it.

Progress was being made, however, in stopping the destruction. According to staff archaeologist Dony George, the Antiquities Department had recovered more than 45,000 artifacts, mostly by offering large monetary rewards.

400,000-year-old spears. Three wooden spears discovered in a mine near Schöningen, Germany, in 1995 were identified in March 1997 as the oldest complete hunting tools. Archaeologist Hartmut Thieme of the Hanover Institute for Historic Preservation in Germany reported that the spears were used about 400,000 years ago.

The spears varied in length—the longest measuring 2.3 meters (7.5 feet) —but they were all fashioned in a similar manner. Much like modern javelins, they are thicker from the point to about one-third the length of the shaft. The remains of more than 10 Ice Age horses—the probable targets of these ancient spears—as well as stone tools used for butchering were found at the site.

Given the spears' extreme age, they were probably made by ancestors of the early human beings known as Neanderthals, who evolved in Europe around 300,000 years ago. Archaeologists have long thought that the first inhabitants of Europe, around 500,000 to 780,000 years ago, were few in number and had not developed complex hunting skills.

Although that still may be true, the Schöningen spears show that planned hunting activities by peoples with substantial physical and mental skills occurred much earlier than once thought.

The discovery of James Fort, the original fortification of the English settlement of Jamestown, was announced in September 1996 by archaeologist William Kelso of the Association for the Preservation of Virginia Antiquities. Jamestown, named for England's King James I, was established by English soldier John Smith in 1607 on a small, swampy island at the mouth of the James River in Virginia. The fort burned in 1608, and during the first year 69 of the 107 colonists died from malaria and starvation or in battles with Indians.

The researchers traced the outline of the buried remains of the three-sided wood fort, which accurately matched written descriptions from the 1600's. The approximately 90,000 artifacts at the site included blue glass beads used in trade, clay smoking pipes, fragments of pottery, coins minted in 1601, and military artifacts, such as sword frag-

The first artists?

Archaeologists at a site in Australia's Northern Territory, *below,* study rock carvings believed to be at least 75,000 years old. The researchers, led by archaeologist Richard Fullagar of the Australian Museum in Sydney, published their findings in September 1996. A close-up view of the carvings, *inset,* shows the remarkable uniformity of the round indentations tapped into the rock by the prehistoric artists. Because the carvings depict no recognizable images, the researchers were uncertain of their meaning, but Fullagar and others believed they are evidence of early artistic expression.

Destruction of Iraqi artifacts
A piece of an ancient alabaster wall, *above,* from the palace of the Assyrian king Sennacherib, who ruled around 700 B.C., appeared for sale in late 1996. The fragment had been broken out of the wall by thieves. A 1991 photo, *left,* shows the wall before the piece was removed. The red line identifies the part of the wall from which the fragment came. This artifact was one of thousands that had appeared on the world's art markets since 1991. Economic hardships in Iraq, due to United Nations sanctions, are believed to have prompted the widespread looting.

ments, a helmet, and chest armor.

A surprise discovery was the skeleton of a man in his early 20's buried in a wooden coffin. A musket ball was imbedded in his lower right leg, and he had possibly also suffered from a shoulder wound. Speculating about the man's death, forensic anthropologist Douglas W. Owsley of the Smithsonian Institution in Washington, D.C., noted a written account about a Jamestown man killed during a mutiny, as well as another account of a settler killed by an Indian who had seized a gun from him.

The National Geographic Society agreed to sponsor continued excavations at James Fort and Jamestown, hoping to have new data for the 400th anniversary of the settlement in 2007.

Excavation of La Salle's ship. In April 1997, a team of archaeologists led by James Bruseth of the Texas Historical Commission finished excavating a remarkably well-preserved French ship, the *Belle,* which sank in the Matagorda Bay on the Texas coast in 1686. The *Belle* was one of four ships under the command of French explorer Sieur de La Salle, who had intended—but failed—to establish a fort at the mouth of the Mississippi River and claim the territory for France.

After sinking, the *Belle* and its cargo were quickly covered by mud, which preserved about 40 percent of the ship's hull and thousands of artifacts. In order to excavate the ship, the archaeologists built a *cofferdam* (temporary enclosure) around it and pumped out the water, enabling them to work on dry land.

Artifacts included the ship's rope riggings, barrels of glass beads for trade, iron axeheads, and boxes of supplies. Two ornate bronze cannons were found in the cargo hold, along with boxes of muskets and the complete skeleton of one of the French crewmen or perhaps a colonist who had returned to the ship. Conservation and restoration of the *Belle* began in April under the leadership of archaeologist Donny Hamilton at Texas A&M University's Nautical Archaeology Program in College Station.

In September 1996, the accidental discovery of eight buried cannons near Matagorda Bay allowed archaeologists to

Treasures of a Scythian tomb

The intact tomb of a Scythian prince who lived about 2,300 years ago in what is now Ukraine was uncovered by archaeologists in summer 1996. The tomb's apartmentlike burial chamber, *below*, included pots and a cooking stove. The Scythians were nomadic warriors who controlled much of present-day Ukraine and surrounding areas from the 600's to the 200's B.C.

The tomb was discovered near the town of Ryzanovka, Ukraine, *below*. Artifacts found in the tomb included a Greek-made silver drinking cup depicting fighting animals, *top*, and a gold bracelet, *left*.

also verify the location of a fort that La Salle established close to the bay in 1685. In the winter of 1687 and 1688, the native Karankawas overran the fort and killed all the colonists, except for five children.

Dispelling myths of New York City. Excavations in lower Manhattan's Five Points district revealed that the neighborhood's reputation in the mid-1800's as an immigrant "slum" riddled with gangs, vice, and poverty may have been a myth. Many popular writers of that time condemned Five Points, but archaeologist Rebecca Yamin of John Milner Associates in Philadelphia reported findings in March 1997 that summoned up a much different image.

German-immigrant residents in Five Points began subdividing their houses in the 1830's so they could rent rooms to other immigrants, mostly laborers from Ireland. The archaeological record of the people who lived in these houses is best preserved in their *privies* (outhouses). The privies, which also served as household garbage dumps, provided unusual but remarkable time capsules of the cultural artifacts of the 1800's.

One privy sealed in the 1830's at the house of a German family yielded expensive tableware and glassware from England; a variety of glass containers for perfume, medicines, and snuff; and clay smoking pipes. Other privies used between the 1850's and 1870's at one tenement with mostly Irish immigrants yielded more English dishes and teaware. The archaeological team's innovative research included using an 1867 catalog with the prices of these kinds of ceramics and census records indicating the occupations of residents to estimate family incomes.

The researchers determined that 57 percent of the families had an annual income of about $600—rather high for what had been described as a "slum." Rather than a "nest of vipers," as one author called it, the archaeological record revealed a working-class neighborhood in which residents could spend a considerable part of their income to acquire household goods and create comfortable homes.   [Thomas R. Hester]

See also ANTHROPOLOGY.

Astronomy

Comet Hale-Bopp streaked into the inner solar system in 1997, making its closest approach to the sun on April 1. With its bright *coma* (envelope of gas and dust) and long tail, Hale-Bopp gave viewers in the Northern Hemisphere the best cometary sky show of the past 100 or 200 years, according to astronomers. Even more important, Hale-Bopp shed from its icy *nucleus*—a core of rock and ice—molecules similar to those in interstellar clouds. Such molecules may be chemical precursors of the earliest forms of life on Earth. Hale-Bopp's final surprise was evidence of a type of tail never before seen in a comet.

Hale-Bopp is a *long-period* comet, one that orbits the sun in periods of thousands or millions of years. Hale-Bopp last visited the inner solar system 4,200 years ago, and it will return in 2,400 years. Like other long-period comets, Hale-Bopp probably originated in the Oort Cloud, a region that lies 1,000 times farther from the sun than Pluto, the farthest planet in our solar system.

As Hale-Bopp drew closer to the sun and was heated by it, the ices in the comet's nucleus vaporized, creating the display of coma and tail. Using *spectrometers* (instruments that break light up into its component colors, or wavelengths), astronomers identified about a dozen molecules in the comet's ices by the wavelengths they produced. The astronomers were able to begin studying the gases released by Hale-Bopp in September 1995—well before its closest approach to the sun—partly because of its exceptional size. Hale-Bopp's nucleus was about 40 kilometers (25 miles) wide, while most comets' nuclei are less than 10 kilometers (6 miles) wide.

One of the first gases detected in Hale-Bopp was carbon monoxide, a common molecule in the gas and dust clouds that exist throughout the Milky Way. These clouds may be the sites of star and planet formation.

In March 1997, a research team headed by astrophysicist Harold Weaver at Johns Hopkins University in Baltimore reported that it had also found methyl alcohol, formaldehyde, hydrogen sulfide, and methyl cyanide in Hale-Bopp. These molecules are made up of car-

Comet Hale-Bopp displays its *coma* (envelope of gas and dust) and two of its three tails as it travels through the inner solar system in March 1997. Like most comets, Hale-Bopp had an *ion tail*—a tail of electrically charged particles—(the blue streak) and a dust tail (the white streak). But astronomers discovered that Hale-Bopp also had a sodium tail, positioned near the ion tail and visible only with an instrument called a spectrometer. The reddish patch in the upper right of the image is a far-away nebula, or gas cloud.

bon, hydrogen, nitrogen, sulfur, and oxygen. Their presence in Hale-Bopp—and in other long-period comets like Hyakutake, observed in early 1996—suggests that the comets are rich in molecules that serve as starting points for making amino acids, the building blocks of proteins. The discovery of such molecules in long-period comets prompted astronomers to consider whether comets delivered most, or all, of the water and carbon-bearing molecules that were the source of oceans and life on Earth.

Teams of astronomers at Padova Astronomical Observatory in Italy; Queens University in Belfast, Northern Ireland; and La Palma Observatory in the Canary Islands announced another startling fact about Hale-Bopp in April 1997: The comet had three tails. Most comets have two—a dust tail and a fainter tail of *ions* (electrically charged atoms or molecules), both easily seen with the naked eye. Hale-Bopp had a third tail of sodium atoms, positioned near the ion tail and visible only as an electronic image on a spectrometer.

Signs of life in Mars meteorite? Geologist David S. McKay at the National Aeronautics and Space Administration's (NASA) Johnson Space Center in Houston and his colleagues captured the imagination of people throughout the world in August 1996 with a startling announcement: The scientists revealed that they had found apparent evidence of past life in a meteorite from Mars.

The rock—officially known as ALH84001—was found in the Allan Hills of Antarctica in 1984. It was one of 12 meteorites in which trapped gases, minerals, or other chemical clues strongly suggest a Martian origin. Researchers believe that ALH84001 was blasted into space when an asteroid struck Mars, shattering its rocky surface. Through chemical testing, they determined that ALH84001 was formed some 4.5 billion years ago.

The evidence in the meteorite that Mars once harbored life, in the form of primitive microorganisms, was threefold. McKay and his associates found that the rock contained carbonate, a mineral which forms on Earth when water and carbon dioxide chemically erode surface rock. The scientists reasoned that the carbonate in the Martian rock may have formed at a time when

Mars had a warm climate and liquid water. The rock also contained molecules called polycyclic aromatic hydrocarbons (PAH's), which on Earth are formed through biological processes, and the mineral magnetite in a form that on Earth is usually made by bacteria.

Finally, images taken with an electron microscope—which can see features 1,000 times smaller than the thickness of a hair—revealed tiny spherical and wormlike forms in the meteorite. The team suggested that these were the remains of the primitive microorganisms themselves.

The team's conclusions were challenged by scientists who contended that the chemical and microscopic evidence in the meteorite could have resulted from nonbiological processes. But the discovery also helped to accelerate plans to bring a rock sample back from Mars with a robotic spacecraft, perhaps as early as 2005.

Galileo and the moons of Jupiter. Throughout 1996, new images and data from the Galileo spacecraft revised astronomers' ideas about Jupiter's largest moons. The four satellites—Callisto, Ganymede, Europa, and Io—are known as the Galilean moons. Like the spacecraft that went to study them, they are named for the Italian astronomer Galileo Galilei, who discovered them in 1610.

The Galileo spacecraft, which began orbiting Jupiter in December 1995, mapped the giant planet's magnetic field, studied its atmosphere, and made multiple passes by Callisto, Ganymede, and Europa. (Io, the innermost of the four moons, was the least studied, because its orbit is too deep in Jupiter's belts of intense radiation to permit multiple close fly-bys.) Scientists used an electronic camera and a spectrometer to examine Jupiter's moons in detail.

Callisto, outermost of the Galilean moons, was thought from images taken by the Voyager probe in 1979 to be heavily cratered and geologically quiet. However, the Galileo images, analyzed by Michael Belton at the National Optical Astronomy Observatories in Tucson, Arizona, and his colleagues, revealed that although Callisto has many large craters, it has few small ones. Belton's team reported its findings at the Lunar and Planetary Science Conference in Houston in March 1997. The team noted that the most plausible explanation for the lack of small craters was that the water ice that is part of Callisto's crust—and hence part of its craters—may have evaporated over time, causing the larger craters to weaken and collapse but remain visible. The smaller craters simply disappeared. This explanation, if proved correct, would support the view that Callisto has no geologic way to renew its surface and thus has remained for billions of years a passive moon whose surface features have slowly crumbled away.

Images of nearby Ganymede, Jupiter's largest satellite, showed long grooves across its surface. These grooves are signs of geologic activity in the moon's interior earlier in its history.

Data from Galileo's instruments also showed that Ganymede has its own magnetic field. Donald Gurnett at the University of Iowa and Margaret Kivelson at the University of California in Los Angeles, astrophysicists who headed the two instrument teams, reported this finding in December 1996. For the moon to maintain a magnetic field, the scientists theorized, parts of its interior must be in motion and must conduct electricity. The scientists suggested that partially melted water ice and dissolved salts inside the moon may act as conductors.

Closer in to Jupiter, the moon Europa stole the show with its icy surface covered with intricate fractures, areas where liquid water may have welled up, along with carbon-bearing compounds. Europa is close enough to Jupiter for the giant planet's gravity to squeeze the moon as it moves in its slightly elliptical orbit. The heat that results from this squeezing may open cracks on the moon and maintain a liquid-water ocean under the surface.

A brownish coloration seen around some cracks in Galileo images of Europa suggested the presence of carbon-bearing molecules reddened by exposure to Jupiter's intense radiation. The spectrometer data, analyzed by Robert Carlson, a scientist at the Jet Propulsion Laboratory in Pasadena, California, and his colleagues, hinted at the presence of such molecules. The fresh appearance of some cracks and other geological features suggested that Europa remains an active world, where biological processes might exist under the thin ice crust. So interesting is this moon that scientists

Here Comes the Sun

The year 2000 may bring solar fireworks to Earth, astronomers predicted in 1997. More and more *sunspots*—dark areas with lower temperatures than the surface around them—began to appear across the face of the sun in 1996. These sunspots signaled the beginning of a new cycle of solar activity. Scientists were betting that the cycle would peak at the turn of the millennium, causing a similar peak in climatic and electrical disturbances all around the Earth.

Sunspots are the most obvious signs of disturbances on the sun. They occur along with *mass ejections*, eruptions that hurl large amounts of particles, energy, and radiation from the sun's surface. Solar physicists believe that sunspots and other disturbances occur when the magnetic field deep inside the sun is disrupted by the sun's rotation. Because the sun is composed primarily of gases, its equatorial region rotates faster than its poles do. This uneven rotation causes the sun's magnetic field to strengthen deep inside the sun. Portions of this magnetic field then buoy to the surface, in some cases preventing heat from reaching the surface, creating the cool sunspots.

Sunspots tend to occur in cycles that last about 11 years. During each cycle, the magnetic field twists, releasing energy in bursts—such as mass ejections—and then relaxes. The cycles progress from no or few sunspots to a large number of spots and back again to a minimum. The sunspots

A large flare on the sun, at the lower center of this image, was captured on April 8, 1997, by an orbiting space telescope. The flare is part of a storm on the sun in solar cycle 23, which began in May 1996.

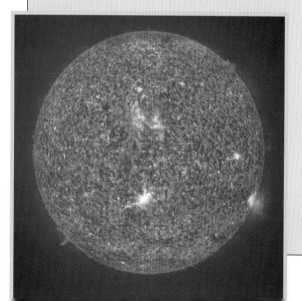

of a new cycle appear in areas midway between the poles and the equator first, and then in areas closer to the equator as a cycle progresses. The energy and radiation from eruptions become part of the *solar wind*—a stream of charged particles, primarily protons and electrons—that blows from the sun, through the solar system, and beyond.

When large bursts of solar energy reach Earth, they create *geomagnetic storms,* severe disturbances of Earth's magnetic field. Geomagnetic storms can produce a variety of effects on Earth, most of them disruptive. Among the most striking and best understood effects of increased sunspots and solar activity is an upswing in the occurrence of *auroras* (the northern and southern lights). Strong gusts of solar wind send clouds of charged particles from the sun toward Earth. The particles follow Earth's magnetic field lines into the Earth's atmosphere. There, the particles collide with atmospheric atoms and molecules producing the auroras—vivid, diffuse arcs and rays of multicolored light that dance across polar skies.

Another effect of the barrage of space particles is a shut-down of electric power transmission grids, the systems of electric power lines that carry electric current from producers to users. In 1989, the last time that the number of sunspots peaked, the flow of charged particles from the sun so disrupted the Earth's magnetic field that a hydroelectric power grid in Quebec, Canada, was knocked out of operation. The collapse shut down electric power throughout the province.

Abrupt power blackouts and more frequent auroras are the more obvious effects of the increased magnetic activity that accompanies a rise in the number of sunspots. But this increase in magnetic activity can also confuse the delicate electronics aboard spacecraft, causing potentially dangerous false or "phantom" commands to be given to the spacecraft. On a larger scale, the Earth's atmosphere often responds to a geomagnetic storm by heating and swelling, pushing the edge of the atmosphere outward. A higher, expanded atmosphere increases drag on low-orbiting satellites and can shorten their useful life by hastening their reentry into the atmosphere.

People, too, may be at risk from solar outbursts. Astronauts on a spacewalk must seek shelter in their spacecraft because high-energy radiation from a geomagnetic storm can destroy cells in the human body.

Thus, predicting how strong the solar cycle will be and when it will be at its maximum—the time when the sun is covered with the most sunspots and is producing the greatest number of eruptions—is important to our technological society and to human health. Such prediction is largely a process of looking back to find a pattern of activity that can then be successfully projected forward.

The prediction of solar activity is a relatively recent development in astronomy. Although ancient Chinese astronomers recorded sunspots, the first regular observations were not made until 1749, when astronomers at the Zurich Observatory in Switzerland began recording the cycle that modern astronomers call solar cycle 1. The 22 solar cycles since that date have been extremely irregular, making prediction difficult. Moreover, scientists now believe that truly reliable observations began in 1848, covering only 13 of the 22 cycles of the short historical record.

In many cases, according to Karen Harvey, a solar physicist at the Solar Physics Research Corporation and a Visiting Astronomer at Kitt Peak National Solar Observatory, both in Tucson, Arizona, the length of a particular cycle of sunspots is not clear until the new cycle begins. The reason for the uncertainty is that both old- and new-cycle sunspots are visible during the minimum period between cycles. One way that scientists can distinguish new sunspots from those of the preceding cycle is by plotting the points at which the spots appear on the sun. Spots from the old cycle are near the equator while spots from the new cycle appear at solar latitudes greater than 25 degrees.

To help astronomers today predict the solar cycle and monitor solar activity, the National Oceanic and Atmospheric Administration and the U.S. Air Force jointly operate a service known as Space Weather Operations. This facility in Boulder, Colorado, issues forecasts and warnings of impending solar disturbances. Such disturbances were forecast with about 30 percent accuracy in the mid-1990's, roughly the same as for weather forecasts before continuous observations of the Earth were possible with weather satellites. Solar scientists hoped that a new satellite, scheduled for launch in August 1997, would improve the accuracy.

Known as the Advanced Composition Explorer (ACE), the new satellite was to be placed about 1.5 million kilometers (930,000 miles) sunward from the Earth, at a point where the gravitational fields of the sun and Earth are balanced. From that location, ACE will sample the composition and magnetic characteristics of the solar wind flowing to Earth and provide warnings of hazardous solar gusts that will reach Earth about an hour after being detected by ACE.

Further improvement in long-term prediction, however, will have to await the results of studies

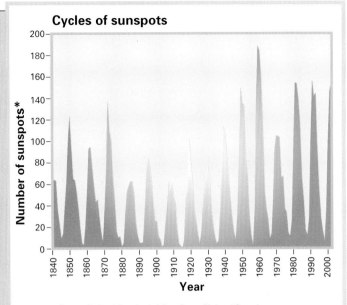

Cycles of sunspots

Number of sunspots*

Year

Source: National Geophysical Data Center/National Oceanic and Atmospheric Administration (NOAA).
*Numbers for the years 1997 through 2000 are estimates by the Space Environment Center at NOAA.

being conducted by a number of ground-based instruments as well as by spacecraft from around the world. Ulysses, a joint mission of the National Aeronautics and Space Administration (NASA) and the European Space Agency (ESA), was launched in 1990 to orbit and observe the sun. The Solar and Heliospheric Observatory (SOHO), also a joint effort of NASA and ESA, has been surveying the sun with a battery of instruments since 1995. A Japanese satellite, Yohkoh, was launched in 1991 to study the sun's *corona* (outer atmosphere) by observing the X rays it emits.

Scientists spent much of early 1996 watching a nearly spotless sun and waiting for the first sign of the next round of sunspots to appear. In May, they noted a new sunspot region at about 29° N latitude, indicating the start of solar cycle 23.

After determining that a new solar cycle had begun, scientists turned to predicting the timing of the coming maximum and its effects on Earth. In September 1996, NASA assembled a scientific task force to make a "best guess" about the timing and size of the next solar maximum. The panel reported a "reasonable consensus" that solar cycle 23 will be comparable in magnitude to cycles 21 (1976 to 1986) and 22 (1986 to 1995), but will probably not exceed cycle 19 (1954 to 1964), the most active on record. The task force said the probability for severe geomagnetic storms would be greatest from 1999 through 2005. With those expected storms, the celestial fireworks of the new century would begin.   [Joann Temple Dennett]

A close-up view of Callisto, one of Jupiter's largest moons, taken by the spacecraft Galileo in November 1996, shows part of a chain of impact craters. Though Callisto has many large craters, astronomers were surprised to find that it has relatively few small ones. The scientists theorized that much of the water ice that is part of Callisto's crust may have evaporated over time. The evaporation caused the larger craters to crumble but remain visible, while small craters disappeared. Fresh ice surfaces gleam brightly in areas where parts of crater walls have crumbled, exposing underlying ice.

planned to make it the focus of an extended Galileo investigation beginning in late 1997.

Doubts about new planets. From June 1996 to early 1997, astronomers reported finding several more *extrasolar planets* (planets orbiting other stars), bringing the number of such planets known to more than a dozen. In February 1997, however, astronomer David F. Gray of the University of Western Ontario in Canada questioned some of the discoveries.

None of the supposed new planets was seen by astronomers—all were too dim and too close to their stars to be sighted directly. Rather, astronomers inferred their existence by the small motion detected in each star, caused by the pull of the planet's gravity. By analyzing the motion, astronomers estimated the *mass* (quantity of matter) of each planet, which ranged from about one-half to nearly 10 times the mass of Jupiter. (Jupiter has 318 times the mass of Earth.)

But Gray threw a little cold water on the excitement over extrasolar planets.

He suggested that in at least some cases—particularly that of 51 Pegasi, the first new planet discovered—the detected motions were probably the star's normal pulsations and not orbital motion. Gray said the same could also be true of three other suspected planets discovered in 1996, those orbiting the stars Tau Boötis, Upsilon Andromedae, and Rho[1] Cancri.

Supporters of the planetary theory argued that pulsations such as Gray proposed should be accompanied by variations in the stars' brightness, which were not seen. They also noted that stars that pulsate usually do so at more than one frequency, and 51 Pegasi and the other planets showed no such variations.

Galactic plume of antimatter. In April 1997, a team of astrophysicists announced the discovery of a giant fountain of *antimatter* flowing from the core of the Milky Way Galaxy. Antimatter is identical to ordinary matter but opposite in electrical charge. Antimatter was produced by the *big bang*—the explosion of matter and energy that most astrophysicists believe gave birth to the universe—and continues to be produced by celestial processes.

Astrophysicist William Purcell at Northwestern University in Evanston, Illinois, and his collaborators at the Naval Research Laboratory in Washington, D.C., used NASA's orbiting Compton Gamma Ray Observatory to measure and record *gamma rays*. Gamma rays are a form of high-energy radiation. When a particle of matter collides with a particle of antimatter, the two annihilate each other, producing energy that can be detected as gamma rays.

Purcell's team proposed that *supernovae* (exploding stars) at the center of the Milky Way may have caused the antimatter plume. Other researchers theorized that a supermassive *black hole* (a concentration of matter in such a small volume that gravity prevents even light from escaping) at the center of the Milky Way may be the cause.

New molecule in the Milky Way. In November 1996, astronomers Thomas Geballe at the Joint Astronomy Centre in Hilo, Hawaii, and Takeshi Oka at the University of Chicago reported that they had found H_3^+, an elusive molecule in the dusty clouds between the stars of the Milky Way Galaxy. Astronomers think H_3^+, which consists of three joined hydrogen atoms but with one electron missing, may play a role in star formation, helping gas clouds cool until they become dense and collapse to form stars.

Astronomers had been searching for H_3^+ since 1961. Analyses of the molecule in the laboratory had led them to believe that H_3^+ may be an intermediate step between H_2 (two joined hydrogen atoms), the simplest molecule in gas clouds between the stars, and more complex molecules.

Geballe and Oka used the United Kingdom Infrared Telescope at the Mauna Kea Observatory in Hawaii, aiming it at young stars in the dark clouds. The astronomers knew they had found H_3^+ when they noted its signature in the *infrared* part of the light spectrum. (Infrared radiation is identical to visible light except that its longer wavelengths cannot be seen by the human eye.)

A black hole in every galaxy? From October 1996 through February 1997, astronomers found new evidence supporting the theory that many galaxies—perhaps most or all of them—contain supermassive black holes at their center. Astronomers think that black holes form when massive stars collapse at the end of their lifetime; when huge quantities of matter fall together during galactic formation; or when galaxies collide. The black holes make their presence known through high-energy activities, such as rapid star and gas-cloud motions and emissions of intense radiation.

Astronomers have found considerable evidence of an immense black hole in the Milky Way Galaxy. They have long suspected that a tiny bright spot seen in radio and infrared images, called Sagittarius A* (Sgr A*), may be the central object around which the Milky Way's giant spiral-shaped disk rotates. They have also observed that stars and gas clouds near Sgr A* move very rapidly, indicating the probable presence of a black hole. However, since the center of the Milky Way is almost 25,000 *light-years* away, even rapid motions have been very hard to measure. (A light-year is the distance light travels in one year, about 9.5 trillion kilometers [5.9 trillion miles].)

In October 1996, astronomers Andreas Eckart and Reinhard Genzel at the Max Planck Institute for Extraterrestrial Physics in Garching, Germany, announced that they had accomplished the equivalent of measuring such rapid motions in stars near the galactic center. Eckart and Genzel used the New Technology Telescope in La Silla, Chile, to make a series of precise measurements of the positions of stars near Sgr A* over a period of five years. When they compared the results, they found that the overall velocities of the stars near Sgr A* were too high to be explained by anything other than a supermassive black hole. Thus, the Milky Way is almost certainly one of the galaxies that has a huge black hole in its core.

Additional evidence that supermassive black holes are common in galaxies was reported in January 1997 by a team of astronomers headed by Douglas Richstone at the University of Michigan in Ann Arbor. The team used the Hubble Space Telescope (HST) to observe the motions of stars near the centers of more than a dozen galaxies and found that the motions were so rapid that a very large central mass must exist in each of the galaxies. The researchers estimated that the masses range from 2 million to hundreds of millions of suns.

The idea that many, or even all, galaxies have black holes was further bolstered in February 1997. A team of astronomers led by Roeland P. van der Marel at the Institute for Advanced Studies in Princeton, New Jersey, reported that it had found clear evidence of a black hole with the mass of a million suns in the center of a small nearby galaxy called M32. Van der Marel and his colleagues used the HST to measure the motions of stars near the center of M32. They found star velocities in the core region of the galaxy to be so high that a mass of at least 3 million suns must be contained within a volume of space just two light-years across. Only a black hole can squeeze so much matter into such a small volume.

New images of quasars. In November 1996, teams of scientists led by John N. Bahcall at the Institute for Advanced Studies and Michael Disney at the University of Wales in Cardiff released the first images ever taken of the host galaxies of 35 *quasars* (remote, starlike sources of immense quantities of energy). Astronomers had long suspected that quasars reside in galaxies and that they are powered by black holes. Before the launch of the HST, however, no one had seen quasars clearly because their intense light obscured everything around them. The Hubble telescope vastly improved astronomers' ability to detect faint, fuzzy objects.

In the new HST images, every quasar observed lay in the core of a galaxy, and the galaxies differed in outward appearance. Some quasars lay in elliptical galaxies; others, in spiral galaxies. Some host galaxies appeared to be completely normal, while others seemed to have been disrupted, perhaps by a near-collision with another galaxy. Astronomers hoped to determine next whether the black holes that power quasars formed first and then galaxies formed around them, or whether expanding galaxies collided, feeding black holes with matter and turning them into quasars.

Closer to the age of the universe. From mid-1996 to early 1997, several groups of astronomers announced new

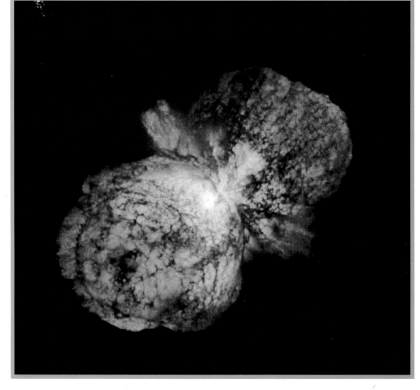

Twin lobes of gas and dust expand from the supermassive star Eta Carinae. The star ejected much of its mass in a huge explosion, seen on Earth in the 1840's, when Eta Carinae briefly became the second-brightest star in the southern sky. Astronomers at the University of Colorado in Boulder and the University of Minnesota in Minneapolis used the Hubble Space Telescope to capture the star in unprecedented detail in this image released in June 1996.

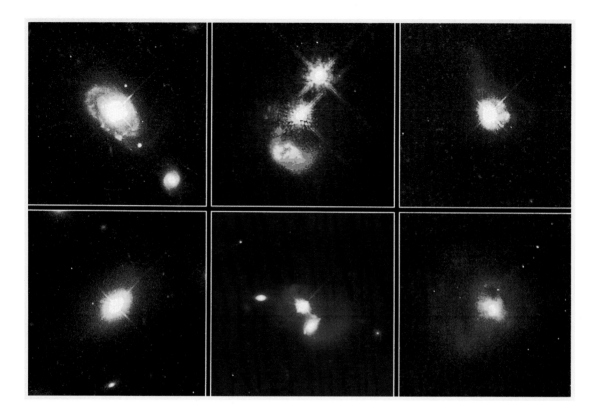

In November 1996, astronomers released new images of *quasars* (remote, powerful sources of immense quantities of energy) and the galaxies in which they reside. The scientists used the Hubble Space Telescope, which improved their ability to detect the faint, fuzzy galaxies, which are usually obscured by the quasars' brilliant light. The quasars were found in a wide variety of galaxies—in a normal spiral galaxy, *top left;* a normal elliptical galaxy, *bottom left;* two colliding galaxies, *center top* and *bottom;* and merging galaxies, *right top* and *bottom.*

calculations for the age of the universe, bringing the conflicting measurements of various teams closer together. Disagreement about the age flared in 1994, when a group led by Wendy L. Freedman at the Carnegie Observatories in Pasadena, California, used data from the HST to calculate that the universe must be about 8 billion to 12 billion years old. That figure was much lower than the traditionally accepted age of 15 billion to 20 billion years, calculated by determining the age of the oldest stars. The Freedman team's figures created a problem by suggesting that the universe was younger than its oldest stars. The debate was further complicated in early 1996, when a team of astronomers led by Allan Sandage—also of the Carnegie Observatories and also using HST data —calculated the age of the universe to be at least 15 billion years.

The disagreement over the age of the universe centered on the rate at which the universe is expanding. Astronomers calculate the expansion rate from the speed at which an object, usually a galaxy or cluster of galaxies, is moving

away from the Milky Way. They then use the expansion rate to calculate how much time has elapsed since the big bang, the event which most scientists believe began the expansion.

Both Freedman and Sandage calculated the expansion rate by using the HST to observe very bright giant stars called Cepheid variables in faraway galaxies and thereby determine the distance of the galaxies. (The brightness of Cepheids is an indicator of their distance.) However, the two teams used the Cepheid information in different ways: Freedman's team observed the farthest Cepheids that can be seen with the HST, those in galaxies 50 million to 100 million light-years away. Sandage's group used Cepheids to determine distances to galaxies where supernovae had been observed, as a means of determining the exact brightness of supernovae. Supernovae can be seen up to billions of light-years away, so once their brightness is known, they can be used to calculate the distances to extremely faraway galaxies.

The Sandage team's calculations yielded a slower expansion rate and thus an older universe, consistent with the ages of the oldest stars. The expansion rate found by Freedman and her colleagues, on the other hand, was more rapid, implying a younger age for the universe and causing a conflict with the ages of the stars.

In mid-1996, both teams announced refined measurement results. The Sandage team slightly increased its expansion rate estimate, while Freedman's group slightly decreased its estimate. The ranges of possible values from the two groups overlapped for the first time, at a figure of about 10.5 billion years.

Then, in February 1997, astronomers Robin Catchpole at the Royal Greenwich Observatory in Cambridge, England, and Michael Feast at the University of Cape Town in South Africa reported a revised brightness scale for Cepheids, based on direct measurements of the distances to 26 Cepheids in the Milky Way. The astronomers used extremely accurate instruments aboard the European satellite Hipparcos to measure the Cepheids' *parallax*—their apparent shift in position in the sky over the course of a year due to their being observed from opposite points in the Earth's orbit around the sun. The parallax measurements enabled the astronomers to calculate distances for the Cepheids that were 100 times more precise than previous ones.

Catchpole and Feast found that the stars are a bit farther away than astronomers had thought and thus that Cepheids in general have a greater inherent brightness than had been assumed. This recalibration of Cepheids' true brightness resulted in an increased distance scale—and an older age—for the universe. The revision changed both the Sandage and Freedman groups' estimates of the universe's age, shifting the overlap point from 10.5 billion years to 11.5 billion years, a better match with the estimated age of the oldest stars.

Two other groups of astronomers reported in late 1996 that their research showed the universe to be about 14 billion years old.   [Jonathan I. Lunine and Theodore P. Snow]

(In the Special Reports section, see PROBING THE PLANETS.)

Atmospheric Science

Many important areas of atmospheric science were explored by researchers in 1996 and 1997. Some scientists investigated the possibility that excess nitrogen in the atmosphere was causing environmental problems. Others gained new insights into the role that clouds play in influencing climate. Computer models enabled researchers to learn more about how wind and fire affect each other. And radar helped scientists gain a better understanding of the dangerous, swirling winds of tornadoes.

Excess nitrogen. "Excess nitrogen is causing serious and long-term environmental consequences across large regions of the Earth," according to a study published in April 1997 by a group of scientists affiliated with the Ecological Society of America, a professional association based in Washington, D.C. Air is about 78 percent nitrogen, making nitrogen the most common gas in Earth's atmosphere. In a natural process known as the global nitrogen cycle, nitrogen circulates through the atmosphere, soil, water, and plants and animals.

The nitrogen cycle is essential to life. The study indicated, however, that human activities are disturbing the cycling of nitrogen by releasing quantities of the chemical almost as large as those released by natural processes. Humans release nitrogen into the environment in fertilizers, partially treated and untreated sewage, inefficient combustion in automobile and truck engines, and emissions into the air by fossil-fuel-burning power plants.

Excess nitrogen in bodies of water causes algae to undergo population explosions called blooms. When large numbers of the algae die, bacteria in the water decompose them, which depletes the oxygen in the water. As a result of the oxygen depletion, many fish die. Another problem with blooms is that certain kinds release toxic chemicals into the water, killing more fish.

On land, excess nitrogen seems to favor the growth of certain weeds, which then grow out of control at the expense of desirable plant species. As the desirable plants disappear, animals that normally feed on them may starve.

Excess nitrogen may contribute to the

greenhouse effect, the warming of Earth's lower atmosphere, by weakening the ability of plants to remove carbon dioxide from the air. (Carbon dioxide is one of the so-called greenhouse gases that trap heat in the atmosphere and which, in excessive quantities, may contribute to global warming.) Nitrous oxide, a compound containing nitrogen, is one of the gases contributing to the destruction of *ozone,* a form of oxygen in the upper atmosphere that protects people and other organisms from the sun's harmful ultraviolet rays. Another compound containing nitrogen—nitric oxide—is absorbed by water in clouds and falls to Earth as acid rain.

To reduce the amount of nitrogen released by human sources, the scientists suggested a more conservative use of fertilizer and the development of more efficient internal combustion engines. They said that over a longer term, environmental nitrogen could be further reduced by using *genetic engineering,* the manipulation of an organism's genetic material, to create crops that could survive with less fertilizer.

Clouds and global warming. In 1997, research continued to indicate that the concentrations of carbon dioxide, methane, and other greenhouse gases were increasing in Earth's atmosphere, mainly because of the burning of fossil fuels and the clearing of forests. While atmospheric scientists generally agreed that these increasing concentrations would lead to higher temperatures over time, they disagreed about the magnitude of the warming.

One of the reasons for the disagreement was that scientists did not fully understand the role that clouds play in influencing climate. In February 1997, atmospheric scientists at the Scripps Institution of Oceanography in La Jolla, California, published a report discussing a recently found piece of the global warming puzzle—the fact that one of the ways that clouds influence global temperatures is by absorbing a significant amount of solar energy.

The scientists, led by Veerabhadran Ramanathan, found that clouds may retain as much as 8 percent of the solar energy passing through the Earth's at-

Hurricane Fran, with winds clocked at 185 kilometers (115 miles) per hour, is captured in a satellite image in early September 1996 as it approaches the East Coast of the United States. The hurricane struck the coast at Cape Fear, North Carolina, on September 5, causing 17 deaths and more than $1 billion in property damage.

mosphere. The solar energy stored in clouds may lead to lower daytime temperatures and higher nighttime temperatures than predicted by most theoretical models of global warming.

Ramanathan's research was part of the Atmospheric Radiation Measurement Program, a project begun in 1989 by the United States Department of Energy to examine the role that clouds play in influencing climate. In 1997, 50 teams of scientists from more than 70 institutions were associated with this project, which included arrays of meteorological sensors spread over the steppes of the Alaskan high Arctic, the plains of central Oklahoma and southern Kansas, and remote islands and atolls of the far western Pacific. The sensors obtained data on the vertical distribution of water vapor, clouds, and solar radiation in the atmosphere. From these data, scientists could see how the sun's energy is retained in the lower atmosphere. The knowledge gained from the Atmospheric Radiation Measurement Program was expected to help scientists make more accurate predictions about the long-term future of Earth's climate.

Wildfires in the computer. A computer model to simulate the interplay between wind and wildfire was presented at the December 1996 meeting of the American Geophysical Union in San Francisco, California, by atmospheric scientist Terry Clark of the National Center for Atmospheric Research. A wildfire is one of the most dynamic expressions of nature's fury. Wildfires come in many forms and can turn a wooded mountainside or a grassy plain to ashes in a matter of minutes. Winds play a key, though not fully understood, role in the spread and behavior of wildfires.

The behavior of wildfires is unpredictable because of the complex terrain in which they often occur and by the fact that fires may modify local winds in ways that, in turn, cause the fires to grow more rapidly. Using a supercomputer to model a large wildfire in a forest and the flow of winds in and around the blaze, Clark and his colleagues showed that the fire's growth depended on a delicate balance between its heat output and the surrounding winds.

For example, the computer model suggested that in the presence of weak winds, a fire is unstable because the winds create sudden fingers of flame. (Previously, researchers thought that these extensions of a fire were due mainly to effects of the terrain.) In extreme cases, such a wildfire can create its own wind and unleash unpredictable "blow-ups" that surge out rapidly to advance the fire front. Where there are relatively strong winds, in contrast, a fire is unlikely to create its own wind, and its behavior becomes more predictable.

The model also suggested that air temperatures near a wildfire may be lower than expected, because a fire's updraft pulls in surrounding cooler air as the fire's heat output increases. The cooler air keeps air temperatures adjacent to the fire in the range of 60 to 100 °C (140 to 212 °F)—even when the fire itself has a temperature of about 800 °C (1,420 °F).

The model by Clark and his colleagues was expected to be a useful new tool in wildfire prediction and management. It was also expected to lead to computer models that would simulate other characteristics of wildfires.

Chasing twisters. A study published in June 1996 described the work of atmospheric scientists who placed an electronic monitoring device in the path of a Texas tornado and collected the most detailed information ever obtained on the structure of twisters. Scientists have been trying to learn more about the rotating funnel clouds of tornadoes, which contain the most violent winds on Earth and can destroy almost anything in their path. The 1996 study was conducted by Joshua Wurman and Jerry Straka of the University of Oklahoma in Norman and Erik N. Rasmussen of the National Oceanic and Atmospheric Administration's National Severe Storms Laboratory, also in Norman.

The researchers used a new type of radar device of their own design. The instrument, called Doppler on Wheels, or DOW, which was mounted on a small truck, was a mobile version of a *Doppler radar* station. Doppler radar, a type of radar often used to make precise speed measurements, transmits radio waves of a constant frequency, which are reflected back at altered frequencies when they strike moving objects. By measuring the difference between a transmitted and received frequency, scientists can determine the speed of an object. DOW transmits its energy waves in pulses, each one lasting a few millionths of a second. By scanning a beam of pulses over an area, the researchers were able to make radar maps indicating the speeds and locations of winds and material in the funnel.

The scientists positioned DOW about 3 kilometers (2 miles) from a tornado funnel near Dimmitt, Texas, on June 3, 1995. This was a very violent tornado that destroyed a home, lifted automobiles, and removed huge chunks of asphalt from roads. Because DOW was positioned right in the path of the tornado, it was able to obtain information about the funnel at much higher resolution, or in much more detail, than stationary weather radars could obtain. The measurements made by DOW helped verify various aspects of theoretical models of tornadoes.

DOW found that the Dimmit tornado had an *eye,* a central area with very little material in it, as models indicated a tornado should have. The eye penetrated the full depth of the funnel cloud, which was more than 800 meters (2,600 feet) high. Surrounding the eye were circular bands of material consisting of raindrops and various kinds of debris. Some of this material occasionally moved into the eye. Winds in the funnel were measured at speeds of more than 70 meters (230 feet) per second.

DOW detected the presence of a downdraft, a downward movement of air, in the center of the eye. Although some scientists had suspected that tornadoes contain downdrafts, this was the first time that such a flow of air had been found. The downdraft was surrounded by the tornado's updraft, the much-feared winds responsible for lifting objects off the ground.

The device used in this study was replaced by two new, improved DOW's in early 1997. As of May 1997, scientists had used DOW's to study 10 tornadoes and 1 hurricane. Plans called for DOW's to be used in many more studies of tornadoes and hurricanes—studies that promised to greatly clarify our understanding of these devastating windstorms.   [John T. Snow]

Biology

A shrub that may be the world's oldest living organism is growing in two river gullies on a remote mountainside in Tasmania, Australia. Botanists determined in 1997 that the shrub, which was discovered in 1993, is perhaps 40,000 years old. That makes it much older than the previous record holder, an 11,700-year-old creosote plant in California. The discovery was announced in October 1996 by Stephen Harris of the Tasmania Parks and Wildlife Service.

Informally known as King's holly, the shrub stands as high as 8 meters (26 feet) in places, and produces bright red flowers every summer. It is the only known specimen of the species *Lomatia tasmania.*

Scientists first assumed they had found several plants belonging to the species, but they later determined that there is only one plant. The plant is sterile, meaning it does not grow from seed, but regenerates itself by spreading into new territory. As its roots spread, they die off at the tail end.

A fossil of one of the plant's leaves found nearby was dated at 43,600 years old. The fossilized leaf's structure was identical to those growing on the plant today, indicating that the present-day plant was growing when the leaf fell.

Penguin research. Male emperor penguins in Antarctica incubate a single egg for 105 to 115 days, sitting on their nest through the frigid polar winter without eating. This feat has long puzzled scientists, who suspected that penguins could not store enough body fat to survive the ordeal. In January 1997, scientists reported that although an isolated penguin cannot survive the winter without eating, groups can do so because they huddle together to conserve energy.

Biologist Yvon Le Maho and her colleagues at the Centre National de la Recherche Scientifique in Strasbourg, France, studied 8 male emperor penguins living in a huddled group of 3,000 and 10 kept in outdoor pens. They found that the huddled penguins used 17 percent less energy than those living in the pens. Without huddling, the team concluded, penguins would run out of energy three weeks early and have to abandon their eggs.

In April 1997, the first known sighting of an all-white emperor penguin was reported by Gerald Kooyman of the Scripps Institution of Oceanography in San Diego. The all-white chick was 5 months old and just under 0.6 meter (2 feet) tall. Normally, penguins have dark wings, tail feathers, bills, and feet, and dark rings around their eyes. Kooyman said he does not think the white penguin was an albino, because its eyes were not the characteristic pink of albinos.

Tiny frog found. The Northern Hemisphere's smallest frog—only 10 millimeters (0.4 inch) long—was discovered by researchers from Pennsylvania State University in State College and the Institute of Forest Investigations in Havana, Cuba. The frog, found in a Cuban rain forest in late 1996, is so small that four could fit comfortably on a nickel. Penn State biologist S. Blair Hedges reported in December that the frog, informally dubbed "eleuth" after its genus *Eleutherodactylus,* shares many characteristics with other unusually small species: It produces only one egg at a time, it lays its eggs out of the water, and it hatches directly into a frog instead of a tadpole.

Red-furred marmoset discovered. A squirrel-sized monkey informally called the Satere marmoset is the latest of seven new primate species found in the rain forests of South America's Amazon valley since 1990. The newly discovered animal, called *Callithrix saterei* after the Satere Indians of the region, has a coat of reddish fur, researchers from the Amazon Forest Foundation reported in August 1996. The marmoset uses its razor-sharp teeth to slice open tree bark, then laps up the sweet, energy-rich sap.

The oldest fossils of animals that lived on land in North America were reported in December 1996 by biologist Patricia Gensel of the University of North Carolina at Chapel Hill. The 400-million-year-old fossils include scorpions, millipedes, and other creatures up to about 10 centimeters (4 inches) long. Until recently, scientists had believed that only plants lived on land that long ago. The fossils took more than a decade to identify and were found during the 1980's in Canada's Gaspé Bay, Quebec, and New Brunswick.

Life on Earth emerged at least 3.8 billion years ago, scientists studying rocks on Akilia Island, Greenland, reported in November 1996. That finding, if correct, means that life is markedly older than the 3.5 billion years previously estimated. (Earth is at least 4.5 billion years old.)

The signs of life, discovered by scientists from the University of California at Los Angeles and the Scripps Institution of Oceanography in La Jolla, California, included traces of carbon isotopes and other organic chemicals characteristic of primitive metabolisms in microscopic grains of a mineral called apatite. The rocks had been crushed and heated too much over time for physical fossils to have survived. But the chemical clues provided strong evidence to evolutionary biologists that life on Earth must have formed very early, even while the planet was in the midst of intense bombardment from the rubble of the early solar system. One researcher, geochemist John M. Hayes of Woods Hole Oceanographic Institution in Massachusetts, said the evidence suggests that primitive life may have emerged 3.8 billion years ago, been wiped out, and reemerged later.

Singing a genetic song. Biologists have long argued whether songbirds' songs are learned from their parents or controlled by genetic inheritance. A remarkable experiment by neurobiologist Evan Balaban of the Neurosciences Institute in San Diego, reported in March 1997 indicates that birds' songs are, in fact, genetic.

Working with fertilized eggs only two to three days old, Balaban transplanted brain cells that control song from Japanese quail into chickens. First, he cut a small window in the quail-egg shells to expose the neural tubes, the bundle of cells from which the brain grows. Using special stains, Balaban identified and removed the brain cells thought to be responsible for song. He then implanted the cells in a chicken egg from which the corresponding cells had been removed, closed the shell, and allowed the egg to develop to maturity.

The chicks that hatched sang like quail. Although chickens normally emit a single squawk without much head movement, these chicks bobbed their heads up and down rapidly and emitted the characteristic three-note quail song. The rest of their behavior, however, was characteristic of chickens.

The east African butterfly *Bicyclus anynana, above,* can take on either of two colorations to fool predators. If born in the wet season, bottom, it has "eyespots" on its wings to attract predators to the wings rather than to the vulnerable body. If born in the dry season, top, it looks like a dry leaf. A group of U.S. and European researchers reported in November 1996 that they had bred groups of the butterflies in laboratory conditions that mimicked either a permanent wet season or a permanent dry season. Within 20 generations, two distinct new species had evolved, one with eyespots and one without, showing that the butterflies were able to adapt quickly to changing conditions by altering relatively few genes.

Earless frog. An earless species of frog found in Panama apparently hears by detecting sound waves through its lungs, researchers at Ohio State University reported in December 1996. The Panamanian golden frog, which lives only along remote mountain streams, possesses a typical amphibian inner ear, but lacks a middle ear and external ear. Nonetheless, the frogs call out to each other and respond to sound, a fact that has puzzled biologists.

Researchers led by zoologist Thomas Hetherington concluded that the frog uses its lungs, which lie very close to the water surface, as ear substitutes. When sound waves hit the frog's side, its lungs vibrate. In experiments, they found that the frogs responded to sound waves that bounced off their lungs, but had difficulty hearing when barriers blocked sound waves from that area. The scientists had yet to learn how vibrations detected in the frog's lungs are transmitted to its brain.

The frogs supplement their hearing with a form of visual communication, waving their front legs. In the laboratory, the frogs waved at their own reflections in a mirror, at a miniature flag that flashed their characteristic yellow color, and at speakers emitting frog sounds.

How insects fly. With the help of a robotic hawk moth, British researchers made a crucial discovery about how insects' wings generate enough upward force, or lift, to fly. The finding was reported in December 1996 by entomologist Charles P. Ellington and his colleagues at Cambridge University.

In general, wings generate more lift as they increase their *pitch*—the angle of the wing relative to the direction of flight. But aerodynamic calculations show that for insects to generate enough lift to support their weight, the pitch must be so high that it would disrupt the flow of air over their wings. This would cause turbulence, which in turn would make the insects *stall* (lose aerodynamic lift) and crash.

The Cambridge scientists first tethered real hawk moths—large, brightly colored moths with streamlined bodies—inside a wind tunnel and observed the flow of smoky air over their wings. The moths did, in fact, have their wings at a very high pitch on each downstroke. A small *vortex*—a spinning mass of air, like a tornado—traveled from each insect's body to the tip of its wing on each stroke. But before the vortex could reach the end of the wing and cause turbulence, the hawk moth began a new stroke, thereby avoiding a stall.

The researchers then built a robotic hawk moth 10 times the size of the real insect. The robot flapped its wings once every three seconds, 100 times slower than a real hawk moth, and released smoke from its body so that the team could track air movements over its wings. When the wing pitch reached the angle at which a stall should occur, each vortex would pull smoothly away from the wing just as an upstroke began. Scientists believe other insects use the same exquisite timing to fly.

Repelling gypsy moths. The green ash, a common American tree, has a natural defense system against gypsy moth larvae that could be adapted to protect other trees, University of Wisconsin researchers reported in November 1996. The gypsy moth attacks more than 300 species of trees and has denuded trees in large areas of the United States. But moth larvae that come into contact with the green ash turn tail. Those that do nibble on its leaves die, said University of Wisconsin entomologist Dale Norris.

Norris and an associate, Ingrid Markovic, analyzed vapors released by green ash trees and discovered that their primary component was a mixture of two chemicals, called linalool and methyl salicylate. The larvae were able to detect the odor of the mixture several yards from the trees. The leaves are so toxic to the larvae that no more than 4 percent of a green ash's leaves are ever eaten—too few to be noticed by casual observers. The chemicals also disrupt the larvae's hormones, preventing any surviving nibblers from maturing into adult moths. Norris suggested that a cloth soaked in the compounds could be wrapped around the trunks of vulnerable trees, discouraging larvae from crawling up to eat the leaves.

Living thermometer. The male striped tree lizard of Arizona changes color as the temperature rises and falls, making it a kind of living thermometer.

The smallest-known frog in the Northern Hemisphere, the "eleuth," rests on a Cuban coin the size of a nickel. The frog, which is just 10 millimeters (0.4 inch), was found in a Cuban rain forest in late 1996 by researchers from Pennsylvania State University in State College and the Institute of Forest Investigations in Havana, Cuba.

A type of shrimp called *Synalpheus regalis* lives in a cooperative community similar to that of bees, ants, and other so-called eusocial creatures, biologist J. Emmet Duffy of the Virginia Institute of Marine Science in Gloucester Point reported in June 1996. Duffy studied more than 30 colonies of the shrimp on coral reefs off Belize and found that most of the shrimp in a colony are the offspring of a single female, or queen. *S. regalis* is the first marine animal known to be eusocial.

The lizard, formally known as *Urosaurus ornatus*, is pale green in the relative coolness of morning but becomes progressively bluer as the temperature rises, passing through turquoise to a bright cobalt. That finding was reported in February 1997 by *herpetologist* (reptile expert) Randall Morrison and his colleagues at Hood College in Frederick, Maryland.

Morrison speculated that the green color helps the lizard blend into the background in the morning, when the cold-blooded reptile is sluggish and unable to evade predators easily. The bright colors, in contrast, help the lizard attract mates when the afternoon heat increases its *metabolism* (energy production), enabling it to run fast.

The color changes when the lizard's pigment cells expand with rising temperatures. As a result, when light is reflected from the patches' surface, some wavelengths are removed, producing different colors.

Mongoose immunity. Biologists have generally assumed that the mongoose uses its speed to avoid the lethal bite of snakes it tries to kill, but new evidence reported in December 1996 by immunologist Sara Fuchs of the Weizmann Institute in Rehovot, Israel, suggests that the animal has an additional hidden advantage: It is apparently immune to snake venom.

The most common poison in snake venoms is a protein called alpha-neurotoxin. The poison works by attaching itself to certain molecules, called acetylcholine receptors, on the surface of muscle cells. The receptors normally receive signals from the brain telling muscles to contract or expand. When alpha-neurotoxin is bound to them, they are unable to function. As a result, a bitten animal is paralyzed and dies.

Fuchs studied the acetylcholine receptors of snakes and mongooses. She found that the receptor in poisonous snakes has an unusual shape that alpha-neurotoxin cannot bind to, which explains why snakes do not poison themselves. Surprisingly, the mongoose has a nearly identical acetylcholine receptor, which is also resistant to alpha-neurotoxin. [Thomas H. Maugh II]

Here are 16 important new science books suitable for the general reader. They have been selected from books published in 1996 and 1997.

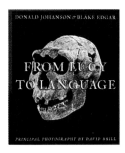

Anthropology. *From Lucy to Language* by Donald Johanson and Blake Edgar— a paleoanthropologist and a science writer, respectively—examines the mystery of human origins. The study documents more than 20 years of Johanson's field work in Africa, including his discovery of "Lucy," the oldest, most complete skeleton of a prehuman ancestor ever found. Johanson and Edgar also show in stunning photographs more than 50 important human fossils and discuss the significance of the tools, art objects, and cave paintings associated with them. (Simon & Schuster, 1996. 272 pp. illus. $50)

Astronomy. *The Hunt for Life on Mars* by Donald Goldsmith, a science writer, explores the possibility of extraterrestrial life. Goldsmith provides an authoritative and entertaining review of the evidence of microscopic organisms found in a meteorite that originated on Mars. Scientists announced the discovery in 1996. Goldsmith presents the case for and against the possibility of Martian life and discusses the scientific and philosophical implications of the discovery. (Dutton, 1997. 267 pp. illus. $24.95)

Prisons of Light by Kitty Ferguson, a science writer, is a clearly written account of perhaps the strangest things in the universe—black holes. Black holes are concentrations of matter in such a small volume that their gravity prevents even light from escaping from them. Ferguson explains how black holes behave and how astronomers have discovered them in the Milky Way and other galaxies. (Cambridge University Press, 1996. 214 pp. illus. $24.95)

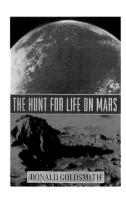

Biology. *Darwin's Dreampond* by Tijs Goldschmidt, a biologist, recounts his experiences during a decade-long study of the fish of Lake Victoria in Africa. In the waters of the lake, small, perchlike fish called cichlids had branched into hundreds of species, providing a unique environment for the study of evolution. But beginning in the 1980's, more than two-thirds of the species of cichlids became extinct. Goldschmidt provides an excellent study of this mass extinction and an exciting account of the rewards and trials of doing field work in a re-

mote, poverty-stricken part of the world. (MIT Press, 1996. 274 pp. illus. $25)

Life Itself: Exploring the Realm of the Living Cell by Boyce Rensberger, a science writer for *The Washington Post,* introduces the reader to the smallest units of life. Rensberger relates how cells move, repair themselves, and reproduce and explores what happens when cells malfunction. (Oxford University Press, 1996. 290 pp. illus. $30)

General Science. *The Science Explorer* by Pat Murphy, Ellen Klages, and Linda Shore, staff members of San Francisco's Exploratorium Museum, describes how to perform 52 scientific demonstrations at home using simple materials. Detailed instructions on such entertaining experiments as building a "bubble bomb" and producing static electricity from human hair teach basic scientific principles while providing hours of enjoyment for parents and children. (Henry Holt, 1996. 127 pp. illus. $12.95)

Mathematics. *Fermat's Last Theorem* by Amir D. Aczel, a mathematician, relates how generations of deep thinkers came to grief over a theorem that scholar Pierre de Fermat claimed to have proved in the 1600's. Fermat, in a marginal note, stated that he had found a "truly marvelous" proof that no whole number, when raised to the third or a greater power, could be expressed as the sum of two other whole numbers raised to the same power. But Fermat left no details of his supposed proof, and the problem turned out to be more vexing than anyone had imagined. In 1995, mathematician Andrew Wiles made front-page news when he finally announced a 200-page solution to the theorem. (Four Walls Eight Windows, 1996. 140 pp. illus. $18)

Natural History. *In the Company of Mushrooms* by Elio Schaechter, a microbiologist and *mycophile* (lover of mushrooms), traces the history of mushrooms from the Stone Age and describes the amazing properties of fungi and the pleasures of hunting them. While some mushrooms are good to eat, many are poisonous, so that even lovers of mushrooms gather them with caution. Schaechter lists clubs around the country where people can learn to hunt and identify mushrooms from knowledgeable enthusiasts. (Harvard University Press, 1997. 274 pp. illus. $24.95)

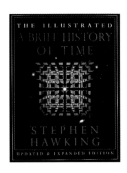

The Modern Ark by Vickie Croke, a wildlife journalist for the *Boston Globe,* examines how zoos have changed over the years and how today's zoos are redefining their role in an age of shrinking natural habitats. Croke thoughtfully explores the views of those who believe that animals can be free only in the wilderness and those who believe zoos provide the best hope for the preservation of diverse species. (Scribner, 1997. 272 pp. $26)

Oceanography. *The Universe Below* by William Broad, a science reporter for *The New York Times,* describes the technological advances that have opened up to scientific study the 70 percent of the Earth's surface that lies underwater. Broad notes that only in recent years have the watery depths been mapped and explored in a systematic way and explains the scientific, commercial, and military factors that have motivated the growing interest in the oceans. (Simon and Schuster, 1997. 432 pp. illus. $30)

Paleontology. *Dinosaurs of the Flaming Cliffs* by Michael Novacek of the American Museum of Natural History in New York City relates the exciting story of Novacek's expedition to the Gobi Desert of central Asia. The remote Gobi has been known as a remarkable source of fossil remains since 1922, when the author and explorer Roy Chapman Andrews found the first nest of preserved dinosaur eggs and the bones of many previously unknown dinosaurs. Seventy years later, Novacek led another team of scientists to the Gobi, where they uncovered a site with many more dinosaur fossils and eggs. (Anchor Books, 1996. 367 pp. illus. $24.95)

Physics. *The Illustrated A Brief History of Time* by the renowned British physicist Stephen Hawking is a revised and expanded version of Hawking's best-selling 1988 work. Hawking includes new information about wormholes and time travel and uses more than 240 illustrations, photographs, and computer-generated images to explain the mysteries of cosmology. (Bantam Books, 1996. 256 pp. illus. $37.50)

Stuff by Ivan Amato, a science reporter whose articles have appeared in *Science News* and *The Washington Post,* describes recent developments in creating a host of materials that don't occur in nature. In the past, according to Amato, the recipes for such useful substances as steel were discovered quite by accident. Now, new technology and a new understanding of physics and chemistry make it possible for scientists to design materials to meet specified requirements. Amato suggests that in the future, researchers may produce lighter, more durable fabrics, substances harder and cheaper than diamond, and structures that repair themselves. (BasicBooks, 1997. 304 pp. illus. $25)

The Fusion Quest by T. Kenneth Fowler, a physicist at the University of California at Berkeley, describes some of the challenges researchers face as they try to produce energy by fusing atomic nuclei. For example, one problem researchers have had is building a container capable of holding a gas that can be up to 300 million °C (540 million °F), far hotter than the core of the sun. Duplicating the reaction by which the sun fuses hydrogen into helium and thereby releases energy would make it possible to construct nonpolluting power plants that produce limitless amounts of inexpensive electricity. (Johns Hopkins University Press, 1997. 250 pp. $29.95)

Psychology. *Born to Rebel: Birth Order, Family Dynamics, and Creative Lives* by Frank J. Sulloway, a scholar at the Massachusetts Institute of Technology, provides evidence to support the common wisdom that eldest children approach life differently than their younger brothers and sisters. Reporting on a massive study of the lives and attitudes of famous thinkers from Martin Luther to Charles Darwin, Sulloway explains how the data show that younger children tend to be more adventurous, more open to new ideas, and more creative in all aspects of their lives than eldest children. (Pantheon Books, 1996. 653 pp. illus. $30)

Technology. *The Invention that Changed the World* by Robert Buderi, a science writer, traces the history of radar and its spin-offs. Buderi notes that the ability to track airplanes and ships at a distance was critical to the Allied victory in World War II (1939-1945). After the war, this technology led to such important inventions as lasers, microwave ovens, air-traffic control systems, high-speed computers, and radio astronomy. (Simon and Schuster, 1996. 544 pp. illus. $30)   [Laurence A. Marschall]

Three research groups, working independently, reported in August 1996 that they had induced organic *polymers* (long chains of molecules with carbon "backbones") to produce laserlike beams of light. This feat could pave the way for a new generation of lasers made from plastics—a type of polymer. Such devices might be much cheaper to make than the solid semiconductor lasers used in today's compact disc players and computer CD-ROM drives.

The three research groups got thin films of different polymers to emit beams of light in a single wavelength, just as conventional lasers do. But the light was not *coherent* (having all the light waves traveling in step), which is also a characteristic of true laser beams.

The scientists produced the light emissions by pumping, or energizing, the polymers with conventional laser beams. The polymers were an unusual class of *organic* (carbon-containing) materials that conduct electricity.

At the University of California at Santa Barbara, a group led by polymer scientist Alan J. Heeger produced laserlike emissions in different colors from electrically conductive polymers called PPV, PPP, and polyfluorene, either in pure form or chemically modified.

A second research team, at Cambridge University in England, headed by physicist Richard H. Friend, made PPV emit single-wavelength light by using a device called a microcavity, which amplified the light pumped into the substance. A third group, led by physicist Z. Valy Vardeny at the University of Utah in Salt Lake City, also obtained light emission from chemically modified forms of PPV. None of the researchers, however, could get polymers to emit light when stimulated with an electric current, as regular lasers do.

Self-assembling molecules. A new class of molecules that organize themselves into complex structures could eventually have many important applications. That was the prediction of their inventor, chemist Samuel I. Strupp of the University of Illinois at Urbana-Champaign, who described the molecules' properties in April 1997.

Strupp calls his newly discovered

Different images of Bugs Bunny are stored in thin layers of a new plasticlike material unveiled in August 1996 by scientists at the State University of New York at Buffalo. The material is impregnated with a fluorescent dye that changes chemically when exposed to varying intensities of light, creating patterns of dark and light spots. These patterns can be used to encode data in three dimensions. The researchers said 1 cubic centimeter (0.06 cubic inch) of the material can potentially hold as much data as 1,000 CD-ROM's.

Monitoring explosions
Scientists from Lawrence Livermore National Laboratory in California draw gases from the soil at a Nevada site where an underground bomb had been detonated in 1993. The researchers reported in August 1996 that their soil sampling, a test of a new system to detect secret nuclear detonations, had found traces of the explosion. A computer simulation, *right,* shows gases from an explosion moving up through a fracture, center line, with concentration fading from red to blue.

molecules "rodcoils" because they consist of both stiff and flexible segments. The stiff segments are made of rigid molecular groups called biphenyl esters; the flexible parts are composed of molecules of a substance called isoprene, which are in turn connected to molecules of another substance, styrene. At the end of the rigid section are water-attracting molecules known as phenolic groups. The end of the flexible segment contains water-repelling portions called methyl groups.

When the rodcoils are placed in solution, they spontaneously assemble into little mushroom-shaped bundles, in which the rigid sections cluster into a "stem" and the flexible portions spread out to form a "cap." Soon, the mushroomlike clusters pack together to form thin sheets. Finally, the sheets stack on top of each other to form thick films. The top layer of these films, which contains the methyl groups, is slick and water-repellent; the bottom, which has the phenolic groups, is very sticky and water-attracting.

Films with such radically different sides should have valuable applications, Strupp said. Because the films' sticky side clings strongly to metals, he suggested the material might be used as long-lasting antifreeze coatings for aircraft wings. And he speculated that if the films were used to coat artificial blood vessels, the slick side would inhibit the formation of blood clots.

Ceramic contracts when heated. A new kind of ceramic could someday have uses in electronics, energy production, and even dentistry, researchers at Oregon State University in Corvallis and Argonne National Laboratory near Chicago, reported in January 1997. Most solids expand when heated, but the new ceramic, known as cubic zirconium tungstate, contracts with heat. Under certain conditions, however, it loses this remarkable property.

The researchers, led by materials scientist Arthur W. Sleight, said that subjecting cubic zirconium tungstate to forces exceeding 1,000 times the pressure of the air at sea level transforms it into a new *phase* (distinct state of matter) that does not display heat-induced shrinking. But mild heating of this phase restores the ceramic's ability to contract when hot.

Cleaning smoke-damaged art with atomic oxygen
A patch that was cut from a painting and exposed to smoke from an oil fire is black with deposits, *top.* After being exposed to *atomic oxygen* (oxygen atoms that have not joined to form molecules), the patch is clean, *above.* National Aeronautics and Space Administration scientists reported in December 1996 that atomic oxygen could be useful for restoring smoke-damaged paintings.

Sleight said the most likely role of cubic zirconium tungstate would be to modify the heat and pressure properties of *composites* (complex materials composed of two or more separate and distinct solids). Because the new ceramic shrinks when heated, it could be added to composites to lower their overall *thermal* (heat-related) expansion to match that of other materials in contact with the composites.

For example, the material could be added to a composite dental filling to make the filling's thermal expansion match that of a patient's own teeth, thereby making it less likely to come loose. Sleight said the ceramic could also be used in high-efficiency *fuel cells* (devices that produce electricity from a chemical reaction between oxygen and a gaseous fuel, such as hydrogen) and in composite circuit boards for computers.

CO_2: nonpolluting cleanser? In theory, cheap and nontoxic carbon dioxide could replace many of today's polluting industrial solvents and cleaning agents. The reason it has not done so is that few substances are soluble in carbon dioxide (which, though it is normally a gas, can be made in a semiliquid form). But in December 1996, a group of U.S. and Italian researchers reported a way to change that.

The scientists developed a new class of *surfactants* (soaplike molecules) that allow carbon dioxide to dissolve many compounds that are normally insoluble in it. Carbon dioxide modified with the new surfactants might eventually replace conventional solvents for cleaning electronic and optical devices, dry cleaning clothes, and carrying out numerous industrial chemical reactions, said the lead researcher, chemist Joseph M. DeSimone of the University of North Carolina at Chapel Hill.

In their experiments, DeSimone and his colleagues at Oak Ridge National Laboratory in Oak Ridge, Tennessee, and the University of Palermo in Italy used "supercritical" carbon dioxide, a form of carbon dioxide that is intermediate between a liquid and a gas. It has the dissolving power of a liquid but disperses as readily as a gas.

Their surfactants were polymers with backbones made of *hydrocarbons* (hydrogen and carbon compounds) to which two distinct types of chemical groups were attached. One group, which consisted of a *fluorocarbon* (a fluorine and carbon compound), was soluble in carbon dioxide. The other group, made of styrene, another hydrocarbon, was soluble in oils, greases, or hydrocarbons.

The researchers mixed the surfactants with supercritical carbon dioxide and applied the mixture to a plate coated with polystyrene, a hydrocarbon plastic that is normally insoluble in carbon dioxide. The surfactant molecules formed little spheres called micelles that dissolved and dispersed the plastic coating on the plate, which simulated a cleaning operation in industry.

Quicker path to magnetic fluids. A process for using *ultrasound* (high-energy sound waves) to create powderlike clusters of metal atoms was described in November 1996 by chemist Kenneth S. Suslick and his colleagues at the University of Illinois at Urbana-Champaign. The process could provide a short cut to the production of fluids that respond to magnetic fields.

The powders were made by blasting high-energy sound waves into liquid solutions of carbon- and oxygen-containing compounds of metals, such as iron and molybdenum. The sound waves caused millions of microscopic bubbles to form and collapse rapidly in the liquids, a process called cavitation. The bubbles' collapse generated temperatures in their immediate vicinity of about 5000 °C (9000 °F)—almost as hot as the surface of the sun—even though the liquid as a whole warmed only slightly. This intense heat decomposed the metal compounds into tiny clusters of metal atoms measuring about 25 hundred-millionths of a centimeter (1 ten-millionth of an inch) and containing a few hundred atoms.

The metal clusters exhibited an unusual phenomenon called superparamagnetism: The individual atoms in the clusters all had magnetic fields that pointed in the same direction. (The magnetic fields come from the spinning electrons within each atom.) In effect, each cluster was a miniature bar magnet.

The scientists found that they could coat the magnetic clusters with protective molecules and suspend them in liquids to form *colloids* (stable mixtures of liquids and solid particles) known as ferrofluids, which move or vibrate in response to external magnetic fields. Ferrofluids have several uses, including as magnets in stereo speakers and to make magnetic inks for bank checks. Ferrofluids' magnetic particles have traditionally been made by a long and expensive process that involves grinding iron ores into powders over several weeks. By contrast, the new ultrasound process for making the powders is far quicker and potentially cheaper.

Fat substitute from farm wastes. A promising new fat substitute was introduced in August 1996 by investigators at the U.S. Department of Agriculture's (USDA) Biopolymer Research Unit in Peoria, Illinois. The white, tasteless powder, dubbed Z-Trim, is a chemically modified form of cellulose, a polymer that makes up a large part of the cell walls of all plants.

While ordinary cellulose consists of tough, stringy fibers, the Z-Trim powder can be mixed with water to form a smooth gel resembling fat in taste and texture. Like all forms of dietary fiber, the gel contains no calories and passes through the body undigested.

The researchers, directed by chemist George E. Inglett, made the fat substitute from low-cost, cellulose-rich agricultural waste, such as the hulls of oats, soybeans, peas, and rice. They crushed the hulls in a mill in the presence of a highly alkaline solution of water and hydrogen peroxide. This broke apart the walls of the plant cells, releasing their cellulose fibers. It also severed some of the fibers' *hydrogen bonds*, partial chemical links in which hydrogen atoms serve as bridges between oxygen atoms bonded to different molecules. The fibers were then able to separate into the individual cellulose polymers that made them up.

The scientists next spun the mixture in a *centrifuge* (a rapidly spinning device used for separating solids from liquids), to recover the cellulose. They then repeated the milling and spinning. Finally, they dried the purified cellulose to a powder.

According to the USDA, the use of Z-Trim could reduce the fat content of beef patties by 15 percent, and of chocolate brownies by up to 38 percent, without affecting taste or texture.

[Gordon Graff]

In May 1997, for the first time in history, a chess-playing supercomputer defeated a reigning world chess champion in a six-game match played under tournament conditions. The computer, known as Deep Blue, was designed by researchers at the International Business Machines Corporation (IBM). Deep Blue's victory over Russia's Garry Kasparov again raised questions about whether a computer could actually "think."

Deep Blue's triumph. Kasparov, widely regarded as the best chess player in history, had defeated a previous version of Deep Blue in 1996. After that loss, the IBM design team developed a new Deep Blue with more computing power and a better knowledge of chess.

Although the new Deep Blue's playing style appeared "smarter" than the 1996 version, experts maintained that the computer was not thinking at all but merely calculating. Deep Blue used 512 *microprocessors* (collections of tiny transistors that perform computations) working in parallel to examine 200 million chess positions per second.

In the 1997 rematch, Kasparov and Deep Blue split the first two games and played the next three to a draw. The computer then took the final game after just 19 moves, winning the match by a score of 3½ points to 2½. Kasparov promptly challenged Deep Blue to a rematch in a regular, 10-game tournament, with more time scheduled between games to allow him to rest.

DVD finally arrives. *DVD's* (digital video discs or digital versatile discs) and DVD players finally hit the U.S. market in the spring of 1997. This new CD-sized format for delivering movies and computer software to the home consumer was originally scheduled to be the hot item for Christmas in 1996, but last-minute arguments over ways to protect the unauthorized copying of discs delayed the release.

Because a DVD movie is recorded *digitally* (as a code of 0's and 1's), its picture and sound reproduction is superior to movies recorded on videotape. However, since this digital code can be illegally copied over and over again with virtually no reduction in quality, major motion-picture studios were reluctant to release their films on DVD. Months passed while manufacturers and studios struggled to find a copy-protection method that would be acceptable to all parties involved in marketing DVD's and DVD players.

In addition to copy protection, the studios also insisted on international distribution control. New American movies, for example, often debut in foreign theaters months after their release in the United States, usually about the same time as the movie is released on video in the U.S. market. The studios feared that the availability of high-quality films on DVD in North America would undercut theater box-office sales overseas. To counter this, they developed a system called regional coding: Every DVD and DVD player was to receive one of six regional codes, and a DVD could be viewed only on a DVD player purchased in the same region—a disc made for viewing in the United States, for example, would not work with a player purchased in Japan.

Computer hardware and software companies planned to introduce personal computers (PC's) with *DVD-ROM* drives and software programs on DVD later in 1997. DVD-ROM's (read only memory) are discs that contain computer software. The question of whether to use a regional coding system with DVD-ROM was yet to be determined.

With these issues mostly settled, electronics manufacturers quickly got to work building DVD players and producing digital versions of a number of popular Hollywood movies. Consumers greeted the new players with enthusiasm. Because most DVD players could play existing audio CD's in addition to the new discs, many people purchased the players even before there were any movies available to play on them. By April 1997, only about 40 movie titles were available, with another 100 or so scheduled by the end of the year. Most were expected to sell in the $25 range. However, industry insiders predicted that DVD players would not challenge the videocassette recorder (VCR) market until the year 2000.

Trouble at AOL. America Online, Incorporated (AOL), of Dulles, Virginia, the world's largest Internet provider, had more than its share of problems in 1996 and early 1997. The service, which provided Internet access as well as a variety of other interactive features (e-mail, sports, weather, financial news, on-line

The next generation of cellular phones
New cellular phones appeared in 1997 that promised to expand the boundaries of the wireless communication industry. One such device, the Nokia 9000 Communicator, *below,* was a cellular phone that opened like a clamshell to reveal a keypad and expanded liquid crystal display. Built-in software enabled the phone to send and receive faxes and e-mail and to access the Internet. The device weighed about 0.4 kilogram (14 ounces).

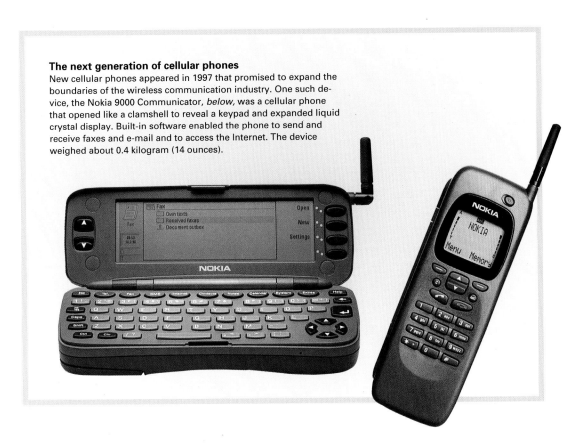

shopping, and chat rooms) to more than 8 million subscribers worldwide, was one of the on-line industry's biggest success stories. But rapid growth dealt AOL a one-two punch that temporarily stopped the giant in its tracks.

The first blow landed at 4 a.m. (EDT) on "Black Wednesday," August 7, 1996, when AOL's entire computer system went down during a software upgrade, leaving millions of individual and corporate subscribers without e-mail or Internet access. Because the system ran seven days a week, AOL engineers often performed upgrades while the system was running. AOL remained off-line for 19 hours before engineers were able to restart the system. The company later reported that switching problems within its network had caused the crash, but the upgrade procedure compounded the problem. This was the biggest service outage in the Internet's short history, and it illustrated the fact that many businesses and individuals had come to rely on Internet and e-mail service as a vital part of their daily routine.

The second punch started as a good deal for subscribers but eventually got AOL into legal trouble. The company had been charging subscribers on a pay-as-you-go basis, but in December 1996, it changed to a flat rate policy—$19.95 a month for unlimited use. AOL expected system usage to increase as a result, but it was overwhelmed by what actually occurred—the volume of traffic on the AOL system more than doubled.

The problem was compounded by an aggressive marketing campaign that was bringing thousands of new users into the system each day. This resulted in a logjam of users trying to connect to AOL. Customers all over the country were greeted with busy signals or other connection problems, and during peak usage times it was almost impossible to access the service at all. Consumer complaints poured in, but AOL could not respond with system upgrades fast enough. Soon, the complaints turned into lawsuits.

Finally, on January 29, 1997, in an effort to avoid further legal problems, AOL signed an agreement with the attorneys general of 36 states. The company promised to invest $350 million in system upgrades, temporarily halt advertising campaigns, and make refunds to users who experienced problems during December 1996 and January 1997.

In the months following the agreement, AOL quickly made major system upgrades and added many new telephone access numbers in most major metropolitan areas. The company eventually resumed adding new members, but at a more manageable rate. Even so, many industry watchers saw the problems at AOL as a sign of things to come for the Internet as a whole. As people became increasingly dependent on e-mail and on-line shopping, they were also learning that the Internet was still developing. Continued planning and forethought would be required by Internet and telecommunications providers to keep capacity in line with consumer demand.

IBM makes a comeback. The International Business Machines Corporation (IBM) was once again reasserting itself as a competitor in the personal computer (PC) market in 1996 and 1997. After developing the market and then dominating it for many years, IBM had been slow to defend its market share against younger, smaller competitors, such as Compaq Computer Corporation of Houston, Texas. Although IBM once controlled close to 100 percent of the PC market, smaller competitors that licensed IBM technology gobbled up market share at an alarming rate, to the point where some computer industry analysts were predicting that IBM would abandon the PC market altogether.

But the mid-1990's saw a big turnaround for IBM. After Louis Gerstner took over as chairman and Chief Executive Officer (CEO) of IBM in 1994, a comprehensive reorganization and streamlining of operations enabled IBM to both cut its prices for new PC's and get them to market more quickly. While prices for IBM PC's may have remained a bit high for the average home user, corporate buyers responded well to the new pricing policy. Due in part to IBM's reputation for strong customer service after the sale, corporate customers traditionally preferred to purchase from IBM when its prices were in line with the competition's. This fact, combined with IBM's new strength in consulting serv-

ices and software areas, helped position the company in 1997 to reclaim its position on top of the PC heap.

Apple polishing. Another PC-industry giant, Apple Computer, Incorporated, of Cupertino, California, was also moving to resolve operational and image problems through mid-1997. A major step in this direction came in late 1996 with Apple's decision to purchase NeXT Software, Incorporated, of Redwood City, California. That brought NeXT's president, Steven P. Jobs, back to the company he cofounded.

Apple was founded in 1976 by Jobs and his partner, Stephen G. Wozniak. In the 1970's and 1980's, the charismatic Jobs led the young company through an amazing growth phase that culminated with the successful debut of the Macintosh computer in 1984. However, in 1985, Jobs ran into problems with John Sculley, CEO of Apple at the time, and was forced out of the company.

Jobs then started NeXT Software, which debuted its NextStep computer in 1989. Designed to compete with the Macintosh, the NextStep computer never caught on, and production was stopped in 1993. But NeXT continued to quietly support its well-regarded NextStep *operating system* (the basic programming that enables a computer to function) and a few successful *software development applications* (software used to help write new computer programs).

By 1996, Apple was losing money and the Macintosh was losing market share. The company's public image was deteriorating, due in large part to its inability to introduce a new, state-of-the-art operating system for the Macintosh to compete with Windows 95, the operating system marketed by software giant Microsoft Corporation of Redmond, Washington. Jobs and NeXT represented an immediate answer to both problems.

On December 20, 1996, Apple announced its acquisition of NeXT, a $350-million deal that gave Apple ownership of NeXT's software development tools and the NextStep operating system to use with the Macintosh. The deal also promised to reassure anxious Apple stockholders by returning the legendary figure of Steve Jobs to Apple's creative team. Jobs became a part-time executive adviser, reporting directly to Apple's new CEO, Gilbert Amelio.

Virtual advertising
Digital insertion of images into a live video picture is the latest option for television advertisers. In a televised soccer match, for example, players and their shadows move across the computerized image as though it is actually painted on the field. The image can be changed at will, and different ads can be inserted by local TV broadcasters in different regions.

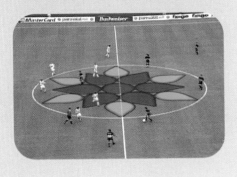

The road ahead for Apple appeared rocky, however. The company faced a huge technical challenge in merging NextStep's technology into the the Macintosh operating system—a project that was not expected to yield results until mid-1998. In the meantime, convincing current users not to abandon their "Macs" in favor of PC's running Microsoft's Windows 95 was seen as the biggest challenge of all.

The internet goes local. A major development in 1996 and 1997 was the business world's move to embrace Internet technology. Not only were companies using the Net to advertise and sell goods and services, they were also developing internal versions of the Internet—called *intranets*—for their own use.

An intranet is a way to connect company personnel to each other and to company databases using the same kinds of systems—such as web pages and e-mail—that people use over the Internet. This enables people who access the company intranet from computers outside the system and those directly connected to it to use the system in exactly the same way. For example, a salesperson with a laptop computer can access the company's customer database to find the phone number of a particular client, or employees working at home can obtain electronic files and exchange messages with co-workers. Unlike the Internet, which is available to the general public, intranets are protected from unauthorized access by a *firewall*, a hardware and software system that admits only preapproved users into the system.

The year 2000 problem. One of the most complicated issues ever to face the computer industry, known as "the year 2000 problem," was looming on the horizon in 1997. As the millennium approached, more and more companies and government agencies were forced to confront the issue.

The problem stemmed from the 1960's and 1970's, when, to save storage space, software programmers used only the last two digits of a year when writing computer code, leaving the "19" as assumed. Therefore, if a computer program in 1997 were to calculate the age of someone born in 1936, it would subtract 36 from 97 and get the correct result: 61. But in the year 2000, the same program would subtract 36 from 00, re-

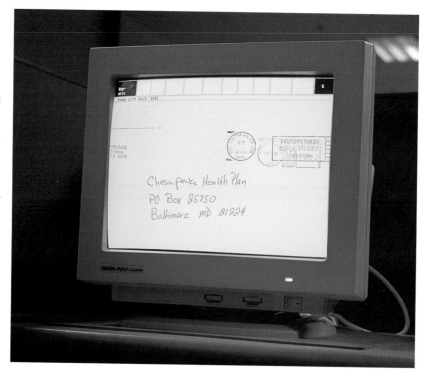

An artificial-intelligence system that could read people's handwriting was being tested by the U.S. Postal Service in 1996 and 1997. The system, which saved more than $1 million in labor costs in 1996, could correctly decipher up to 20 percent of the handwritten addresses it saw. The Postal Service expected to install the system in 250 mail-processing centers by September 1997. By that time, postal authorities hoped, system upgrades would increase the computer's accuracy to 30 percent.

sulting in an answer of −36, because it would assume that "00" stood for the year 1900 rather than 2000.

This kind of error could be disastrous for financial institutions, government records, and other organizations that maintain computer databases because dates are used extensively to calculate everything from paychecks to interest payments. For example, if a payrolling computer program incorrectly calculated a retired worker's age as a negative number, it might conclude that the worker has not been born yet and not issue a pension check.

The solution seemed simple at first— just change the year in the date to four digits. But the vastness of the problem made this easier said than done. To fix the problem, organizations faced the task of locating and changing every reference to every date in every software program they used, and sometimes even in all of the data they had stored and archived. Furthermore, many other systems that used computer chips, such as building security systems, systems that operate elevators, and various office ma-

chines, had to be adjusted as well.

The task was so overwhelming that some experts predicted that many companies would not be done in time and more than a few would go out of business as a result. For companies that were expected to be able to fix the problem, the solution would not be cheap. It was estimated that a typical midsize organization would need to spend about $23 million to remedy the situation. According to the Gartner Group, a noted information industry advisory firm, the total estimated cost of the transition to organizations around the world would be $300 billion to $600 billion.

New chips from Intel. Intel Corporation of Santa Clara, California, a world leader in the development and manufacture of microprocessors, began shipping two new versions of its Pentium chip in 1997, the Pentium MMX and the Pentium II.

Pentium MMX chips, released in January, were designed to process sound, still pictures, and video faster than even ordinary Pentium chips, greatly improving sound and picture quality. Applications such as games, which make use of extensive sound and video, obviously benefited most. But other applications, such as voice recognition, DVD-ROM, and video conferencing programs, also received a welcome boost in performance. However, in order to take full advantage of these capabilities, consumers needed to purchase new software that had been adapted for use with MMX systems.

Pentium II chips, released in May, combined MMX technology with design elements of Intel's Pentium Pro chip, a powerful, high-end microprocessor designed mainly for business workstations. The first Pentium chip, introduced in 1993, ran at 60MHz (cycles per second, a measure of processing speed). In comparison, the first Pentium II's came in 233-, 266-, and 300-MHz versions.

Server push looked to be the next major development in the growth of the World Wide Web. In 1997, most interaction with the Web still relied on a process called client pull. In this system, a software program called a Web browser sent a user's request for a file to a re-mote computer called a server. The server then delivered the file to the browser, which displayed the information on the user's computer.

In a server push system, however, a connection to the server remains open even after a file is sent to the browser, or it is reestablished periodically. If the server's file is updated, the server will automatically forward the new file to the browser, where it can be displayed or stored by the browser for later viewing. Server push became a hot topic after some Internet services, such as news or stock market information providers, began to routinely update the data on their servers several times a day. The system was also seen as a way to deliver advertising on the Web.

Because server push involves additional expense for the user—because the browser must keep a telephone connection open or redial automatically several times a day—there was some question about how widely it would be accepted. However, the technology was expected to be a featured element of future versions of the world's top browsers.

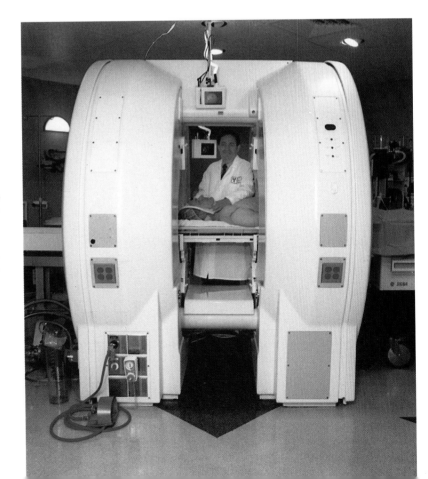

A surgeon at Brigham and Women's Hospital in Boston demonstrates the use of a revolutionary imaging system that combines sophisticated computers and software programs with a magnetic resonance scanner. The system, which enables doctors to view real-time images of structures inside the human body during an operation, promised in 1997 to transform many surgical procedures. For example, by providing color-enhanced, three-dimensional images of tumors, it could enable surgeons to find and remove small bits of cancerous tissue that they might otherwise overlook.

An area of stunning natural beauty, fine fossils, and unusual vegetation in southern Utah was declared the Grand Staircase-Escalante National Monument by President Bill Clinton on Sept. 18, 1996. The monument's 687,990 hectares (1.7 million acres) contain spectacular red, white, and yellow sandstone cliffs, natural arches and bridges, and deep canyons.

The new monument takes its name in part from a vast geological formation called the Grand Staircase, a collection of cliffs and plateaus rising some 1,675 meters (5,500 feet). Other geological wonders include a narrow, meandering canyon 335 meters (1,100 feet) deep that follows the Escalante River; the Cockscomb, two parallel knife-edged ridges with an intervening V-shaped trough; Escalante Natural Bridge, which spans 30.5 meters (100 feet) and rises 40 meters (130 feet) above the ground; and Grosvenor Arch, a rare double arch of rock.

Logs of petrified wood, some up to 11 meters (36 feet) long, and fossils of mollusks and other marine animals are also found in the area. In fact, the rocks contain one of the world's best fossilized records of Late Cretaceous life in the world. (The Cretaceous Period began about 138 million years ago and ended 65 million years ago.)

The new monument has isolated grasslands and stands of pinyon-juniper trees up to 1,400 years old. Warm-desert and cold-desert vegetation mix at the site, and more than 10 percent of the plants are *endemic* species (ones found nowhere else). About 300 species of amphibians, reptiles, birds, and mammals also live in the area.

The monument was opposed by some, including Utah's governor, because it contains one of the largest known deposits of coal in the United States. As a national monument, the area is protected from mining and other commercial development.

New release of California condors. On Dec. 12, 1996, for the first time since 1924, California condors flew over the American Southwest. Biologists released six of the giant birds in Arizona as part of a plan to rescue one of America's

Turtle highway in the Pacific
Leatherback turtles take the same route through the Pacific Ocean every year as they migrate, researchers at Cornell University in Ithaca, New York, reported in November 1996. The scientists tracked eight turtles from 1992 to 1995. Each turtle followed a similar—or even identical—route within a narrow corridor every time it swam the 2,700 kilometers (1,675 miles) from Costa Rica to the Galapagos Islands.

most endangered species from extinction. The location of the release, known as Vermilion Cliffs, includes ridges and other launching points for soaring, as well as caves suitable as nesting sites.

California condors have a wing span of nearly 3 meters (10 feet) and weigh about 9 kilograms (20 pounds), making them the largest land birds in North America. They are members of the vulture family. Their unfeathered heads and necks are usually dull orange but turn bright pink during the breeding season. Condors feed on *carrion* (dead animals), which they locate while soaring over large areas of rugged terrain. The newly released birds were to be provided with calf carcasses as supplemental food until they learned to survive on their own.

Once widely distributed in North America, condors suffered from shooting, poisoning, and egg collecting. By 1987, the wild population had dwindled to fewer than 10 birds, which were removed for captive breeding in a last-ditch effort to prevent the extinction of the species. In the late 1990's, about 90 condors were living in captivity and were producing about 20 chicks each year.

Previously, 17 condors were released in Los Padres National Forest in California. But the condors' historic range in Arizona provides greater security and isolation than California. Biologists hope to eventually see a self-sustaining population of about 150 birds.

Prairie becomes new national park. After years of struggle by conservationists, a 4,450-hectare (11,000-acre) remnant of tallgrass prairie became a national park in November 1996. Congress established the National Tallgrass Prairie Preserve in the Flint Hills of Kansas.

Tallgrass prairie once covered a large region in the midsection of North America, but nearly all of these grasslands were plowed up to create farms. Because the soil at the new preserve is thin and rocky, the site was never plowed. Instead, the land was grazed.

Tallgrass prairies include several species of grasses, of which big bluestem and Indian grass are among the best known. Many *forbs* (broad-leaved, herbaceous plants) also grow there. In season, their flowers add a palate of color to the grassland landscape.

Some farm groups in Kansas opposed federal ownership of land in the state, but their fears were calmed by a provision that most of the park would be owned by a private land conservancy, the National Park Trust. The preserve was to remain open to grazing by private ranchers in the surrounding area.

Record manatee deaths. According to the Florida Department of Environmental Protection, a record number of Florida manatees died in 1996, offsetting recent population gains by the endangered marine mammals. Under strict protective laws, especially the Marine Mammal Protection Act, the manatee population had reached a modern record of 2,639 animals in 1995. But 415 died in 1996.

Toxins emitted by a red tide—a huge clustering of aquatic microorganisms—were blamed for the deaths of 151 manatees. Boats killed 60 others. (Propellers inflict deep and often fatal cuts on the animals, which swim and graze on vegetation in relatively shallow water.) Another 204 manatees died from cold-weather stress, natural causes, and undetermined causes.

Protecting threatened sharks. The National Marine Fisheries Service in December 1996 proposed new regulations designed to protect five species of sharks threatened by overfishing in the Atlantic Ocean and Gulf of Mexico. The service identified basking, bigeye sand tiger, sand tiger, whale, and white sharks as vulnerable to both commercial and recreational fishing.

The new regulations, which went into effect in April 1997, forbade fishing for all of the threatened sharks. Commercial catches of other species of sharks were significantly reduced under the regulations, which were to remain in effect until permanent programs to protect species could be set up.

Bison killings in Montana. A contagious bacterial disease called brucellosis was at the heart of a heated controversy between conservationists and ranchers in 1996 and 1997 over the killing of bison in Montana. Brucellosis infects cattle, bison, and many other animals but poses little threat to people.

A herd of about 3,500 bison lived in Yellowstone National Park in 1996. Deep snows in the 1996-1997 winter made food scarcer than usual at the park. More than 1,000 bison were shot

Vanishing Sumatran rhinos

Sumatran rhinoceroses need special rescue efforts to save them from extinction, scientists at Columbia University in New York City reported in February 1997. Only about 300 Sumatran rhinoceroses, *below,* survived on the Malay peninsula and on the Indonesian island of Sumatra in 1997. A subspecies known as the Borneo rhinoceros, *bottom,* was even more endangered, with only about 70 left in existence. The scientists recommended gathering the remaining Borneo rhinoceroses into a preserve, where they would be protected from poachers and could easily mate.

Source: The World Conservation Union.

or slaughtered when they followed roads and snowmobile trails out of Yellowstone Park and onto adjoining Montana public lands and ranches.

The bison were killed because ranchers feared the spread of brucellosis, which would lead to a quarantine on their cattle. Coupled with other losses from the hard winter, the killings reduced the Yellowstone bison herd to about 1,300.

Brucellosis in Yellowstone bison was first reported in 1917. About 45 percent of the herd in the late 1990's tested positive for exposure to the brucellosis bacterium, but not all of those animals were actually infected. Large numbers of elk also tested positive, but Montana allows the elk to roam free.

Brucellosis was introduced into North America with imported cattle, so the bacteria originally traveled from livestock to wildlife. In cattle, the disease causes the spontaneous abortion of calves, reduced milk production, infertility, and other reproductive disorders. The risk of transmission between wild bison and cattle is unknown.

No effective treatment or cure exists for animals infected with brucellosis, but the disease can be prevented with a vaccine. On average, the vaccine is 65 percent to 75 percent effective in cattle, but less so in bison.

Because of the controversy, Secretary of the Interior Bruce Babbitt asked the National Academy of Sciences to conduct a study of brucellosis in the Yellowstone bison herd. The academy was due to complete the study in October 1997.

Climate change and bird migrations. The World Wildlife Fund in September 1996 warned of serious threats that climate change may pose to millions of migratory birds. According to the report, migratory birds with habitats as dissimilar as the Zambezi Basin in Africa and Arctic wetlands are at risk because of global warming.

Scientists think the global climate is growing warmer, in large part because of a build-up in the atmosphere of so-called greenhouse gases. The most abundant of these gases is carbon dioxide, created in enormous quantities by the burning of coal and oil. Greenhouse gases trap solar energy near Earth's surface, thereby increasing temperatures. Global warming may imperil birds because their migratory patterns could be disrupted by changes in the timing of seasons, drier weather, and especially by rising sea levels, which would destroy prime feeding and breeding habitat.

Shore birds, for example, migrate long distances—thousands of miles in some cases. To prepare for such journeys, they must eat large amounts of food to build up the fat that serves as fuel for the long-distance flights. En route, the birds land at stopover locations where they feed again before continuing along their migratory route. Some birds consume double their weight in food.

However, only a few places provide suitable amounts of food, and these have become traditional feeding areas for generations of birds. Most of these food-rich sites are coastal, including marshes and mudflats in Chesapeake Bay, Maryland; Port Philip Bay in Australia; parts of the Danube Delta in Romania; and along the Mediterranean Sea. If these coastal locations are flooded by rising sea levels, vital habitats will be lost and bird populations will suffer.

The timing of biological events can also be crucial to the survival of some kinds of birds. While migrating to the Arctic each spring, for instance, ruddy turnstones, red knots, and other shorebirds stop at Delaware Bay, between New Jersey and Delaware. Their arrival coincides with the spawning of horseshoe crabs. The birds gorge on the immense supply of energy-rich crab eggs, which provide the fuel necessary for the remaining segment of the long northward migration. A single red knot, for example, may consume 135,000 horseshoe-crab eggs during its brief stop at Delaware Bay. If global warming were to alter the schedule of either birds or horseshoe crabs by just a week, the birds would have nothing to eat when they arrived at the bay.

Finally, a drier climate has serious implications for pintails, mallards, and other ducks. About half the duck population in North America breeds in wetlands known as prairie potholes, which are sometimes called "duck factories" because of their importance as nesting habitats. These wetlands depend on snowmelt for water. Hence, with a drier climate, many prairie potholes might disappear. [Eric G. Bolen]

Kenneth T. Bainbridge

Charles B. Huggins

Mary Leakey

Notable scientists and engineers who died between June 1, 1996, and June 1, 1997, are listed below. Those listed were Americans unless otherwise indicated.

Bainbridge, Kenneth T. (1904–July 14, 1996), physicist who directed the Trinity Test—the testing in 1945 of the first plutonium bomb. Bainbridge said that during the test, a moment of great personal triumph, he realized that enormous problems were being unleashed upon the world and that it would be the scientists who created such weapons who would be expected to control them. Bainbridge produced the world's first double-focusing *mass spectrometer* (an instrument that enables scientists to separate ionized atoms and molecules according to their mass and electric charge) before being recruited to work on the Manhattan Project. (The Manhattan Project was a government-sponsored undertaking, launched in 1942, to devise an atomic bomb.) Bainbridge's spectrometer established the principle and technology underlying modern instruments that separate atomic nuclei.

Erdos, Paul (1913–Sept. 20, 1996), mathematician who founded the field of discrete mathematics. Erdos, a legendary figure during much of his life, concentrated so completely on the study of mathematics that he lived without home or property. Commuting from one international math meeting to another, he stayed with colleagues who considered it an honor keeping him fed, clothed, and in spending money. In return, Erdos fed mathematicians ideas and challenges. A child prodigy who discovered negative numbers at age 3, Erdos gained international recognition at the age of 20 by working out a proof of the Chebyshev theorem—that for each number greater than one, there is always at least one *prime number* (a number that has no divisors other than itself and one) between it and its double. His greatest achievement, however, was the introduction of discrete mathematics, the computational foundation of computer science. Ernst Straus, who worked with both Erdos and Albert Einstein, wrote in 1983: "[Erdos] has remained the prince of problem solvers and the absolute monarch of problem posers."

Herman, Robert (1914–Feb. 13, 1997), physicist who predicted in the 1940's that echoes of the *big bang*, the enormous explosion of matter and energy that most astrophysicists believe gave birth to the universe, still existed in space and could, theoretically, be detected. Herman based his prediction on calculations suggesting that, under the physical laws governing the universe, such echoes must exist. In the 1960's, Bell Laboratory scientists, working to lessen microwave noise picked up by radio antennae, decided that the problematic noise was, in fact, the remnants of radiation released during the big bang—the echo predicted by Herman. In the 1950's, Herman left scholarly research to join the General Motors Research Laboratory, where he created a new field of study, traffic sciences, in which statistical models are developed and employed to predict traffic patterns. Herman's models are still employed by most traffic engineers.

Huggins, Charles B. (1902–Jan. 12, 1997), physician who with F. Peyton Rous won the 1966 Nobel Prize for physiology or medicine for establishing the relationship between hormones and prostate and breast cancer. Huggins's research proved that many cancers are not self-governing and self-perpetuating but, rather, dependent on chemical signals. His discoveries laid the foundation for new cancer therapies based upon depriving cancerous cells of the chemical signals on which they depend. The Nobel committee cited Huggins's work as providing "an active and useful life to patients with advanced cancer, . . . patients who would have been lost [with] other forms of therapy."

Leakey, Mary (1913–Dec. 9, 1996), paleontologist and matriarch of a family renowned for its fossil discoveries. Leakey, who worked in East Africa's Rift Valley for decades with her husband, Louis, and son, Richard, in 1959 discovered an early *hominid* (humanlike) species called *Zinjanthropus boisei* (later renamed *Australopithecus boisei*). The discovery she was most proud of, however, was the so-called Laetoli footprints, 3.7-million-year-old tracks in volcanic ash, which proved that hominids walked upright far earlier than previously believed.

Sagan, Carl (1934–Dec. 20, 1996), astronomer who became internationally known as the host and narrator of the 1980 public-television series "Cosmos." While Sagan was intensely inter-

Carl Sagan

Clyde W. Tombaugh

Chien-shiung Wu

ested in the possibility of *extraterrestrial life* (life originating away from Earth), his career was built on a solid foundation of research, scientific articles, and more than a dozen books, including the Pulitzer Prize-winning *The Dragons of Eden*. Sagan, early in his career, concluded that mysterious radio emissions issuing from Venus were being produced by Venusian surface temperatures reaching about 500 °C (900 °F), a theory later confirmed by Soviet spacecraft. His theory that the variable color of Mars was the result of wind storms shifting surface dust was also eventually confirmed, by U.S. Mariner spacecraft. The National Aeronautics and Space Administration invited Sagan to participate in the planning of a number of unmanned explorations of Mars and other planets, including the Mariner 9, Viking 1 and Viking 2, Pioneer 10 and Pioneer 11, and Voyager 1 and 2 missions.

Spitzer, Lyman (1914–March 31, 1997), astrophysicist who inspired the Hubble Space Telescope. Spitzer, who was instrumental in the World War II (1939–1945) development of sonar, in 1947 proposed placing a satellite in orbit around Earth. In 1954, three years before the Soviet launch of Sputnik, the first artificial satellite, Spitzer proposed installing an observatory hundreds of miles above Earth, where the universe could be studied without atmospheric interference. Spitzer, as head of Princeton University's Plasma Physics Laboratory, then spent decades shepherding his brainchild toward fruition: initially as the Copernicus Orbiting Astronomical Observatory, launched in 1972, and ultimately, as the Hubble Space Telescope, launched in 1990. Spitzer also pioneered research on controlled nuclear fusion. In 1979, he was honored by President Jimmy Carter with the National Medal of Science for "important contributions to the theory of star formation and evolving stellar systems and plasma physics, including use of fusion as a [future] source of energy."

Tombaugh, Clyde W. (1906–Jan. 17, 1997), astronomer who discovered Pluto, the smallest and, usually, most distant planet orbiting the sun. On Feb. 18, 1930, Tombaugh examined two photographic plates taken six days apart at the Lowell Observatory in Flagstaff, Arizona. Among the tens of thousands of stars on the images, Tombaugh found a starlike speck that appeared to have changed position from one plate to the other. The speck proved to be the so-called Planet X, the predicted ninth planet that U.S. astronomer Percival Lowell had been searching for since 1905. Lowell had claimed that the irregularity of Neptune's orbit could only be explained by the existence of Planet X. Tombaugh, who in 1930 lacked formal education and training, found the planet—later named Pluto—by ignoring Lowell's conclusions regarding its probable location and searching the entire night sky.

Wald, George (1906–April 12, 1997), biologist who, with Haldan K. Hartline and Ragnar Granit, won the 1967 Nobel Prize for physiology or medicine for research on how images are passed from the eye to the brain. The Royal Caroline Institute in Sweden, which awards the prizes, honored Ward for discovering how light triggers molecular changes in the retina's photoreceptive cells, which, in turn, cause impulses to move along the optic nerve to the brain. Ward, who spent much of his career at Harvard University, also completed significant research on the role certain cells play in color perception. In the 1960's and 1970's, Ward became a highly vocal opponent of U.S. involvement in the Vietnam War, and his name appeared on President Richard Nixon's enemies list.

Wu, Chien-shiung (1912–Feb. 16, 1997), physicist who disproved what was once believed to be a fundamental law of nature—the principle of conservation of parity. This law of symmetry held that during a nuclear reaction, nature does not differentiate between left and right. In 1957, Wu subjected the radioactive isotope cobalt 60 to a very strong electromagnetic field. This set all the cobalt nuclei spinning with their axes pointing in the same direction. She then measured what happened when nuclei broke down and shed *beta particles* (electrons). Wu found that most of the particles flew off in the direction opposite the spin. This proved that nature does differentiate between left and right. When the result of the experiment was made public, playwright Claire Boothe Luce noted, "When Doctor Wu knocked out that principle of parity, she established the principle of parity between men and women." [Scott Thomas]

The marketing of new medicines in the United Stated requires formal approval by the federal Food and Drug Administration (FDA). In 1996, the FDA approved 53 new drugs, compared to 28 approvals in 1995 and well above the previous record of 30 approvals in 1985 and 1991. The reasons for this large increase included an FDA initiative to speed up the granting of approvals and an improvement in the quality of new drug applications submitted by pharmaceutical companies. Among the approved medicines were drugs to treat heart attacks, asthma, and cancer. The availability of these treatments promised to provide safer and more effective therapies for a wide variety of human diseases and disorders.

New clot-buster approved. Reteplase, a drug for treating blood clots in heart-attack patients, was approved by the FDA in late 1996. Sold under the brand name Retavase, this new drug was the result of efforts to use genetic engineering techniques to improve the performance of a common *thrombolytic* (clot-dissolving) protein. An estimated 1.5 million Americans experience a heart attack   in medical terminology, acute myocardial infarction (AMI)—each year. Thrombolytics are just one of many kinds of drugs used to treat AMI.

Thrombolysis (clot dissolution) is a natural process activated by a substance in the body known as *tissue plasminogen activator* (t-PA). T-PA promotes the conversion of plasminogen, an inactive component of blood, into an active substance known as plasmin. Plasmin triggers the breakdown of insoluble *fibrin*, the chief component of blood clots, which leads to the dissolution of the clot. Once researchers fully understood the details of this process, they turned their attention to the development of t-PA-based drugs that could be used to dissolve blood clots.

The first product resulting from this research, alteplase (sold as Activase), was made available in the United States in 1988 for the treatment of AMI. Since that time, Activase has dominated this market. One of the chief advantages of Activase is that it acts primarily on a life-threatening clot without interfering with other components of blood clotting. Activase has been highly effective in reducing deaths and subsequent cardiovascu-

lar disease from AMI. But one of the major drawbacks to the use of Activase as a thrombolytic is its relatively short action in the body. This and other considerations prompted researchers to develop improved thrombolytic drugs.

A particular advantage of Retavase is the fact that it remains in the body longer than Activase. Therefore, the new clot-buster can be administered more conveniently—in two quick doses 30 minutes apart rather than as a continuous 30-minute infusion, which is how Activase is given.

Drug therapy for asthma. Two new drugs for the management of asthma, zafirlukast (sold as Accolate) and zileuton (sold as Zyflo), were made available in the United States in 1996. These drugs, which are taken orally, are not useful for acute asthma attacks, but rather offer a convenient way to control mild to moderate asthma.

Some 14 million to 15 million Americans have asthma, including almost 5 million under age 18, and studies indicate that the prevalence of asthma in the U.S. increased by 38 percent from the mid-1980's to the mid-1990's. Furthermore, according to one estimate, asthma deaths in the United States rose 91 percent from 1979 to 1993.

Because the major problem in asthma is *bronchoconstriction* (the narrowing of bronchial airways), drug treatment of the disease has primarily involved the use of *bronchodilators* (drugs that relax muscle tissue surrounding the airways). However, research into what causes asthma indicates that the disorder is actually a chronic inflammatory disease. This finding has led researchers to search for anti-inflammatory drugs that may be more effective and safer treatments for asthma.

There are a number of systems in the body that, when activated by an appropriate stimulus, release chemical compounds that can cause tissue inflammation and smooth-muscle contraction, including bronchoconstriction. One such system involves a substance called arachidonic acid. Researchers have long known that the arachidonic acid system contributes to inflammatory diseases of the joints, including rheumatoid arthritis. In the 1990's, chemical compounds produced by the arachidonic acid system were also implicated in asthma.

Both Accolate and Zyflo reduce the effects of these compounds in asthma either by preventing the formation of substances that facilitate tissue inflammation (Zyflo) or by blocking the action of substances that cause the constriction of airway tissue (Accolate).

Chemotherapy from nature. In 1996, the FDA approved the drugs topotecan (sold as Hycamtin) and irinotecan (sold as Camptosar), for use against cancer. Both are derivatives of a chemical compound called camptothecin, originally isolated from the wood of the Chinese tree *Camptotheca acuminata*.

Initial studies of camptothecin in the 1960's generated a great deal of interest because of the compound's great effectiveness against a number of different tumors. Furthermore, the manner in which camptothecin kills cancer cells was found to be different from that of other kinds of anticancer drugs, which offered doctors a new approach to treating malignancies. Camptothecin interferes with the action of topoisomerase I, a substance involved in the replication of DNA (deoxyribonucleic acid, the molecule that genes are made of), an early step in the process of cell division.

However, the studies also indicated some major problems associated with the use of camptothecin in human chemotherapy. The most important problem was the drug's *toxicity* (harmfulness), which limited the amount of the drug that could be given to cancer patients. Also, camptothecin did not dissolve very easily in water, which presented problems in administering the drug. Hycamtin and Camptosar were developed to overcome some of the disadvantages of the parent drug. Both are more soluble in water and less toxic than camptothecin but still have its broad cancer-fighting properties.

Hycamtin was approved for use in treating ovarian cancer in cases where previous chemotherapy has proven unsuccessful. Ovarian cancer accounts for about 4 percent of all malignancies in women in the United States. Camptosar was to be used to treat cancer of the colon and rectum, a common form of cancer that strikes approximately 1 in 20 Americans.   [Thomas N. Riley]

Ecology

To most ecologists, a construction crane in a tropical rain forest could only mean the destruction of natural habitats. However, as reported at a 1997 symposium, construction cranes have been enabling ecologists to explore a relatively unknown part of rain forests, the canopy. Also in 1997, ecologists found that a type of butterfly believed to be extinct was still flying and that the World Wide Web, a computerized communication network, may not be the ideal forum for scientific meetings.

At the tops of the trees. The canopy is the place in a tropical rain forest where the tops of the trees converge and where, biologists estimate, 90 percent of the rain forest's organisms live. In March 1997, a Tropical Forest Canopy Symposium was held in Panama to discuss canopy research being done there using a crane 42 meters (138 feet) tall. The conference was organized by the Smithsonian Tropical Research Institute (STRI) and the United Nations Environment Programme (UNEP).

Researchers have been using the crane since 1990 in Panama City's Parque Natural Metropolitano, where a relatively dry type of tropical rain forest is being protected. Scientists study the rain forest's canopy from a gondola suspended from the crane. Before the crane brought the canopy within reach, most research in tropical rain forests was limited to the floor of the forest. Scientists who wanted to study the canopy had to climb up to it, shoot parts of it down, or hang precariously above it from a raft suspended by a balloon.

Among the topics of canopy research discussed by scientists who had used the crane were biological diversity and insect populations. The symposium participants also discussed a new crane set up in a very wet type of tropical rain forest in Panama and other cranes that, inspired by the work in Panama, have been established elsewhere, including Washington state and Australia.

Trees and global warming. Also at the Panama symposium, STRI researchers Catherine Ellen Lovelock and Klaus Winter discussed evidence they had found indicating that trees are more limited than previously thought in the

When the Rains Stop

There's probably nothing more devastating to a farmer than drought. Entire fields of crops can be lost, and a family's finances can be left in ruin. Industries and homeowners, too, can be seriously affected, as their water supplies dwindle. Drought parched most of the Southern Great Plains, the Southwestern United States, and northern Mexico from the fall of 1995 through the summer of 1996. Though the drought was relatively short-lived, crop losses in the region totaled more than $4 billion, according to the National Climatic Data Center. In addition, forest fires, sparked by a combination of the drought and a hotter-than-average spring and summer, burned millions of acres.

Meteorologists believed the drought was caused by two main factors, which worked together to prevent the moisture-bearing jet stream from reaching the region. The first factor was a cool water current, known as La Niña, that periodically flows along the surface of the Pacific Ocean. The current cooled the air above it, producing a high-pressure system in the upper atmosphere. This system diverted the jet stream from its typical path over the Southwest to a path over the Pacific Northwest. The second factor causing the drought was a low-pressure system over the mid-Atlantic Ocean, which pushed the eastern edge of

the jet stream away from the Southern Plains. In most of the affected region, the drought was broken in August 1996 when new weather systems, including tropical storm Dolly, brought rain to the area.

Though devastating to agriculture, the drought had only a minor affect on ground-water and reservoir levels, because it followed two of the wettest decades in centuries, according to researchers at the University of Arizona Laboratory of Tree-Ring Research. Based on their studies, which reveal wet years as wide rings in tree trunks and dry years as narrow rings, the most severe drought in the recent history of the Southwest and Southern Plains occurred during the 1950's. During that decade, there were two-to-three-year clusters of dryness, each separated by a wet year or two. The region's worst-known drought occurred during an approximately 20-year period in the late 1500's.

Because of the short duration of the 1995-1996 drought, ecologists believed that it was unlikely to have long-term effects on plant and animal populations. More extensive past droughts, however, resulted in the death of large numbers of plants and animals. Droughts kill plants and animals not only by depriving them of water but also by creating conditions favorable to the spread of certain pests and diseases. For example, drought makes it easier for bark beetles to feed on pine trees and to spread fungal diseases among them, because the drought-stressed trees cannot produce enough of the resin that normally protects them from insect attack.

On a Texas farm, dead fish lie on dry, cracked ground that had been the bottom of a small lake—reduced by drought to a pond. A severe dry spell baked the Southwest and Southern Great Plains in 1995 and 1996, but its effects were not expected to be long-lived.

Drought-induced ecological changes are most evident where different types of plant communities meet. For example, creosote bushes normally live in dry areas, such as deserts. But because severe droughts may deplete the available water in desert soils, creosote bushes may invade adjacent, relatively moist areas, such as grasslands.

Some plants and animals have evolved adaptations to help them survive droughts. Certain amphibians burrow into the ground and surround themselves with a cocoon made of shed skin to help prevent water loss. The animals then go into a state of dormancy, called *estivation,* emerging when rain soaks the surrounding soil. A number of drought-adapted plants produce seeds that can remain viable for many dry years, germinating when eventually exposed to water.

The Southwest's thin soils, which retain little moisture, provide a poor buffer against the effects of drought. But even in less-arid areas with richer soils, droughts can produce major ecological changes. Ecologist David Tilman and his colleagues at the University of Minnesota tracked the effects of drought on an oak forest and prairie in the Cedar Creek Natural History Area, north of St. Paul. After three consecutive years (1987-1989) of drought, the researchers found that 38 percent of the plant species in their study area had been wiped out. And while one of the area's two main species of oaks suffered a high mortality rate, the other species took over dominance of the forest community. It took six years for plant diversity in the area to return to predrought levels.

Although meteorologists cannot accurately predict when droughts will strike or how long they will last, they have found that droughts tend to alternate with wetter-than-normal periods in an irregular cycle. Scientists and engineers are exploring a variety of ways to help us cope better with droughts. Plant researchers, for example, are trying to develop drought-tolerant crops, which would reduce the need for irrigation during dry spells. And in the Southwest, where cities have grown rapidly since the 1980's, engineers have attempted to minimize the effects of drought on municipal water supplies by building pipelines to bring water from distant rivers. Homeowners in drought-prone areas can help by landscaping with native plants, which generally use less water than large expanses of lawn.

Ecologists warn that plans to cope with droughts should address the potential effects of major, prolonged dry periods such as those that struck the Southwest and Southern Plains during the 1950's. If a similar drought were to strike the Southwest today, with all of the residential and industrial development that the region now has, the economic consequences would be much more serious than in the 1950's. [Alison J. Mack]

amount of carbon they can use in *photosynthesis,* the process by which plants use the energy of sunlight to convert carbon dioxide and water into food.

The evidence compiled by Lovelock and Winter, which they obtained from studies of the canopy, is relevant to the current debate over how fast global warming, an increase in global temperatures due partially to an increase in atmospheric carbon dioxide, may proceed. Some scientists believe that trees will be able to absorb enough excess carbon dioxide to offset global warming. But Lovelock and Winter found that although the rate at which a plant carries out photosynthesis initially increases when it is exposed to carbon dioxide, the effect lasts only a short time. After that, additional carbon dioxide does not result in extra photosynthesis. This finding implied that we should not expect trees and other plants to remove large amounts of the carbon dioxide that we are adding to the atmosphere.

Not extinct after all. Among the most studied of butterflies are the bay checkerspot butterflies found among the grasslands of Stanford University's Jasper Ridge preserve in northern California. In an annual survey of these butterflies conducted in March 1997, researchers counted five male bay checkerspots and one female bay checkerspot. These numbers, though low, were higher than expected, because no bay checkerspots were found in a 1996 survey, and researchers suspected that this population of the butterflies had become extinct. After discovering that the Jasper Ridge bay checkerspots were not extinct, researchers speculated that, in 1996, unfavorable spring weather may have caused the butterfly larvae to remain in a state of *diapause,* a type of hibernation, which prevented them from changing into adults in time for the survey.

Though not a separate species, the bay checkerspot is a distinct subspecies, and those found at Jasper Ridge make up an isolated population confined by natural barriers. Stanford University biologist Paul Ehrlich has made numerous studies of these butterflies since 1960. In the 1990's, Ehrlich's research indicated that the Jasper Ridge population was in serious decline. A number of factors, including local pesticide use and invasion

Butterflies on radar

In summer 1996, Canadian ecologists use radar to track the movements of the Apollo butterfly in the meadows of the Kananaskis Mountain Range in Alberta, Canada. The researchers hoped to learn how the butterfly is adapting to the shrinking of the meadows, caused by expanding areas of forest. An Apollo butterfly sits on the flowers of a stonecrop plant, *right*. Glued to the butterfly's abdomen is a thin aluminum antenna that can reflect radar signals.

Above, an ecology student wearing head-phones listens for radar signals sent out by the transmitter she is holding and reflected back by antenna-tagged Apollo butterflies. Beyond her, a student uses a net to capture other Apollos. A captured butterfly also gets a three-letter code written on its wing, *right*. The code will enable researchers to identify the butterfly if it is later recaptured. This system of marking and recapturing butterflies makes it possible to monitor their movements over time.

of the area by foreign species of plants (which reduced the range of the plants eaten by the bay checkerspot's larvae), contributed to the bay checkerspots low numbers.

The precarious existence of the bay checkerspot ignited a controversy among ecologists. Should every effort be made to save the Jasper Ridge population, or should it be allowed to eventually slide into extinction? Ehrlich was among the scientists who believed that more could be learned from studying the extinction of the population than from trying to save it.

If the population eventually becomes extinct, researchers may have an opportunity to study not only extinction but also recolonization. Another population of the bay checkerspot exists south of Stanford, and butterflies from this population could be used to recolonize Jasper Ridge.

Ecology meeting on the Web. Most scientific meetings, where scientists discuss their research, take place in hotels or at universities. These meetings usually last about a week and necessitate traveling to distant cities. In order to cut down on the time and expense involved with such conferences, the North American Amphibian Monitoring Program (NAAMP) held what it believed was the first large-scale scientific meeting on the World Wide Web, from November 1996 to February 1997.

Scientists presented papers over their computers on such topics as amphibian monitoring techniques and the effects of pollution on amphibians. Biologist Sam Droege of the U.S. Geological Service's Biological Resources Division, who headed the on-line meeting, said he was pleased that the NAAMP reached a much wider audience than in its previous meetings. However, not all the participants were happy with the meeting. Biologist Stanley Sessions of Hartwick College in Oneonta, New York, said, "A cyberconference such as this one is no substitute for a conventional conference, because the important face-to-face social interactions are not happening." The NAAMP decided that its next meeting would be a conventional one.

[Robert H. Tamarin]

Energy

A demonstration project of the world's largest fuel cell power plant was completed in March 1997. The system had been generating power for the Santa Clara, California, municipal electric system since April 1996. A fuel cell is a device that converts chemical energy to electrical energy by combining a fuel and an *oxidizer* (a substance that removes electrons in a chemical reaction).

The Santa Clara Demonstration Project power plant, connected to the Santa Clara municipal electric system during the year of tests, held four garage-sized modules called fuel cell stacks. These stacks used natural gas and oxygen to produce electricity. Researchers hope that as technology improves, *biomass* (vegetation) or coal can be used as fuel sources rather than natural gas.

In the Santa Clara project, natural gas was fed directly into the fuel cell. This system differed from some other types of fuel cells, in which the fuel first goes into an external fuel processor that produces a hydrogen-rich gas, which is then fed into the fuel cell. The project researchers said the Santa Clara system had accomplished many of the goals they had set. They said that the system used in Santa Clara was simpler and more efficient than the other systems used by fuel cell power plants.

The Santa Clara fuel cell plant generated two megawatts of electricity, which was enough to light about 2,000 homes. The fuel cell technology used in the plant got its start as an onboard power supply for U.S. manned spacecraft. Energy researchers believe that because of fuel cells' high efficiency, reliability, low noise, minimal pollution, and adaptability to use various fuels, future fuel cells will be considered attractive options for energy production.

Hazardous waste to energy. Energy engineers in 1997 were putting the finishing touches on a $25-million plant in Bay City, Texas, designed to convert chemical waste into useful materials, including synthetic fuels. The plant was scheduled to open in late 1997. It uses a processing method called catalytic extraction processing (CEP), which was developed by Molten Metal Technology, Incorporated, of Waltham, Massachu-

Europe's largest "wind farm" began operation in October 1996 on a remote parcel of sheep-grazing land in Wales. The facility's 56 windmills are each 50 meters (164 feet) high and have three-bladed rotors that are 44 meters (144 feet) in diameter. Developed by National Wind Power Limited, the $41-million project's 33.6 megawatt output will power 25,000 homes in the area.

setts. CEP uses a bath of extremely hot molten metal—usually iron—to convert hazardous wastes into useful materials and fuel. The high metal bath temperature—between 1300 °C (2370 °F) and 1700 °C (3100 °F)—acts as a *catalyst* (a substance that promotes a chemical reaction), breaking the wastes into chemical elements. Other materials, such as oxygen, lime, or aluminum, are then added to the bath and cause the elements to combine in new ways to form gases, ceramics, and metals.

The Texas plant will process chemical waste products that are rich in carbon, hydrogen, and oxygen, which will be used to make a high-quality fuel as a by-product of the cleansing process.

A related technology called Quantum-CEP, which also uses a molten metal bath, can be used to break down radioactive waste compounds into their original elements. Scientists recycle the nonradioactive material and discard or recycle the radioactive elements.

Molten Metal Technology has constructed two Quantum-CEP facilities at its Technology Center in Oak Ridge,

Tennessee. The systems, scheduled to be completed in late 1997, were designed to process up to 5 million kilograms (11 million pounds) of mixed nonnuclear and radioactive waste annually for government and commercial customers. The company operates another Quantum-CEP plant in Oak Ridge that processes low-level radioactive waste from nuclear power plants. That facility began commercial operations in December 1996.

Researchers said that catalytic extraction processing is receiving worldwide acceptance. They predicted more CEP plants would be constructed as governments and industry strive to protect the environment from dangerous wastes.

Stronger efficiency standards. The U.S. Department of Energy (DOE) in April 1997 announced new energy efficiency standards requiring refrigerators sold after mid-2001 to operate on almost one-third less electricity than models sold in 1997. In the announcement, U.S. Energy Secretary Federico Peña said the new standards paved the way for "a fridge of the 21st century" that would

Storing nuclear waste in glass

The West Valley Demonstration Project (WVDP) in West Valley, New York, a commercial facility that converts high-level nuclear waste liquids into a solid glass form suitable for long-term storage, began operation in June 1996. The molten glass-waste mixture is poured into stainless steel canisters 3 meters (10 feet) tall *right,* which are then stored at a federal repository. About 300 canisters of radioactive glass will be produced during the program, scheduled for completion in 1998. WVDP was the second project of its type in the country. The U.S. Department of Energy's Defense Waste Processing Facility, located in Aiken, South Carolina, produced the first canister in May 1996. An employee at the Aiken site examines simulated glass waste like that stored inside the containers, *below.*

save electricity for the nation and money for consumers.

The DOE said the stronger efficiency standards for refrigerators would eventually save over 25 billion kilowatt hours of electricity each year. That amount of energy is equal to the energy supplied annually by eight large generating plants, according to the American Council for an Energy-Efficient Economy, a Washington, D.C.-based organization that encourages the adoption of energy-efficient technology and practices.

The new standard was to take effect in July 2001. It was expected to add an average of $80 to the price of a refrigerator, but should save consumers $20 a year—or $380 over the life of the appliance—in reduced energy costs, according to DOE estimates.

The DOE predicted that energy savings for consumers would total $1 billion annually by the year 2010 and more than $2 billion annually by the year 2020. By that time, most of the older, less-efficient refrigerators in the United States will no longer be in use. Refrigerators are the third-largest users of ener-

gy in the average home, behind dryers and stand-alone freezers.

Some refrigerator manufacturers said that they wanted the standards implemented no earlier than the year 2003. They said it would be difficult to meet the standards before that time.

Ceramic parts gain ground. In May 1997, researchers at Solar Turbines, Incorporated, in San Diego, California, studied the use of ceramics to replace metal in some parts of gas turbine engines used to generate power. The research project was part of a DOE Advanced Turbines System program designed to produce turbine engines that have 40 percent more power, operate at a lower temperature, and emit less nitrogen oxide than conventional turbine engines. Researchers at Solar Turbines said they hoped that the ceramic components would be used in existing engine models.

If the technology proves successful, the investigators said, ceramic parts could be ready to use in the commercial market by about the year 2000.

[Pasquale M. Sforza]

In an effort to get more service life out of aging bridges, engineers in 1996 and 1997 worked on the development of new monitoring systems that would enable quicker, less-expensive, and hopefully more thorough assessments of a bridge's structural fitness. One such project, developed by engineers at New Mexico State University in Las Cruces, involved the use of gauges made with laser-treated *optical fibers*—highly transparent strands of glass—to detect wear-and-tear on bridges. Following successful laboratory results, the researchers in August 1996 began full-scale field tests of the system on a section of an interstate highway bridge in Las Cruces.

The engineers installed five gauges, each consisting of a specially treated glass fiber, on the deck of the bridge. The gauges were made at the Optical Science division of the Naval Research Laboratory in Washington, D.C. To create the gauges, researchers repeatedly shined a dual-beam laser onto a strand of fiber 24 meters (80 feet) in length. This process etched grooves 5 millimeters (0.25 inch) wide onto the fiber. A variety of grooves, which function as sensors, were "written" onto the same strand of fiber by repositioning the laser to different sections of the strand and changing the angle of the beams.

The engineers fastened the glass fibers to a bridge with a very strong adhesive. At one end of each fiber, they placed a device called a laser emitting diode, which sends a pulse of light down the strand. The sensors reflect a narrow segment, or wavelength, of the light beam to an electronic monitoring device. The device turns the pulse of light into a digital signal that is relayed to a computer. Stress and strain on a bridge changes the wavelength of the light emitted by the sensors. The wavelength changes enable researchers to pinpoint the locations and types of strain occurring on a structure.

Rola Idriss, a civil engineering professor at New Mexico State University and the lead investigator for the project, said this new technology is more reliable, accurate, and cost-efficient than the traditional monitoring system. Under that system, gauges measure the tautness of wires stretched across the bridge deck. Sensors convert the measurements into an electrical signal, which is conveyed to a computer. But the researchers said that the gauges used in that system are more fragile than the glass fibers and are sensitive to temperature changes.

To determine the accuracy of the fiber-optic system's readings, the engineers placed 30 traditional sensory gauges parallel to the glass sensors. Results were also checked against a computer-based model that predicts the effects that will be produced by various types of strain. The researchers planned to install additional sensors on the bridge deck through 1997 in order to fine-tune the fiber-optic system. They said that their initial round of sensor testing revealed that the devices had functioned well and were providing reliable data.

Bridge fatigue reduction. Tests completed in December 1996 on a special type of "shock absorber" for bridges showed that the device may almost double the life of steel spans that are 18 meters (60 feet) long or longer. The device, called a Semi-Active Vibration Absorber (SAVA), reduces fatigue-causing vibrations and increases bridge *load ratings*—the maximum weight of a vehicle safely allowed on a bridge—according to its inventor, William N. Patten, an associate professor at the University of Oklahoma Center for Structural Control in Norman.

Patten said that by reducing fatigue, the life of thousands of older bridges could be prolonged. The system could also be adapted to protect other steel structures, such as buildings, offshore platforms, and electrical towers.

The SAVA system is made up of two v-shaped pieces of steel called moment arms—each 1.5 meters (5 feet) deep—which are bolted under a bridge *girder* (supporting beam). An extension rod 9 meters (30 feet) long, which has a control mechanism called a hydraulic actuator attached to it, is connected to the pieces of steel. The actuator regulates the flow of hydraulic fluid in the system. The SAVA system collects data about 4,000 times per second from electronic sensors that are located on the bridge and on the control mechanism. The sensors measure vibration from sources such as vehicle traffic and the wind. It can also detect structural problems in the bridge.

Hong Kong's Tsing Ma Bridge, which opened in April 1997, is the longest suspension bridge in the world to carry both road and rail traffic. The 2.2-kilometer (1.4-mile) bridge links the Hong Kong mainland with Lantau Island and the islet of Chek Lap Kok. The bridge is part of a $20-billion development project, which also includes construction of a new airport on Chek Lap Kok.

Using the information, a type of computer chip called a microprocessor takes less than seven *milliseconds* (thousandths of a second) to decide how much to adjust the actuator's hydraulic fluid flow valve. When the valve is closed, the system acts like a spring coiling under a heavy object, which adds to the strength of the girder. When the valve opens, hydraulic fluid is released to reduce vibration on the bridge. The process is similar to an automobile shock absorber in action.

Preliminary studies showed that the SAVA system reduced stress on the bridge by up to 65 percent. Patten said the system could increase the maximum per-vehicle weight capacity of some bridges from 36,000 kilograms (80,000 pounds) to 54,000 kilograms (120,000 pounds) or could extend the life of a bridge by a minimum of 40 years.

New paint-removal technique. An easier way to remove paint from large surfaces was announced in March 1997 by the U.S. Department of Energy's Oak Ridge National Laboratory (ORNL) in Oak Ridge, Tennessee. A piece of equipment called a cryogenic pellet accelerator uses frozen carbon dioxide pellets to do the job.

The device works by shooting thousands of tiny frozen carbon dioxide pellets from a rapidly spinning wheel. The wheel slings the pellets off its outer edge at speeds up to 330 meters (1,100 feet) per second. The speed at which the pellets are released is controlled by the speed of the wheel. Depending on how fast the pellets strike an object, they can strip paint or contaminants such as grease from a surface, while leaving the base unaffected. The pellets then evaporate, leaving only tiny particles of the contaminant to clean up.

The Oak Ridge researchers said the system's precision and relatively low energy requirements made it superior to traditional paint-removal methods. The scientists predicted that the new device would be used to clean ships, barges, and processing equipment and to remove old paint from storage tanks.

Improved contaminant detection. In April 1997, the ORNL announced that it had developed a portable instrument

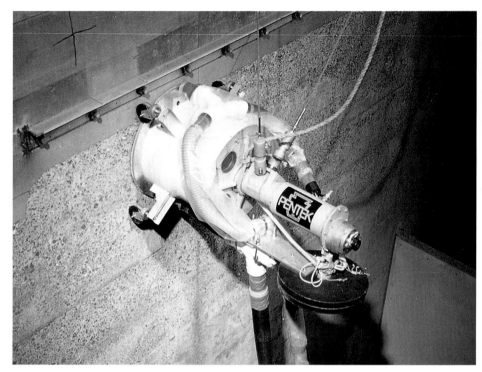

The WallWalker, a robotic wall-cleaning device, can aid in scrubbing the walls of nuclear reactors. The WallWalker was developed by Pentek, Incorporated, of Coraopolis, Pennsylvania, under a $150,000 grant from the U.S. Department of Energy. The unit is suspended from two cables connected to computer-controlled motors. A map of the surface of the wall is programmed into the computer, which directs the robot's motions. A vacuum attached to the Wall-Walker captures dust and debris and stores it in large drums.

designed to detect, measure, and monitor pollutants in soil or water and give instantaneous readouts.

The device, marketed under the brand name Luminoscope by Environmental Systems Corporation of Knoxville, Tennessee, can be taken to a work site and used to detect the presence of pollutants such as gasoline, oil, polychlorinated biphenyls (PCB's), and pesticides in soil or water. Engineers need to know what type of pollutant, if any, is at a job site. If hazardous waste is present, they must also know how much of the soil or water is affected and find a way to clean the area before they can begin working on a project.

Many existing methods of sampling pollutants require the physical separation of the contaminants, which can be a slow and costly process. However, scientists know that certain pollutants naturally emit different *spectral signatures* (bands of light). The Luminoscope detects these light emissions from contaminants present in soil or water through a technique called ultraviolet synchronous scanning. The scanner is

linked to a laptop computer in the field that stores and analyzes the collected data and serves as the instrument's control panel.

Monitoring radioactive wastes. Tests of a modified space shuttle component in September 1996 showed that the device can help in obtaining information and samples from underground storage tanks containing hazardous radioactive wastes. Engineers modified the joints of a portable robotic arm used on the space shuttle to create the Light-Duty Utility Arm (LDUA).

The work was conducted as part of an Energy Department project. Engineers want to use the LDUA to inspect, sample, and retrieve the hazardous waste stored in aging underground storage tanks across the entire United States. Because of the high levels of radiation and difficulty in reaching the waste through the small access-pipe openings, called risers, engineers must use a remotely operated system to collect data about the tank and waste conditions.

During a test, the LDUA system, built by SPAR Aerospace of Toronto, Ontario, used a specially mounted video system to take three-dimensional color pictures of the inside of a tank that had been contaminated with radioactive waste. Three days, later the device, fitted with a gripper tool, was used to remove a steel measuring tape that had been dropped into the tank.

Underwater construction. One of the most costly components of underwater construction is called a habitat, a watertight enclosure that enables workers to make dry welds on submerged steel structures and pipelines. Habitats must be custom designed and are typically used only once, pushing the cost of a single underwater weld as high as $250,000, according to underwater construction contractors. But in February 1997, researchers began the second phase of testing on specially formulated wet-welding rods that one day should enable divers to make underwater welds directly, without the need for a habitat.

The project, called the Joint Industry Underwater Development Program, is a cooperative effort between Global Divers & Contractors, Incorporated, and the Colorado School of Mines in Golden. During the tests, researchers in New Iberia, Louisiana, successfully made wet welds in simulated depths of 1 meter (3 feet) to 120 meters (400 feet). The experiments were carried out in a *hyperbaulic chamber*, a pressurized tank that can produce water pressures corresponding to depths as great as 360 meters (1,200 feet) below the surface. By conducting the tests on land, the investigators were able to avoid the risks of bad weather but were still able to gather needed information.

The Colorado School of Mines was to analyze the data gathered during the tests. The team expected the first commercial applications of the technology shortly after completion of the research in late 1998.

Success at greater simulated depths could lead to widespread adoption of the system and large savings in underwater construction as habitats are made obsolete. The researchers said the system would be useful at locations such as offshore oil platforms and possibly underwater pipelines. [Andrew G. Wright]

Environmental Pollution

Exposure to electromagnetic fields associated with power lines, appliances, waterbed heaters, and other sources does not pose a health risk to humans. That conclusion was reported in October 1996 by a 16-member committee of the National Research Council, a branch of the National Academy of Sciences. The panelists based their conclusion on a three-year analysis of 500 studies conducted over the previous 17 years on the potential health effects of extremely low frequency electromagnetic radiation. The report was commissioned by the United States Congress to address widespread concern over possible health effects of low-level electromagnetic fields.

According to the report, the bulk of the scientific evidence suggests that exposure to residential electric and magnetic fields does not cause cancer, neurological or behavioral problems, or damage to reproductive cells or a developing fetus. The committee said that although several studies had shown small but statistically significant increases in the incidence of leukemia in children living near power lines, there was no clear evidence that the electromagnetic fields generated by these lines were the cause of this form of cancer.

Bird rehabilitation in question. An October 1996 study suggested that well-intentioned but costly efforts to save the lives of birds caught in oil spills may be less effective than once thought.

Daniel W. Anderson, a biologist at the University of California at Davis, reported that only 12 to 15 percent of the 112 rehabilitated brown pelicans he tracked following oil spills off the California coast in 1990 and 1991 were alive two years after release. Nearly one-half of the birds were dead within six months. The normal two-year survival rate for a population of pelicans is 80 to 90 percent.

Anderson's study supported an April 1996 report that some seabird species survive an average of just four days after being cleaned of oil and released. In that report, Brian E. Sharp, an Oregon ornithologist who for 25 years studied seabirds living off the Pacific Coast, concluded that rescuing and cleaning birds is ineffective.

Birds immersed in oil often swallow

or inhale oil, which contains many potentially toxic chemicals. Exposure to this mix of chemicals can result in *anemia* (a reduction in red blood cells), hormonal disorders, internal tissue damage, and suppression of the immune system. Rehabilitated birds, while apparently healthy at the time of release, may lack the strength to survive the rigors of life in the wild.

However, David Jessup, a senior wildlife veterinarian with the California State Department of Fish and Game, said the high mortality in Anderson's study may have resulted from a slow response time in oil spills—the amount of time it takes officials to begin cleanups. The slower the response time, the greater the oil exposure to birds. He also noted that some bird species in Sharp's study are reluctant to come ashore even when they are covered with oil. They may, therefore, remain trapped in oil for days before being rescued. If those birds could be more quickly found and cleaned, he said, they might ingest less oil and thus improve their chances of survival.

Cleaning PCB's from the soil. Engineers said in November 1996 that they had found a cost-effective way to remove polychlorinated biphenyls (PCB's) and other synthetic pollutants from the soil. PCB's were once used as insulators in electrical transformers and have contaminated water and soil in many industrial sites. The soil-cleaning method was devised by William A. Edelstein and his co-workers at General Electric (GE) Corporate Research and Development in Schenectady, New York.

Scientists already knew that PCB's and various other pollutants could be removed from the soil by burning. But that method requires large amounts of soil to be transported and burned—a costly and cumbersome process. By using an intensely hot electric blanket, the GE researchers were able to vaporize pollutants without moving any soil. They demonstrated the blanket at an abandoned racing strip that was contaminated by PCB-laced oil used to control dust.

The researchers laid the specially designed blanket on the surface of the soil. Electric current running through the

A thermal blanket developed in late 1996 by General Electric Corporate Research and Development in Schenectady, New York, proved successful in removing PCB's and other synthetic pollutants from the soil. The blanket heats the top 15 centimeters (6 inches) of soil to 200 °C (392 °F). The intense heat evaporates the pollutants, which are drawn away and burned. The red color of the soil results from the blanket's oxidation of iron.

An 8-hectare (20-acre) pile of tires at Smithfield, Rhode Island, was considered the state's biggest environmental hazard in 1997. The pile, which contains about 10 million tires, covers a wetland and partly covers an underground pit of hazardous waste. The pile is less than 16 kilometers (10 miles) from Rhode Island's main municipal water source.

blanket raised the temperature of the top 15 centimeters (6 inches) of soil to 200 °C (392 °F). The high temperature evaporated the PCB's, which were then drawn away by a vacuum and piped into a device called a flameless thermal oxidizer, in which the PCB's were decomposed by high temperature.

The researchers were able to reduce PCB concentrations from 2,000 parts-per-million to less than 2 parts-per-million over a 9-square-meter (11-square-yard) test area.

PCB's and fetal development. A study of 212 Michigan children published in September 1996 concluded that children who were exposed to PCB's while still in the womb suffer from impaired brain development. The study was conducted by Joseph L. Jacobson and Sandra W. Jacobson of Wayne State University in Detroit. It showed that the intelligence quotient, or IQ, of 30 children, all of them age 11, who had been exposed to fairly high levels of PCB's before birth was an average of 6.2 points lower than that of other children.

Although the PCB-affected children

were in the normal range of IQ, the researchers concluded that the chemical had impaired their short-term memory and planning skills and made them more easily distracted. The children often lagged six months behind their peers in certain skills such as word comprehension. The children are believed to have been exposed to PCB's while in the womb because their mothers ate large quantities of fish tainted with the chemicals.

Nitrogen in the environment. A report released in April 1997 by the Ecological Society of America concluded that human activity adds huge amounts of nitrogen to the environment. The report, issued at the annual meeting of the American Association for the Advancement of Science, held in Seattle, was written by an eight-member panel headed by Peter M. Vitousek, an ecologist at Stanford University in California.

According to the report, human activity annually releases 140 million metric tons (125 tons) of nitrogen and nitrogen compounds into the air, water, and soil through the use of commercial fertilizer, the burning of *fossil fuels* (oil, natural gas, and coal), and the cultivation of crops that draw large amounts of nitrogen from the air into the soil.

All this nitrogen, plus 70 million metric tons (63 tons) of nitrogen released from *biomass* (plant matter) when land is cleared, degrades the planet's air, water, and soil and the many forms of life that depend on them. For example, nitrous oxide is threatening the ozone layer in the upper atmosphere, and nitric acid—formed from nitrogen dioxide and water in the atmosphere—is falling with rain into many lakes and streams, killing or harming fish and aquatic plants.

New rules for pesticides. President Bill Clinton signed legislation in August 1996 that strengthened the rules on pesticides. The legislation requires the U.S. Environmental Protection Agency (EPA) to set identical pesticide residue limits for processed food and raw foods, such as fruits and vegetables. Under the old law, processed foods could not have a greater percentage of pesticide residue than raw food. However, higher levels of some pesticides had been showing up in processed foods because such products are often concentrated forms of raw fruits and vegetables. Improved methods of testing for pesticides in foods also led to the identification of higher levels of pesticides, though experts contended that the amounts never posed a health risk.

The new law addresses other pesticide issues as well. For example, it requires the EPA to set exposure limits of pesticides to protect people from all potential health effects—not just cancer—and to consider the greater susceptibility of infants and children to pesticides.

The President also signed legislation in August that requires municipal water suppliers to tell their customers what contaminants have been detected in their city's water and whether they pose a health risk. The facts must be mailed with each household's bill. In addition, the legislation requires the EPA to announce new drinking water standards for *radon,* a radioactive gas, and review data on the health risks posed by *arsenic,* a poisonous chemical element that is often found in water.   [Daniel D. Chiras]

Fossil Studies

A remarkable discovery by a farmer in the northeastern Chinese province of Liaoning in August 1996 became the center of attention for many dinosaur specialists. The site yielded hundreds of well-preserved fossils from rocks dated tentatively at 120 million to 140 million years old. In April 1997, a team of researchers from the United States and Germany, led by paleontologist John Ostrom of Yale University in New Haven, Connecticut, announced their preliminary findings on the fossils.

A dinosaur or a bird? The most controversial fossils are of an animal resembling a small dinosaur of the genus *Compsognathus* that lived during the Jurassic Period (about 205 million to 138 million years ago). One of the new fossils, however, measuring about 1 meter (3.3 feet) in length, has what appears to be a line of small feathery impressions along the back and tail. Researchers at the National Geological Museum of China in Beijing maintained that the specimen is a bird, which they named *Sinosauropteryx prima.*

Ostrom, who first proposed the theory—now widely accepted—that birds evolved from dinosaurs, had at first hoped that the new specimen would fill a gap in the fossil record. But his team, as well as researchers at the Nanjing Institute of Geology and Paleontology, subsequently argued that the impressions are not true feathers. Rather, they said, the bristlelike features may be *protofeathers,* structures that in time evolved into actual feathers. Those scientists argued that the animal was not a bird but a dinosaur.

Although the debate was not resolved, the researchers agreed that the fossils are an important find. Some fossils of *Sinosauropteryx* contain the preserved remains of soft tissues, including lungs, a liver, muscle tissue, and unlaid eggs in an oviduct, the first evidence identifying the sex of an individual dinosaur. And one specimen contains the jaws of a small mammal in the abdominal cavity—part of the creature's last meal.

Another specimen found at the Liaoning site, a chicken-sized creature called *Protarchaeopteryx robusta* by the Chinese researchers, contributed further to the

Dark impressions along the back of the fossil, *above,* were thought to be feathers, suggesting that the creature was an ancient bird. Further study indicated, however, that the bristly forms are probably not feathers and that the animal was a dinosaur. The fossil also contains internal organs, *arrow.* Two fossils of what definitely were birds were among hundreds at the site. The fossils were buried 120 to 140 million years ago.

debate about the link between dinosaurs and birds. *Protarchaeopteryx* had some characteristics similar to *Archaeopteryx*, the earliest known bird. For example, the front limbs of *Protarchaeopteryx* were much like the wings of the primitive bird. Also, the creature may have had tail feathers, though the feathers could be the remains of another animal.

Although the features of *Protarchaeopteryx* suggested a link to the first birds, the dating of the site made it improbable that the new species could have been ancestral to birds. If the fossils are 120 million years old, then the creatures would have lived as much as 20 million years after *Archaeopteryx*. Also, in a layer of rock just above the specimen, the researchers found hundreds of fossils of *Confuciusornis,* a more advanced, pigeon-sized bird that at other sites had been dated later than *Archaeopteryx.*

An important question in the debate was whether all of the organisms died at once. The condition of all the fossils suggested that the creatures were killed quickly in a disaster, such as a volcanic eruption. However, some researchers

believed that the site may be the result of more than one disaster occurring at different times. The researchers said further studies would be required to confirm the ages of the fossils and determine their significance.

The evolution of bird flight. Two reports in 1996 and 1997 offered clues to the evolution of flight. In April 1997, paleontologists Fernando E. Novas of the Argentine Museum of Natural Sciences in Buenos Aires and Pablo F. Puerta of the Patagonian Paleontological Museum in Trelew announced the discovery in southern Argentina of a small dinosaur fossil that may be the strongest evidence yet linking birds and dinosaurs.

The researchers determined that the shoulder socket of the dinosaur would have allowed it to make a full flapping motion with its front limbs and to tuck its limbs close to its body in the same way a bird folds its wings. Also, the pelvis and hind legs resemble those of ancient birds. Despite these similarities, the researchers determined that the body was too large and the forelimbs too short to allow the creature to fly. Moreover, the

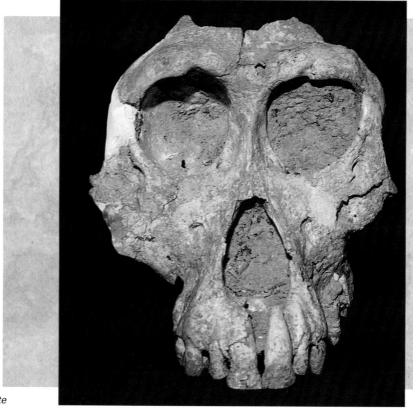

The discovery in Turkey of the nearly complete skull of a 10-million-year-old ape, called *Ankarapithecus meteai,* was reported in July 1996 by paleontologist Berna Alpagut and her colleagues at Ankara University in Turkey. Features of the skull led the researchers to conclude that, contrary to what was commonly believed, this species was not a direct ancestor of modern apes or humans. Instead, Alpagut's team contended, all three evolved from an earlier common ancestor.

fossil has no evidence of feathers. The ability to flap nonetheless supported the theory that flight may have begun with short, hopping flights from the ground rather than gliding from trees.

The fossil, dated at 90 million years, could not have been an ancestor of ancient birds. But the similarities between the dinosaur and birds led the scientists to conclude that the creature may have branched off from a lineage of dinosaurs that later evolved into birds.

Controlled flight. A remarkably well-preserved fossilized bird from 115-million-year-old deposits in the Cuenca province of Spain provided insights into the evolution of controlled flight. The discovery of the fossil was reported in August 1996 by paleontologist José Sanz of the Autonomous University of Madrid and *ornithologist* (bird specialist) Lewis Chiappel of the American Museum of Natural History in New York City.

The specimen, the size of a goldfinch, belonged to a primitive group of birds called enantiornithes, which existed during most of the Cretaceous Period (about 138 million to 65 million years ago)—later than *Archaeopteryx*. The feature of this fossil that sets it apart from earlier specimens is the presence of an *alula,* or *bastard wing*, a cluster of feathers on the first digit.

Modern birds use the alula to control the flow of air over the wing. Directing the airflow prevents turbulent eddies from developing around the wings and, therefore, allows for controlled flight at low speeds when taking off and landing. The discovery of this fossil indicates that birds had developed smooth, controlled flight by at least the middle part of the Cretaceous Period, much earlier than scientists had previously believed.

Largest dinosaur. In October 1996, Brian Curtice, a graduate student in paleontology at the State University of New York (SUNY) at Stony Brook, reported that the reconstruction of 145-million-year-old dinosaur remains from Upper Jurassic *strata* (geologic layers) resulted in the largest known dinosaur.

Since the partial remains were discovered in Colorado in the 1970's, many paleontologists believed that they belonged to two different genuses, called *Supersaurus* and *Ultrasauros*. Previous estimates had ascribed a length of about 31 meters (102 feet) to the plant-eating *Supersaurus*. However, *Ultrasauros* was considered to be even larger.

Some of the *Ultrasauros* bones had been crushed, but after reconstructing them, Curtice found that they fit perfectly into the *Supersaurus* skeleton. Curtice determined that *Ultrasauros* never existed and that the bones were all from just one species—belonging to the genus *Supersaurus*. Moreover, by transferring the bones into the skeleton of *Supersaurus*, Curtice discovered that the dinosaur may have been 37 to 40 meters (120 to 130 feet) long. This, indeed, would represent the longest dinosaur ever found. Moreover, based on the structure of the pelvis and the lack of complete fusion of the pelvis to the spine, Curtice concluded that the dinosaur may have been immature when it died. Therefore, even larger *Supersaurus* dinosaurs may have existed.

Cambrian Explosion reconsidered. The fossil record shows the apparently rapid evolution of *metazoans* (multicellular animals) during the Cambrian Period (about 540 million to 500 million years ago). Within a 10-million- to 15-million-year span, nearly all of the *phyla* (major body forms of animals) appear in the fossil record. This so-called Cambrian Explosion occurred at the end of a period of about 3 billion years during which the Earth was populated by only single-celled organisms. Many researchers, however, have doubted the abrupt evolution of metazoans.

In an October 1996 report, molecular biologist Gregory Wray and his colleagues at SUNY at Stony Brook argued that major groups of animals may actually have appeared as much as 1.2 billion years ago, more than 600 million years before the commonly accepted date of the Cambrian Explosion. The SUNY researchers based their claim not on fossils, but on the degree of similarity among genes from groups of modern animals in seven different phyla.

By studying the variations of particular genes in different living organisms, the researchers estimated the rate at which various groups of organisms diverged from common ancestors. Assuming that genetic *mutations* (molecular changes) occur with predictable frequency, the investigators calculated a "genetic clock," an estimate of the number of mutations every 1 million years.

The researchers then used the clock to determine that metazoans must have emerged no later than 1.2 billion years ago. Experts anticipated much debate about this finding since known animal fossils date back only 600 million years.

Discovery of soft-bodied animals. Exquisitely preserved fossils of soft-bodied animals were discovered in a 424-million- to 430-million-year-old fossil bed in the county of Herefordshire, England, in the United Kingdom. The finding was reported in July 1996 by paleontologists Derek Briggs of the University of Bristol, David Siveter of the University of Leicester, and Derek Siveter of Oxford University.

The fossils included specimens of bristly worms, tiny shrimps, and previously unknown animals with lobelike appendages. The finding was remarkable because few soft-bodied animals from the Silurian Period (435 million to 410 million years ago) are known from the fossil record. The researchers noted that the creatures had been buried in volcanic ash. They believed that geochemical changes around the decaying organisms triggered cementation of the ash entombing the organisms.

Earliest chordate discovered. The discovery of a 530-million-year-old chordate, the earliest specimen of the phylum to which human beings belong, was reported in November 1996. The report was made by paleontologists S. Conway Morris of Cambridge University in the United Kingdom and Shu Degan and Zhang Xingliang of Northwest University in Xi'an, China.

The 2.2-centimeter (0.87-inch) specimen, called *Cathaymyrus diadexus*, was found in the Yunnan province of China. Although the fossil resembles a worm, it contains possible gill slits, segmented muscles, and a central groove that appears to be a notochord, a cartilage rod supporting a central nerve cord.

The researchers also determined that what was believed to be the oldest chordate, *Yunnanozoon lividium,* did not actually have a notochord. What had been interpreted as a notochord in a 1995 study, Shu discovered, was really the creature's gut.　　　[Carlton E. Brett]

See also GEOLOGY, OCEANOGRAPHY.

Genetics

Researchers at the Roslin Institute in Edinburgh, Scotland, in February 1997 announced that they had *cloned* (made an exact genetic duplicate of) a sheep from one of the animal's mammary cells. Although scientists had already cloned mammals from cells taken from *embryos* (a prebirth stage of an organism), this was the first time that a mammal had been cloned from an adult cell. Before this procedure, geneticists believed that once cells had *differentiated*—become, for example, skin, or eye, or brain cells—their DNA would no longer be able to form a complete organism. DNA—deoxyribonucleic acid—is the molecule genes are made of.

Every cell in the body originates from a single fertilized egg, which contains in its DNA all the information needed to construct a whole organism. Each cell carries in its nucleus a full complement of DNA. Because embryo cells are undifferentiated, they can give rise to all of the other cells in the body. But that soon changes as an embryo develops into a fully formed organism with differentiated cells. In those cells, most of the genes are "turned off." For that reason, scientists had assumed that adult cells could not be used for cloning. But the Roslin Institute researchers, led by embryologist Ian Wilmut, successfully activated the DNA in an adult cell by creating a mock embryonic state.

The researchers extracted cells from the udder of a 6-year-old Finn Dorset *ewe* (female sheep). To stop the cells from dividing, the scientists deprived them of nutrients for a week. In response, the cells fell into a *quiescent* ("sleeping") state. Using a procedure called nuclear transfer, the researchers then removed the nucleus of an unfertilized egg from a Blackface ewe and fused the empty egg cell with a nucleus of one of the quiescent cells. The egg accepted the new nucleus and began the process of cell division. A week later, the embryo that had started growing was implanted in the uterus of another Blackface ewe. On July 5, 1996, the Blackface ewe gave birth to a Finn Dorset lamb, named Dolly, that was genetically identical to the donor of the adult cell.

The genetics of cloning

Scientists in Scotland announced in February 1997 that they had successfully cloned a sheep using a cell taken from an adult animal. It marked the first time scientists were able to use a body cell from an adult mammal to create a clone, or exact genetic duplicate.

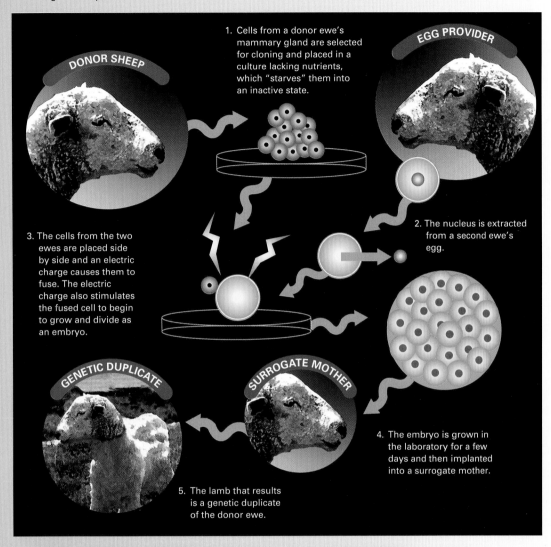

1. Cells from a donor ewe's mammary gland are selected for cloning and placed in a culture lacking nutrients, which "starves" them into an inactive state.

DONOR SHEEP

EGG PROVIDER

3. The cells from the two ewes are placed side by side and an electric charge causes them to fuse. The electric charge also stimulates the fused cell to begin to grow and divide as an embryo.

2. The nucleus is extracted from a second ewe's egg.

GENETIC DUPLICATE

SURROGATE MOTHER

4. The embryo is grown in the laboratory for a few days and then implanted into a surrogate mother.

5. The lamb that results is a genetic duplicate of the donor ewe.

Embryologist Ian Wilmut of the Roslin Institute in Edinburgh, Scotland, poses with Dolly, the first mammal to be successfully cloned from an adult cell. Although Wilmut dismissed the idea of creating human clones, he said there was "no reason in principle why you couldn't do it."

Although the procedure was heralded in the science community as a major accomplishment in the field of genetics, news of the experiment stirred public concern—especially over the issue of possibly cloning human beings. In the wake of the news, several countries—including the United States—took action to either ban or restrict research on cloning humans. Many scientists objected to the bans, however, proposing instead the adoption of ethical guidelines for cloning research.

According to scientists, the object of cloning mammals is not to set the stage for cloning humans but to produce improved livestock. Through cloning, herds could be improved so animals would produce better meat, eggs, wool, or milk. And animals could be made more resistant to disease.

Following the breakthrough at Roslin Institute, scientists focused their attention on cloning cows, an advance in animal cloning that would be far more useful to science and agriculture than cloned sheep. In February 1997, researchers at the University of Wisconsin at Madison fused differentiated cells—in this case, skin cells—from a 30-day old calf fetus with unfertilized cows' eggs. The scientists hoped that the experiment would produce a calf by the early months of 1998.

Human gene map. An international group of researchers reported in October 1996 that it had mapped more than 16,000 human genes as part of the Human Genome Project. That large endeavor is designed to produce a gene "blueprint," giving scientists the computer and laboratory tools needed to understand the genetic instructions that make each person unique.

It is estimated that the human *genome* (complete set of genetic material) contains between 50,000 and 100,000 genes. Scientists were optimistic in 1997 that all of these genes would be found and described by the year 2005.

The new map was expected to greatly accelerate this process. The map should also help scientists identify more genes associated with diseases and improve treatments and find cures for diseases such as diabetes, cystic fibrosis, and certain forms of cancer.

Genes, which carry coded instructions for the production of all the proteins needed by the body, are contained in short segments of DNA. All of a cell's DNA is packaged into 23 pairs of chromosomes within the cell's nucleus. Each chromosome carries thousands of genes arranged like beads on a string. The map shows where different genes are located on the chromosomes.

Scientists considered the development of the map a significant achievement because it provides a framework in which to organize the information available from several other types of human genetic maps. Some maps, for example, are only for particular chromosomes, such as a map completed in 1997 of the X chromosome, one of a pair of sex chromosomes that determines whether a child is a boy or a girl.

The genome map combines much of the information from previous maps by defining a large number of genes in terms of their DNA makeup, and by assigning locations to these genes along the length of individual chromosomes. Researchers working on the map described it, in part, as a human gene catalog, because it is a collection of information describing what is known about most of the human genes that have been studied to date.

Glaucoma gene discovered. Scientists announced in January 1997 that they had discovered a gene that may let doctors detect a form of glaucoma early enough to prevent thousands of people from losing their sight. The gene, called TIGR, may cause a form of glaucoma that strikes young people, often under age 20. The researchers, led by molecular geneticists Edwin Stone and Val Sheffield of University of the Iowa College of Medicine in Iowa City, reported that the gene may also be responsible for a small percentage of cases of adult glaucoma and may be involved to some extent in half of all glaucoma cases.

Glaucoma, which every year causes 10,000 Americans to lose their sight, is the second leading cause of blindness in the United States. Glaucoma occurs when fluid builds up inside the eyeball, causing dangerous pressure that over time destroys the optic nerve. By the time people notice vision loss, the damage is often irreversible. The discovery of the gene will allow doctors to test the relatives of people with juvenile glaucoma to identify anyone on the verge of

An electronics technologist at Lawrence Livermore National Laboratory (LLNL) in Livermore, California, tests a portable, battery-operated DNA analysis system designed by LLNL researchers. The United States Army began using a prototype of the system in November 1996. The suitcase-sized system can be used to test food and water in remote locations for contamination by disease-causing microbes, to diagnose certain diseases, and to identify human remains.

developing the condition, the investigators said.

The researchers tracked the gene to a section of chromosome 1. They then focused their hunt on three genes in the chromosome after studying the genetic material of more than 100 people with glaucoma. The scientists found that one of those genes—the TIGR gene—contained a *mutation* (molecular change) in people afflicted with juvenile glaucoma. They also discovered the mutated gene in 3 percent of adults with glaucoma.

According to the researchers, the abnormal protein produced by the mutated TIGR gene may be responsible for causing the disease. The protein may hinder the functioning of a group of cells that are responsible for filtering fluids out of the eye.

Genetic link to blood disease. The discovery of a gene associated with a disease called hemochromatosis was reported in August 1996 by three teams of scientists in the United States. Hemochromatosis, a common inherited disease caused by excess iron absorption, afflicts about 1.5 million people in the

United States. The study, conducted by geneticist Roger K. Wolff of Mercator Genetics in Menlo Park, California, and researchers from Stanford University and the St. Louis University School of Medicine, found that the gene, called HLA-H, may be useful in the diagnosis and treatment of the disease.

Small amounts of iron are necessary for the proper functioning of all cells in the body. Iron is especially important to the health of red blood cells, which use the element to form *hemoglobin*, a substance that carries oxygen from the lungs to other tissues in the body. The body normally excretes excess amounts of iron. Hemochromatosis accelerates the iron absorption process, allowing dangerous levels of iron to build up in the heart, liver, and other organs. If untreated, the iron can damage these organs, and may contribute to illnesses such as heart disease and cirrhosis.

For many years, scientists knew that HLA-H resided on chromosome 6, but they were unable to pinpoint its exact location. To find the gene, Wolff and his colleagues examined 15 different genes, including HLA-H, in 178 people diagnosed with hemochromatosis. They discovered that in 85 percent of the people the HLA-H gene was mutated.

The researchers reported that the mutated form of the gene may carry a blueprint for a faulty protein that causes the body to absorb too much iron. It is also possible, they said, that the gene is not the cause of the disease but only an indicator that the disease is present.

Key cancer gene found. Two teams of researchers reported in March 1997 the discovery of a gene that codes for an *enzyme* (a substance that promotes biochemical reactions) that blocks the development of cancer. Many people suffering from forms of prostate, breast, brain, and kidney cancers are missing the gene, according to a study led by Ramon Parsons, assistant professor of pathology at Columbia-Presbyterian Medical Center in New York City and molecular biologist Michael Wigler of Cold Spring Harbor Laboratory on Long Island, New York. The same conclusion was reached in another study, led by cell biologist Peter Steck of the M. D. Anderson Cancer Center in Houston, Texas, and Sean Tavtigian, director of cancer research at Myriad Genetics in Salt Lake City, Utah.

The investigators discovered that a piece of chromosome 10 known to contain a particular gene was missing in cells taken from breast, brain, and prostate cancer tumors. The group led by Parsons and Wigler called this gene "phosphatase and tensin homolog deleted on chromosome 10" (PTEN); the other team called it "mutated in multiple advanced cancers 1" (MMAC1). The researchers said the gene is apparently a tumor suppressor—it prevents cells from becoming cancerous. When tumor suppressor genes are missing or mutated, cancer has a better chance of developing and of spreading.

PTEN (or MMAC1) produces an enzyme called a phosphatase, which counteracts other enzymes called kinases. Kinases stimulate cell division. When phosphatase enzymes are not present, according to the researchers, kinases stimulate cells to divide uncontrollably—that is, to form a tumor. The researchers hope to use this gene to develop betters tests for early detection and more effective treatments of cancer.

Closing in on prostate cancer. Scientists in the United States and Sweden announced in May 1997 that they were getting close to finding a gene that may cause about one-third of all inherited prostate cancers. At least three research teams were attempting to locate a gene, called hereditary prostate cancer 1 (HPC1), that geneticists think increases the risk of prostate cancer in men, especially men with a family history of the disease. The investigators said they hoped to zero in on HPC1 by the middle of 1998.

The scientists—at the National Center for Human Genome Research in Bethesda, Maryland; Johns Hopkins University in Baltimore; the University of Michigan in Ann Arbor; and Umea University in Sweden—reported in November 1996 that they had determined that the gene lies on chromosome 1. They tracked the gene to that chromosome by analyzing genetic material from 2,500 families with a history of prostate cancer. In 66 of the families, at least three men had developed the disease.

The chromosome 1 found in men who were suffering from prostate cancer differed slightly from the chromosome found in men without the disease. The researchers also discovered that prostate cancer cells often have extra copies of chromosome 1.

Experts estimate that about 3 percent of all prostate cancer results from an inborn genetic flaw that is passed through the generations and that HPC1 plays a role in about 30 percent of these inherited cases. Moreover, evidence suggests that men with HPC1 get a more aggressive form of prostate cancer than men whose cancer is not inherited. And the gene may be especially important in triggering cancer in men at relatively young ages. According to scientists, the gene is responsible for about half of all inherited cases of prostate cancer that strike before the age of 65.

More than 300,000 American men are diagnosed with prostate cancer every year, and more than 40,000 die of it. Geneticists said that finding HPC1 would help doctors screen and treat men who come from families in which prostate cancer is common. It would also improve understanding of the genetic flaws that trigger the disease.

[David S. Haymer]

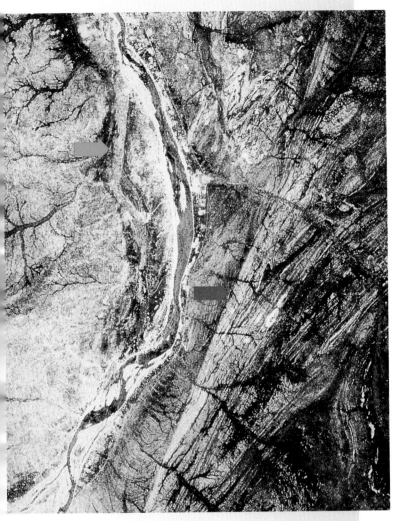

A radar image taken from a U.S. space shuttle shows the boundary, *red arrow,* at which the ancient continents of East and West Gondwanaland collided about 650 million years ago. The collision zone is visible only in radar images because it is buried beneath the sands of the Sahara. As well as revealing the collision boundary, the image may also help scientists explain how geologic forces have altered the course of the Nile River, the narrow yellow band running from top to bottom near the center of the image. The ancient—and now also buried—course of the Nile, *blue arrow,* lies to the west of the modern river.

Evidence presented in late 1996 indicated that primitive organisms may have populated the Earth much earlier in its history than previously thought. The discovery also pointed to the possibility that the emergence of life from nonliving material happens far more rapidly than currently thought.

A team of geochemists and geologists from Australia, the United Kingdom, and the United States reported in November 1996 that they had found evidence that primitive life forms existed on Earth about 3.85 billion years ago—more than 300 million years earlier than had previously been established. Prior to this discovery, the oldest known evidence of life on Earth had been a collection of fossilized bacteria that were approximately 3.5 billion years old. Those fossils were discovered in a rock formation in western Australia and were publicized in 1993.

The new evidence was found in a rock formation on Akilia Island, off the southwest coast of Greenland. The researchers found no fossil remains from these ancient organisms because they had been obliterated long ago by the intense heat and pressure of geologic activity. However, using a new instrument called an ion microprobe, the scientists detected traces of two *isotopes* (variant forms) of carbon in grains of a mineral known as apatite taken from the rock formation. The relative proportions of the two isotopes indicated that biological processes had been occurring in the rock when it was formed from the sediments of the ancient ocean.

Carbon has two stable isotopes, carbon-12 and carbon-13. In *inorganic* (nonliving) chemical processes, carbon-12 and carbon-13 are found in proportions close to their natural ratio: 98.9 percent carbon-12 and 1.1 percent carbon-13. However, processes carried out by living organisms treat the isotopes differently—they prefer carbon-12 over carbon-13. When the researchers found a higher-than-normal ratio of carbon-12 to carbon-13 in the apatite, they concluded that *organic* (living) processes had been at work within the rock formation in the distant past. Because the rock was found to be 3.85 billion years old, the scientists concluded that the carbon deposits were of the same age.

In an article discussing the signifi-

"Planet" Within the Earth

If you were to go on a journey to the center of the Earth, you would first have to dig through 8 to 40 kilometers (5 to 25 miles) of rocky *crust*, the "skin" of the Earth. If you were able to accomplish that feat, you would then have to find a way to get through the *mantle*, another rocky layer—this one about 2,900 kilometers (1,800 miles) thick. As you passed through this layer, you would need some sort of magical suit of armor to survive the intense pressures and infernal temperatures that grow greater as you move deeper. The next layer down, the *outer core*, reaches a temperature of about 6100 °C (11,000 °F). This layer consists mainly of melted iron and nickel, flowing and swirling around in a soup some 2,250 kilometers (1,400 miles) thick. After miraculously surviving a passage through the outer core, you would come to the *inner core*, a sphere of iron at the center of the Earth. The inner core is 2,600 kilometers (1,600 miles) wide. Though temperatures here are even greater than in the outer core, the incredible pressure at this depth forces the inner core's iron to remain solid.

Of course, a human could not really survive a journey to the center of the Earth. The trip described above is just a fantasy. It is inspired, however, not only by Jules Verne, the author of the novel *A Journey to the Center of the Earth*, but also by the work of scientists. Geophysicists have discovered much about the composition of the Earth's interior by using instruments such as *seismographs*, which amplify and record vibrations within the planet. In July 1996, geophysicists announced a new discovery about the center of the Earth—the inner core rotates faster than the rest of the planet. It is virtually a planet unto itself.

This discovery was made by geophysicists Xiaodong Song and Paul G. Richards, both of Columbia University's Lamont-Doherty Earth Observatory in Palisades, New York. Song and Richards were inspired to do their research by work that other scientists—geophysicists Gary A. Glatzmaier of Los Alamos National Laboratory in Los Alamos, New Mexico, and Paul H. Roberts of the University of California at Los Angeles—did in 1995. Glatzmaier and Roberts used a highly sophisticated computer simulation to conclude that the inner core rotates faster than the rest of the Earth. Song and Richards tested and confirmed this conclusion by analyzing almost 30 years of data from seismographs.

The vibrations detected by seismographs are known as seismic waves. Created by literally Earth-shaking events, such as earthquakes and nuclear explosions, they pass from one end of the planet to the other, and they move faster going northward or southward than when going eastward or westward. That is because as the waves pass through the center of the Earth, they encounter a feature of the inner core called the *axis of anisotropy*. Anisotropy is a variation in physical properties in different directions of measurement. The axis of anisotropy within the Earth refers to the direction in which the iron crystals of the inner core are pointing. These crystals are oriented at a 10° angle to the north-south axis around which the Earth spins. Therefore, the axis of anisotropy is said to be oriented at a 10° angle to the Earth's axis. The more closely the path of seismic waves matches the axis of anisotropy, the faster the waves travel. If the inner core is in fact rotating faster than the mantle and crust, the axis of anisotropy should, over time, change its orientation with respect to any particular point on the Earth's surface. And if this sort of wobbling is occurring, seismic waves moving from a particular source at one end of the planet to a particular site at the other end of the planet should move faster or slower over time.

Song and Richards found that seismic waves from earthquakes in the South Sandwich Islands, between South America and Antarctica, reached a seismic station at College, Alaska, one-third of a second faster in 1995 than in 1967. They explained this discrepancy by concluding that the axis of anistropy pointed more toward the seismic station in 1995 than in 1967, and therefore that the inner core must have rotated faster than overlying layers of the Earth. Their data indicated that the inner core rotates eastward about 1° per year faster than the mantle and crust. In other words, the inner core makes one complete revolution in relation to the Earth's surface every 360 years.

In December 1996, geophysicists Wei-jia Su and Adam M. Dziewonski, both of Harvard University in Cambridge, Massachusetts, and Raymond Jeanloz of the University of California at Berkeley announced the results of their own study of seismic waves. They used methods similar to those used by Song and Richards, but they analyzed data from about 2,000 different seismic stations collected over a 29-year period. They found, as Song and Richards did, that the inner core is spinning eastward faster than the rest of the planet. But their data indicated that the core's rate of rotation is about 3° per year faster than that of the mantle and crust.

Why does the inner core rotate at a different rate than the rest of the planet? Or, as scientists ask, why does it display differential rotation? Su, Dziewonski, and Jeanloz suggested that the differential rotation could be driven by either gravita-

A diagram of the Earth shows the inner core as a reddish sphere. The solid line through the core represents the axis along which *seismic waves* (vibrations) traveled fastest through the Earth in 1996. Records of seismic waves from past earthquakes show that this axis has changed over the years. The change indicates that the inner core has made more than a quarter of a revolution in relation to the Earth's surface since 1900.

tional or electromagnetic forces. They noted that scientists have learned that the rotation of the Earth's mantle and crust is slowing down over time due to friction caused by the gravitational pull of the moon and sun. The result of the deceleration of the mantle and crust is that the length of a day on Earth is increasing by about two thousandths of a second every 100 years. Perhaps the deceleration of the inner core simply lags behind that of the mantle and crust, because the fluid of the outer core acts as a buffer. The other possible explanation offered by Su, Dziewonski, and Jeanloz is that physical forces involving the Earth's magnetism may be causing the differential rotation.

The computer simulation of Glatzmaier and Roberts provided a detailed explanation of how magnetism may be driving the rotation rate of the inner core. The simulation indicated that melted iron in the outer core is flowing eastward, carrying a magnetic field that is dragging the inner core along—much as the rotating armature of an electric motor causes its central shaft to turn. This theory implied that, over time, the rotation rate of the inner core may become faster or slower, depending on the movements of the fluid in the outer core. The gravity theory of Su, Dziewonski, and Jeanloz implied only a gradual deceleration of the inner core. Therefore, continued monitoring of seismic waves was expected to eventually reveal which, if either, of these theories is correct.

As scientists gained a better understanding of the core of the Earth, they were also learning more about the origin and workings of the planet's magnetic field. Near each of the Earth's geographic poles (the North and South poles) is a magnetic pole. The magnetic poles act like the ends of a bar magnet. The north magnetic pole, for example, attracts the north pole of a compass needle. The magnetic field extends far into space, where it surrounds the Earth and attracts electrically charged particles, such as electrons and protons. Since the 1950's, scientists have explained the Earth's magnetic field with the *geodynamo theory*. According to this theory, the magnetic field is generated by the motion of the melted iron in the outer core. The metallic fluid is stirred as some of the iron solidifies and sinks toward the inner core and as lighter elements present in the outer core, such as oxygen and sulfur, rise toward the mantle. An electric current forms in the stirred fluid, and the movement of this current produces the magnetic field.

The computer simulation by Glatzmaier and Roberts supported much of the geodynamo theory. It also added a new twist to the theory by finding that the rotation of the inner core may cause additional disruption of the fluid motion in the outer core, which in turn would increase the magnetic force generated.

One indication that Glatzmaier's and Roberts's simulation was accurate was that it produced a reversal of the magnetic field. Studies of the alignment of crystals in ancient volcanic rocks (which oriented themselves relative to the Earth's magnetic field when the rocks solidified) have shown that the magnetic poles periodically trade places. Using more than 2,000 hours of supercomputer time to simulate about 40,000 years of real time, Glatzmaier and Roberts detected one reversal of the magnetic field—approximately what scientists could expect for that length of time.

Perhaps it is not exactly what Jules Verne had in mind, but the center of the Earth has begun to reveal some long-buried secrets to us. We will never actually see the innermost parts of our planet, but learning about them is nonetheless a fascinating journey.

[Henry T. Mullins]

Glacial flooding in Iceland

A satellite-radar image of southeastern Iceland, *right,* shows a huge glacial flood that struck the area in 1996. Geothermal heat sources beneath Iceland's glaciers periodically cause floods, called *jökulhlaups.* But the 1996 flood, triggered by the eruption of the Grimsvötn volcano, was among the biggest on record. The eruption, which occurred beneath Vatnajökull, Iceland's largest glacier, melted a vast quantity of ice, creating a surge of water and ice that poured down the southern slope of the glacier, *arrows.* For a short time, the flow formed the world's second largest river.

Heated water flowing beneath the ice of the Vatnajökull glacier melts a chasm, *above,* measuring 6 kilometers (3.7 miles) long, ½ to 1 kilometer (0.3 to 0.6 mile) wide, and 100 to 200 meters (330 to 660 feet) deep. As the torrent flowed to the sea, it smashed three bridges and destroyed parts of the only road running along Iceland's southern coast. However, there was reportedly no loss of human life.

cance of the new discovery, geochemist John M. Hayes of the Woods Hole Oceanographic Institution in Woods Hole, Massachusetts, noted that some experts support the theory that huge asteroids hit the Earth as late as about 3.8 billion years ago—close to the time that primitive organisms were living in the warm seas around what is now Greenland. These were the last large impacts of what many experts speculate was a period of "late heavy bombardment" of the Earth by debris from outer space during the formation of the solar system.

Such a tremendous collision would have generated enough heat to boil away the planet's entire ocean, thereby obliterating all life on Earth. Therefore, Hayes wrote, it could be that life on Earth reemerged "with breathtaking rapidity" only a few hundred million years after the impact. If life can develop in such short periods of time, it raises the possibility that organisms may have originated on Earth more than once, perhaps several times, prior to 3.5 billion years ago. These earlier life forms could also have been destroyed by asteroid impacts, only to be replaced by new organisms many millions of years later.

Anatomy of an asteroid strike. The Chicxulub Crater on the Yucatán Peninsula of Mexico is thought to be the impact site of an asteroid that struck the Earth about 65 million years ago. Many experts believe this impact could have caused the extinction of many organisms, including the dinosaurs. New investigations of the crater by geologists Peter Schultz of Brown University and Steven d'Hondt of the University of Rhode Island suggested that the asteroid struck at a low angle, which may explain the riddle of why the catastrophe affected different parts of the world so unevenly. The scientists reported their findings in November 1996.

The Chicxulub Crater lies buried beneath the surface of the Yucatán Peninsula, but it can be imaged by a satellite using a device that measures the intensity of gravity. The rocks that form the crater are denser than the rocks surrounding it because they were compressed by the force of the impact. Therefore, the gravitational pull over the crater is measurably higher than over the rest of the Yucatán Peninsula.

Schultz and d'Hondt used a comput-er to assemble these data into a detailed image of the crater. They discovered that the crater, 300 kilometers (185 miles) wide, is not circular, but *elliptical* (oval-shaped) and opens toward the northwest. This finding suggested that the asteroid did not fall from directly above, but came in at a low angle.

Impact tests in the laboratory have shown that an asteroid striking the Earth at an angle between 45 and 90 degrees produces a circular crater. This is because the impact vaporizes both the asteroid and the rock at the impact site so suddenly that it creates a circular blast pattern, throwing debris in all directions at once. However, if the impact occurs at a lower angle, the asteroid plows a furrow in the ground as it strikes the Earth, and the rock vaporizes more slowly. This results in an elliptical blast pattern, in which a greater proportion of debris is thrown out ahead of the impact in the asteroid's direction of travel.

According to the new theory, the asteroid, estimated at about 15 kilometers (9 miles) in diameter and traveling at a speed of about 20 kilometers (12 miles) per second, entered the atmosphere from the southeast at an angle of 20 to 30 degrees above the horizon. As it entered the atmosphere, friction heated the air around the asteroid to a white-hot glow. As the lower part of the asteroid touched the ground, it began to vaporize and plow out the crater. The upper part of the asteroid continued along its path but was shattered by the explosion caused by the vaporization of the lower part.

A cloud of superhot vapor continued northwestward across North America (areas that are now west Texas, New Mexico, and Colorado), incinerating all life in the region. This was followed by a hail of scorching debris from the explosion. This hail and fire storm may explain why the plant life in this region of North America was replaced by ferns in the years after the event, while forests in other areas were not destroyed. A northwesterly direction of travel would also explain why the asteroid's effects were most severe in the Northern Hemisphere, while the Southern Hemisphere was relatively protected. This pattern of devastation had puzzled scientists since 1980, when the "doomsday asteroid" theory was first proposed.

Earth's early atmosphere, experts think, contained only traces of oxygen. But in December 1996, geochemist Hiroshi Ohmoto of Tohoku University in Japan and Pennsylvania State University reported findings indicating that the amount of oxygen present between 3.5 billion and 1.8 billion years ago may have been greater than previously believed. Ohmoto reached this conclusion after using a new method to examine the chemical composition of *paleosols* (fossil soils).

Almost all of the oxygen in the atmosphere is produced by plants, which sustain themselves through *photosynthesis* (the use of sunlight to convert carbon dioxide and water into nutrients). Oxygen, created as a result of this reaction, is used up by many natural processes. For example, it is breathed by animals and consumed in the decomposition of dead organisms, which uses oxygen to convert organic compounds back into carbon dioxide and water.

The decomposition of iron-bearing minerals in rock deposits, such as magnetite and olivine, also consumes oxygen. These minerals are decomposed by weathering at the Earth's surface, a process that uses oxygen and water to form iron oxide minerals, which remain as part of the soil. If no oxygen is present, the iron in iron-bearing minerals dissolves out of the soil. Older studies of paleosols between 3.5 billion and 1.8 billion years old suggested that they were depleted in iron. As a result, it was assumed that, at the time the ancient soils formed, so little oxygen existed in the atmosphere that most of the iron in the soils must have dissolved.

Ohmoto examined the data collected by these studies, comparing the amount of iron in the samples to the amount of titanium, which is the most insoluble element. He discovered that some of the deposits were in fact not paleosols, but were the result of a reaction between superhot water and rock deep within the Earth. The ratio of iron oxides to titanium in most of the true paleosols showed no iron depletion, indicating that the soil had formed under an atmosphere with an oxygen level at least 1 percent of the present level.   [William W. Hay]

Medical Research

Researchers made several important advances in medicine and surgery in 1996 and 1997. Some of the most significant discoveries were new insights into repairing damaged spinal cords, treating diseased hearts, and understanding how smoking contributes to lung cancer.

Repairing spinal cords. Researchers at the Karolinska Institute in Stockholm, Sweden, made worldwide headlines in July 1996 when they announced a breakthrough in the search for a technique to repair a damaged spinal cord. The researchers showed that they could regenerate small portions of the severed spinal cord of a rat and even restore a degree of muscle function. About 10,000 Americans suffer serious spinal cord injuries each year, and most become paralyzed as a result. The research represented a major milestone by demonstrating the first evidence that spinal cord damage could be reversed and some degree of movement restored.

In the experiment, the Swedish investigators intentionally severed the spinal cords of laboratory rats at chest level, creating a gap of about 6 millimeters (0.25 inch). Then, they surgically transplanted thin nerve fibers from the chest muscles to bridge the gap. These grafts were "glued" into place using *fibrin,* a sticky substance found in clotted blood. The fibrin contained *fibroblast growth factor,* a protein that stimulates nerve growth.

Within three weeks, the rats showed evidence of improvement. After one year, many had regained the partial use of their previously immobilized hind legs. These rats could support their own body weight, flex their joints, and demonstrate some degree of mobility. The recovery was, however, extremely limited. None of the animals could walk or coordinate the motions of their front and hind legs.

Because the technique was so experimental, medical experts cautioned that its use in treating human spinal cord injuries was still many years away. Furthermore, doctors said, unlike the damage inflicted upon the laboratory rats, most spinal cord damage in people is due to crushing injuries, not clean slices.

Another approach to spinal cord re-

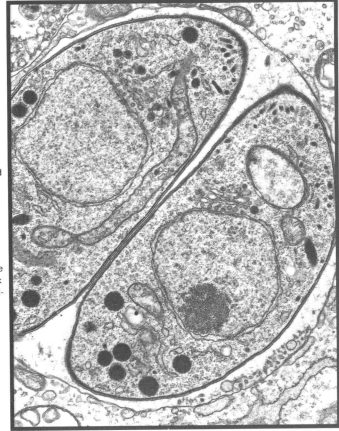

Two parasitic cells within a human cell each contain a structure called a plastid (white oval at right center). The similarity of plastids to chloroplasts in plant cells indicates that plastids may have evolved from chloroplasts captured from green algae cells, U.S. biologists reported in March 1997. Because several disease-causing parasites have plastids, which retain a functioning set of plantlike genes, some experts think the parasites might be vulnerable to drugs that attack the plastid's genes. Such drugs would kill the parasite without affecting normal cells, which contain dissimilar genes.

generation also appeared promising. In October 1996, researchers at Memorial Sloan-Kettering Cancer Center in New York City reported that carefully timed X rays may help the body heal spinal cord damage.

In this study, a single X-ray exposure, in a dose similar to that administered in cancer therapy, was given to rats in the third week after their spinal cords were severed. Four to five months later, one-third of the treated rats had experienced some regeneration of their spinal cords, demonstrated by their ability to move their hind legs.

The researchers believe that X-ray radiation interferes with the activity of *reactive astrocytes*, cells that are produced by the body after spinal damage occurs. These cells somehow prevent injured nerve fibers from regenerating, but the X rays apparently prevent reactive astrocytes from forming in the first place.

The X-ray treatment was effective only when given in the third week after the injury, said neurology researcher Nurit Kalderon, lead author of the study. Early in the recovery from a spinal cord in-

jury, she said, the body attempts to regrow nerve fibers. But at some point that effort stops, and the injury becomes irreversible. In rats, this point appears to be at about three weeks, the time when the reactive astrocyte cells appear.

The investigators expressed the hope that this technique might someday help prevent paralysis in humans due to spinal-cord damage. They estimated, however, that two more years of animal research were necessary before studies on humans could be undertaken.

Cigarettes' "smoking gun." Although studies have repeatedly demonstrated a statistical link between cigarettes and lung cancer, a study published in October 1996 identified the biochemical mechanism involved. Using genetic techniques, investigators at the M. D. Anderson Cancer Center in Houston were able to identify a specific chemical produced by tobacco smoke that apparently causes *mutations* (changes) in a particular human gene in a manner commonly seen in lung cancer.

This gene—p53, a so-called tumor suppressor gene—is vital to fighting cancer because, in normal circumstances, it blocks the uncontrolled division of cells that produces a cancerous tumor. But the researchers found that a substance called BPDE, which is manufactured in the body from benzo[a]pyrene, a compound in cigarette smoke, forms strong chemical bonds with p53 at three sites. Those bonds would prevent the gene from functioning and would presumably cause permanent mutations when cells reproduce. The same mutations are often seen in lung cancer. According to a number of cancer and genetics experts, this finding at last established a direct link between smoking and lung cancer.

The promise of cord blood. A study at Duke University in Durham, North Carolina, published in July 1996, concluded that the use of blood cells taken from the placental and umbilical cord tissue of newborn babies may save the lives of many individuals with leukemia or other life-threatening illnesses that are commonly treated by a bone marrow transplant. The researchers evaluated 25 children and young adults with life-threatening blood diseases. The patients needed new bone marrow to replace their *stem cells* (the building blocks of both blood and immune-system cells), which had been destroyed by disease or cancer treatments. All received transfusions of cord blood, which, like bone marrow, is rich in stem cells.

The results showed that cord blood stimulated the patients' bodies to produce white blood cells and other vital blood components. In addition, these benefits occurred even though the transplanted blood was not a perfect match to the patient, because stem cells from placental blood are less likely to be rejected than those from adult bone marrow. The survival rate, 12 of 25 patients, was greater than would be expected with a bone-marrow transplant.

Many people die each year while waiting for a bone marrow transplant, due in part to the difficulty in finding a compatible bone marrow donor. Donors are located for less than 40 percent of patients, and this figure is even smaller for minorities. But because a perfect donor-patient match is not necessary, blood transfusion from placental and umbilical cord blood could be used far more widely, providing a life-saving option for many. Blood from umbilical cords and placentas had long been routinely discarded after a baby is born. But the potential benefit to bone marrow transplant patients led to calls in 1997 for this blood to be frozen and stored for that purpose.

Painless laser for dentistry. A laser "drill" that can be used on teeth without the need for anesthesia received approval from the United States Food and Drug Administration (FDA) in May 1997. In tests, the laser caused virtually no pain because it vaporized decayed tooth tissue without the pressure and vibration generated by an ordinary dental drill. It also eliminated the upsetting noise associated with drilling teeth.

Laser drills were first tested on teeth in the early 1990's. However, those early devices generated excessive heat, which damaged teeth. The manufacturer of the new laser, Premier Laser Systems Incorporated of Irvine, California, said the new laser uses wavelengths of light that enable it to cut teeth without significantly raising temperatures. Tests were conducted on more than 1,300 teeth. Only three patients requested local anesthetic, Premier spokespeople said. But the FDA cautioned that some patients did report mild discomfort from the laser drill. The FDA also prohibited the use of the dental laser on children until further testing could be done and required dentists and dental assistants to wear protective goggles while using the laser.

Understanding SIDS. Although sudden infant death syndrome (SIDS) remained the leading cause of death in infants in 1996 and 1997, its incidence was declining. A large two-year study by researchers in the United Kingdom published in July 1996 confirmed earlier findings that parental smoking increases the risk of SIDS. They noted that almost two-thirds of SIDS deaths could be avoided if parents did not smoke during pregnancy and after the baby's birth. For parents who cannot quit smoking, the researchers recommended keeping the baby in a "smoke-free zone."

The investigators also questioned the practice of putting babies to sleep on their sides. The study found that, compared with babies who slept on their backs, those who slept on their sides had twice the risk of dying from SIDS. The researchers also noted that side-sleeping infants can roll over onto the their stom-

A different approach to heart surgery

A new heart surgery technique gaining favor in 1997 enabled surgeons to avoid making a large incision in the chest to gain access to the heart, *top*. Instead, several small cuts are made in the torso, *bottom,* through which small surgical instruments and fiberoptic cameras are inserted.

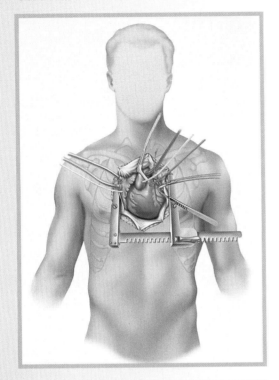

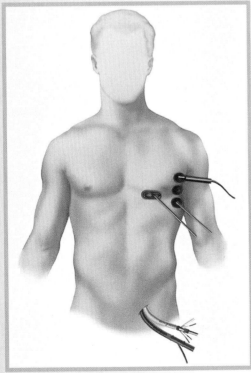

achs during the night. Sleeping on the stomach has been found to increase the risk of SIDS ninefold.

Surgery through a keyhole. A new surgical technique that could become an alternative to the traditional open-heart method of coronary artery bypass surgery was becoming more widely used in 1997. In the procedure, known as "minimally invasive coronary artery bypass surgery" or simply "keyhole surgery," a surgeon uses special instruments to perform the operation through several small openings in the torso. A fiberoptic camera and video monitor enable the surgeon to see inside the body.

About 400,000 open-heart bypass operations are performed in the United States each year. In the conventional technique, the patient's breastbone is sawed open and the ribcage is spread apart. While the surgeon grafts new veins to carry blood around blocked or narrowed arteries, the heart is stopped and the patient is kept alive with a heart-lung machine. By eliminating the need for such a large, severe opening in the chest, the new procedure requires a much shorter recovery period than the traditional operation and also results in fewer postoperative complications.

In a study of 103 patients at Allegheny University of the Health Sciences in Pittsburgh, first reported in November 1996, patients who underwent the new procedure experienced fewer complications, including a decreased loss of blood, than those receiving the traditional operation. This group also spent less time in the hospital (an average of 3.3 days versus 7.8 days), and had 40 percent less in-hospital charges. In a separate study conducted at the Dresden Cardiovascular Institute in Germany and reported in March 1997, patients who had minimally invasive surgery spent only one day in the intensive care unit and returned home three to four days earlier than those who underwent the conventional operation.

In December 1996, the first use of the keyhole procedure to correct blockages in three coronary vessels was completed at New York University Medical Center. However, because the new technique was designed primarily to correct blockages in just one or two arteries that were relatively easy to reach, it was not con-

Science News Update **243**

AIDS Drugs Offer Hope

A growing number of scientists and researchers expressed optimism in 1997 that the tide had finally turned in the fight against AIDS. The main cause of their optimism was the newest generation of AIDS-fighting drugs, called protease inhibitors.

The new drugs block production of an enzyme called a protease, which HIV (the human immunodeficiency virus) needs to *replicate* (produce copies of) itself. When the virus is unable to reproduce, it cannot multiply in the body to cause its usual devastating effects. Nor can it *mutate* (genetically change) into a strain that resists drug therapy.

For years, the only drug available for the treatment of AIDS patients was zidovudine, also called AZT. This drug decreases the amount of the virus in the bloodstream. However, HIV can develop a resistance to AZT, so the drug often has a short-lived effect.

Protease inhibitors made their debut in Decem-

Protease inhibitors have been successful in fighting AIDS in many patients, but the drugs can be costly, and patients must take as many as 20 pills a day.

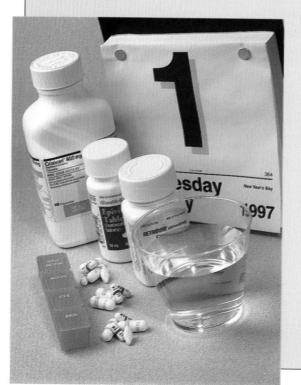

ber 1995, when saquinavir, sold under the trade name Invirase, became the first of the drugs to receive approval from the United States Food and Drug Administration (FDA). In March 1996, other protease inhibitors—ritonavir, marketed under the name Norvir, and indinavir, sold under the name Crixivan—were approved by the FDA.

Protease inhibitors proved to be most effective when combined into a "cocktail" with one or more other antiviral compounds, such as AZT or a drug called 3TC. These drug combinations attack the HIV virus from multiple directions, leaving it no room for escape or retreat.

In July 1996, an international panel of scientists issued a report on protease inhibitors. The researchers announced that in clinical trials, protease inhibitor drug combinations had reduced blood levels of HIV to undetectable levels in up to 85 percent of patients. The drugs were so effective in cutting down the virus, the panel said, that it is possible the treatment might permanently halt the progression of the disease in patients who respond to the drugs.

Other studies also confirmed the effectiveness of protease inhibitors. One such study was reported in July 1996 at the 11th International Conference on AIDS in Vancouver, British Columbia, by researchers from the Aaron Diamond AIDS Research Center in New York City. The lead investigator, Martin Markowitz, said his team gave a triple-drug cocktail (ritonavir, AZT, 3TC) to a small number of patients newly infected with HIV. The medications turned nine patients *aviremic* (free of detectable virus) for up to 300 days. "We simply cannot find evidence of viral replication," Markowitz said. "Active viral replication has been turned off."

In a New York University study reported at a Washington, D.C., conference in January 1996, researchers administered a three-drug cocktail—indinavir, AZT, and 3TC—to 26 HIV-infected patients. Six months later, no HIV could be detected in the blood of 24 of the patients.

The study compared a group of patients taking only indinavir to two other groups—one were taking a combination of AZT and 3TC, and a third group that took all three drugs. "This is the best response of any antiretroviral therapy that has been seen to date," said Roy Gulick, one of the study's researchers.

The apparent success of the drug cocktail was celebrated in February 1997, when the U.S. Centers for Disease Control and Prevention (CDC) in Atlanta, Georgia, reported that AIDS deaths in the United States were declining. The CDC said that 13 percent fewer Americans with AIDS died from the disease in the first half of 1996 than during the same period in 1995. According to the CDC, about 22,000 AIDS deaths were reported in the first six months of 1996, compared with 24,900 deaths one year earlier. The CDC said this was the first decline in the death toll from AIDS since the disease emerged in the early 1980's.

Although many scientists credited protease inhibitors with the decline in AIDS-related deaths, other experts claimed that it was also due to the growing availability of health care for people afflicted with AIDS and the impact of prevention campaigns. All health officials, however, agreed that the declining death rate did not mean the end of AIDS.

Some AIDS patients, for example, did not respond to the new generation of drugs. This was especially true of individuals in the late stages of the disease who had previously taken AZT, according to researchers. Clinical studies showed that protease inhibitors were most successful when taken during the early stages of an AIDS infection. According to David D. Ho, director of the Diamond AIDS Research Center, the drugs were most effective with patients whose brains were not yet infected with HIV. But for such patients, at least, protease inhibitors offered the hope that AIDS could be treated as a chronic, manageable illness, like diabetes.

Nonetheless, doctors expressed some doubts about the long-term effectiveness of the drugs. For example, although studies had shown that the combination drug therapy reduced HIV to undetectable levels in many patients, doctors feared that a small reservoir of the virus might manage to dodge the drugs and survive to re-infect the body at a later date.

Doctors also worried about the side effects of protease inhibitors. Some patients taking the drugs have experienced nausea, diarrhea, fatigue, kidney stones, liver damage, and cramping. The cost of the drug therapy was another cause for concern. One year's treatment with protease inhibitors can cost as much as $20,000, making the drugs too expensive for the uninsured or the poor.

Researchers also warned that the drugs may not be effective unless patients follow a strict regimen, taking 20 or more pills daily at specified times. Some of the pills must be taken with food, and some must be taken on an empty stomach. Patients who do not follow directions risk developing a drug-resistant strain of the virus, which would pose even more dangers.

Researchers agreed that long-term studies were needed before protease inhibitors could be considered the drugs that at last turned AIDS into a manageable illness. Regardless of that word of caution, however, both patients and the medical community embraced the drugs as the best hope yet in fighting AIDS.   [Richard Trubo]

sidered appropriate for more complicated cases. In November 1996, the American Heart Association issued an advisory report on minimally invasive heart surgery, urging caution toward the rapid acceptance of the technique.

New heart-failure treatment. A series of studies published in December 1996 showed that congestive heart failure (CHF) could be considered at least partially reversible with the use of a new drug, carvedilol. In patients suffering from CHF, the heart's pumping action becomes less effective, often because the tissue has been weakened by disease and cannot contract strongly enough to efficiently propel blood through the body. CHF is a major killer of older people.

One major study of the effects of carvedilol on CHF involved 345 patients with mild to moderate, chronic CHF. These subjects received one of three dosages of carvedilol or a *placebo* (inactive substance). After six months, those receiving carvedilol showed improvement in the efficiency of their heart function, with the greatest improvements seen in those taking the highest doses. The drug also improved patient survival over the study period, with a mortality rate of just 1.1 percent in those on the highest dose of carvedilol, compared to 15.5 percent in the placebo group. Use of the medication decreased hospitalization rates by 58 to 64 percent.

Heart reduction surgery. An unusual and dramatic surgical approach to treating CHF caused by an enlarged heart made headlines in 1996 and 1997. The new procedure had the potential to revolutionize care for patients who otherwise would require a heart transplant. The technique, developed by Brazilian surgeon Randas Batista, involves cutting a wedge of heart muscle—about the size of a small slice of pie—out of the left ventricle, the heart's primary pumping chamber. The remainder of the heart is then sewn together, resulting in a smaller organ that is able to pump blood more efficiently.

The new procedure, frequently called left ventricular remodeling surgery, was performed at a number of medical centers in the United States with promising results. In findings presented at the American College of Cardiology meeting in March 1997, investigators from the Cleveland Clinic reported that, of the first 47 patients to undergo the operation at that facility, the heart's pumping efficiency increased from an average of 15 percent before the surgery to 34 percent afterward. There were also dramatic improvements in patients' quality of life after recovery, including greater energy and easier breathing.

One of the early concerns about the Batista procedure had been initial reports of a high death rate among patients—20 percent within the first month after surgery. However, in operations by the Cleveland Clinic team, only 3 of the first 47 patients died—none during the surgery itself. Furthermore, the six-month survival rate was comparable to that of heart-transplant patients.

Unraveling mad cow disease. In October 1996, researchers at Imperial College School of Medicine at St. Mary's in London reported that they had uncovered the first persuasive evidence that bovine spongiform encephalopathy (BSE), a degenerative brain disease popularly known as mad cow disease, could be transmitted from cattle to other mammals. The study may have established the first link between BSE and similar degenerative brain diseases in other mammals, including scrapie in sheep and Creutzfeldt-Jakob disease (CJD) in humans.

The Imperial College researchers isolated abnormal proteins, called prions, from the brain tissue of 10 human patients who had died from what appeared to be unusual cases of CJD—in each case, the pattern of brain damage was different from the pattern usually found in CJD cases. The researchers then compared these prions to ones taken from the BSE-infected brain tissue of cattle, mice, cats, and monkeys and examined the chemical structure of the proteins. The results revealed a strong resemblance between the two groups of prions. However, many experts argued that more conclusive evidence was needed to prove that the variant form of CJD was in fact a human form of BSE infection.

[Richard Trubo]

In the Special Reports section, see ROGUE PROTEINS.

Nobel Prizes

The discoveries of a new form of the element carbon, superfluidity in helium-3, and how the immune system recognizes virus-infected cells were the achievements in chemistry, physics, and physiology or medicine awarded Nobel Prizes in 1996.

The Nobel Prize for chemistry was shared by Richard Smalley and Robert F. Curl, Jr., of Rice University in Houston, and Harold W. Kroto of the University of Sussex in England. In 1985, Smalley, Curl, and Kroto found a new form of carbon—the fullerene. The chemists discovered fullerenes in a substance created when graphite was vaporized with a laser beam in an atmosphere of helium. Fullerenes are large, hollow molecules made up of even numbers of interlocking carbon atoms arranged in closed shells. They can be ball-shaped or form long tubes that are closed at the ends.

While fullerenes consisting of hundreds of atoms have been formed, the original fullerene consists of 60 atoms arranged in a sphere that looks like a soccer ball. It was given the name buckminsterfullerene because its structure matched that of a *geodesic dome* (a dome without interior support made entirely of triangular segments) invented by the American engineer Buckminster Fuller. Buckyballs, as buckminsterfullerenes are commonly called, have graduated since their discovery from being regarded as a scientific oddity to providing the foundation for a new branch of chemistry. Their study may lead to the development of superstrong fibers or materials with unusual electrical or optical qualities.

The prize for physics was awarded to David M. Lee and Robert C. Richardson of Cornell University in Ithaca, New York, and Douglas D. Osheroff of Stanford University in Palo Alto, California. They were honored for their 1972 discovery of superfluidity in an *isotope* (variant form) of helium called helium-3. Lee, Richardson, and Osheroff proved that the helium isotope helium-3, a liquid, becomes superfluid when its temperature is lowered to two thousandths of a degree above absolute zero (−273.15 °C [−459.67 °F]).

When a liquid becomes superfluid, its

Nobel Prize winners in chemistry
University of Sussex chemist Harold W. Kroto, *below,* holds a model of a fullerene, a type of carbon molecule consisting of many interlocking atoms. Kroto and Rice University researchers Richard Smalley and Robert Curl, *bottom,* right and left, were awarded the 1996 Nobel Prize in chemistry for their 1985 discovery of fullerenes.

atoms move in a coordinated, rather than a random, manner, which eliminates friction. Superfluids exhibit properties—for example, flowing up as well as down—that cannot be explained within the limits of classical physics. Such properties, however, can be explained by *quantum mechanics*, which is the branch of physics dealing with the behavior of atoms and subatomic particles. Superfluid helium-3 has properties that exhibit quantum effects ordinarily observed only in molecules, atoms, or subatomic particles. These effects offer scientists the opportunity to directly observe the world of quantum mechanics, which physicists believe may ultimately provide insights into the mysteries of the universe.

The prize for physiology or medicine was shared by Australian-born Peter C. Doherty of St. Jude's Children's Research Hospital in Memphis, Tennessee, and Rolf M. Zinkernagel of the Institute of Experimental Immunology in Zurich, Switzerland. The two scientists were honored for discovering how the immune system recognizes cells infected with a virus. Doherty and Zinkernagel made their discovery while collaborating in the early 1970's at the John Curtin School of Medical Research in Canberra, Australia. Studying how mice respond to viruses, Doherty and Zinkernagel found that white blood cells, which detect and destroy infected cells, locate their targets with the aid of two proteins. The first protein, found on the surface of every body cell, is unique to each individual and helps the immune system distinguish between the body's own cells and an invading virus. The second protein is a fragment of an invading virus displayed on the surface of each infected cell.

The discovery proved to be of great importance to clinical medicine. Understanding how the immune system recognizes cells infected with a virus has been instrumental in efforts both to strengthen the immune response to invading microorganisms and certain forms of cancer and to diminish autoimmune reactions to inflammatory diseases, such as diabetes and multiple sclerosis.

[Scott Thomas]

Nutrition

The long-standing search for a cure for the common cold made headlines in 1996. A study published in July suggested that the mineral zinc, which is an essential trace nutrient, is effective in battling cold symptoms. Several studies of zinc's effect on the common cold had been conducted in the past but had yielded conflicting results.

The latest study, conducted by researchers at the Cleveland Clinic in Ohio, involved 100 subjects who reported having experienced symptoms of a cold for 24 hours or less. The subjects were randomly divided into two groups. One group received lozenges containing zinc, while the other received *placebo* lozenges—ones containing no zinc at all. The subjects were instructed to dissolve one lozenge in their mouth every two hours during periods of wakefulness for as long as they had cold symptoms. They were also asked to keep a daily log, documenting the severity of various symptoms. The patients were instructed to return to the clinic within one day after their cold symptoms had disappeared.

By the end of the 18-day study, all but eight of the subjects reported that their cold had disappeared. The median time for the disappearance of cold symptoms was 7.6 days in the placebo group and 4.4 days in the zinc-treated group, indicating that zinc is indeed effective in fighting a cold.

Nonetheless, the results were of limited value because the researchers collected no evidence to confirm the diagnosis of a cold and took no physical samples to confirm that the subjects had taken the lozenges as directed. The study was further limited because it did not look for a possible beneficial effect of zinc on the performance of the immune system, which might have explained why zinc was effective. Therefore, more studies would be needed before zinc could be considered a proven cold remedy.

Diet and diabetes. Doctors have long theorized that a diet high in certain types of carbohydrates might be linked to an increased risk of diabetes, apart from other risk factors like age, obesity, exercise, and family history. In February 1997, researchers at the Harvard School

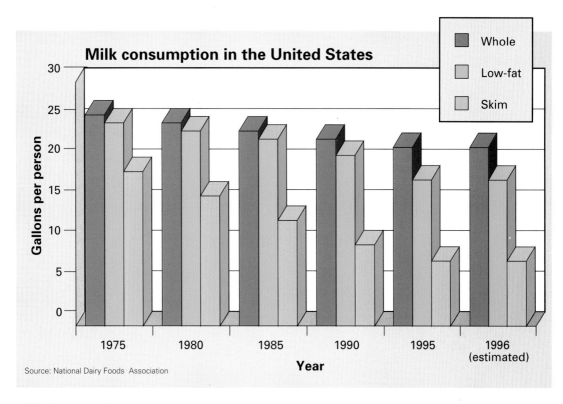

Milk consumption in the United States

Legend: Whole, Low-fat, Skim

Y-axis: Gallons per person (0, 5, 10, 15, 20, 25, 30)

X-axis: Year — 1975, 1980, 1985, 1990, 1995, 1996 (estimated)

Source: National Dairy Foods Association

Milk industry analysts reported in 1996 that the 20-year decline in milk consumption in the United States may be leveling off. Studies had shown that many American adults were drinking less milk because of concerns over its fat and cholesterol content. In 1996, the average American drank just one glass of milk per day.

of Public Health in Boston published the results of a six-year study of this issue. Their findings showed that women who ate a diet high in easily digested and absorbed carbohydrates and low in cereal fiber had more than twice the risk of developing noninsulin-dependent diabetes mellitus (NIDDM), also known as Type II diabetes.

Diabetes is a disorder of *glucose* (blood sugar) regulation caused by insufficient or ineffective insulin in the blood. Insulin is a hormone, secreted in the pancreas, that helps cells absorb glucose. When insulin is in short supply or is not functioning properly, cells have trouble absorbing glucose from the bloodstream, which causes the glucose level in the blood to rise. When that happens, the pancreas secretes more insulin into the bloodstream. High blood sugar levels may cause the pancreas to secrete abnormally large amounts of insulin. Over time, this process can cause the body to become less sensitive to insulin, which means that the hormone loses its effectiveness. NIDDM is characterized by a decrease in the effectiveness

of insulin and the inability of the pancreas to keep up with the body's increased demand for insulin.

In 1986, the researchers began a study of 65,000 American women aged 40 to 65. All were found to be free of cardiovascular disease, cancer, and diabetes. The women completed a detailed questionnaire about the foods they ate, including the types and amounts of carbohydrates. In the six years following the collection of the data, 915 of the women developed NIDDM.

Carbohydrates in food are composed of single-sugar units, known as *simple carbohydrates*, or multiple-sugar units, known as *complex carbohydrates*. Some complex carbohydrates, such as starches found in bread and potatoes, are easily broken down by the digestive system and absorbed into the bloodstream. As sugars from digested food enter the bloodstream, the level of blood glucose rises, causing the pancreas to secrete more insulin.

Other complex carbohydrates, known as fiber, cannot be broken down by the body. Since fiber cannot be digested, eating foods that are rich in fiber will not cause a person's blood glucose level to increase.

In the study, women who said they ate more of the easily digestible carbohydrates and less dietary fiber were 2½ times more likely to develop diabetes as those who ate fewer starchy foods and more fiber, especially fiber from cereal grains. The authors of the study recommended eating more grains that have been minimally refined, and thus have a higher fiber content, in order to reduce the risk of developing diabetes.

Chromium for a better body? The mineral chromium is an essential trace nutrient that helps the body use food, although how it performs this function is unknown. Some studies have suggested that chromium, together with an exercise program involving weights, also promotes the increase of muscle mass and strength and reduces body fat. However, attempts to prove this effect of chromium in the past have yielded conflicting results. In June 1996, researchers at the U.S. Department of Agriculture Grand Forks Human Nutri-

tion Center in Grand Forks, North Dakota, published the results of a study that may help resolve the debate.

In the study, 36 men aged 19 to 29 who were not actively involved in physical training were grouped by physique, amount of body fat, and blood chromium concentration into three groups of 12 men each. Two groups received capsules containing different chemical forms of chromium, and the third group received a placebo. All took the capsules daily for an 8-week period, and all performed weight training exercises five days a week for 60 minutes during the same period.

After eight weeks, all of the subjects showed an increase in their overall fat-free body mass. The men also increased their muscle mass and strength and reduced their body fat. Because similar effects were achieved by all of the subjects, regardless of whether they had received chromium or a placebo, the researchers concluded that chromium supplementation had no beneficial effect in reducing body fat or increasing strength or muscle mass.   [Phylis B. Moser-Veillon]

Oceanography

Scientists in early 1997 conducted an unsuccessful six-week search for a living example of a giant squid. The search—in the South Pacific Ocean at Kaikoura Canyon, located off of New Zealand's South Island—was aimed at learning more about this elusive creature, considered one of the last mysteries of the sea.

Scientists believe the giant squid may live very near the bottom of the ocean. No one has seen a living giant squid. Dead squids, however, have been found in fishing nets or have been washed up on shore. One such squid was over 18 meters (60 feet) long.

The researchers participating in the 1997 squid hunt, led by marine zoologist Clyde Roper of the Smithsonian Institution's Museum of Natural History in Washington, D.C., used a computer-controlled *submersible* (underwater research vessel) about the size of a dolphin to explore the underwater canyon, which is about 1,000 meters (3,300 feet) deep. The submersible cruised at depths of 200 to 750 meters (660 to 2,500 feet) while a video camera recorded the view. The scientists also used a "rope cam"—

video cameras and lights tethered by a line to a surface buoy—to obtain images from depths as great as 800 meters (2,600 feet). The camera was programmed to activate every 15 minutes for two or three minutes. The scientists used liquefied fish as bait to attract giant squids and other deep-sea animals.

The scientists also tried another unsucessful technique to photograph a giant squid. Because the area is home to many sperm whales, the scientists waited for one to surface for air and then fastened a video camera to its back, hoping it might dive deep enough to encounter a squid. The camera was attached with a suction-cup device 30 centimeters (12 inches) in diameter, which was designed to detach within a few hours and allow the camera to float to the surface.

The scientists had a reasonable expectation of success, because sperm whales are predators of giant squids. Partially digested squids have been found inside the stomachs of sperm whales, and sucker marks on the skin of sperm whales indicated they have engaged in underwater battles with giant squids. However,

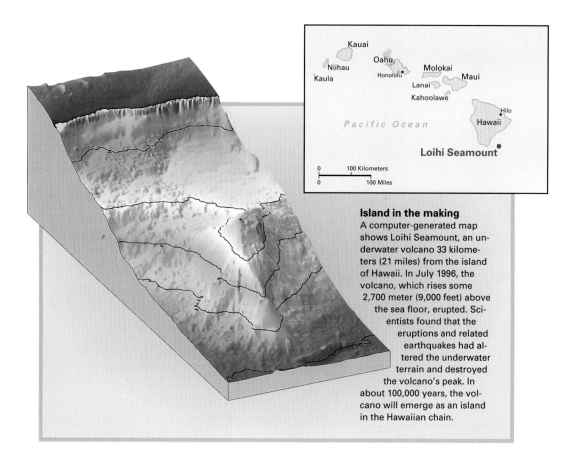

Island in the making
A computer-generated map shows Loihi Seamount, an underwater volcano 33 kilometers (21 miles) from the island of Hawaii. In July 1996, the volcano, which rises some 2,700 meter (9,000 feet) above the sea floor, erupted. Scientists found that the eruptions and related earthquakes had altered the underwater terrain and destroyed the volcano's peak. In about 100,000 years, the volcano will emerge as an island in the Hawaiian chain.

the camera floated off the whale shortly after it was attached.

Although the search did not capture a giant squid on film, it obtained new information about the marine life in Kaikoura Canyon. The scientists planned to use a manned submersible to search the canyon again for giant squids by 1999.

Asteroid evidence. In February 1997, an international team of marine geologists reported the strongest evidence yet that a crater 300 kilometers (185 miles) wide discovered in the 1980's on Mexico's Yucatán Peninsula was formed 65 million years ago by an asteroid impact. The debris tossed skyward by the crash would have darkened the skies worldwide for at least six months, according to scientists. The impact is thought to have caused the extinction of many species, including the dinosaurs.

Scientists led by Richard Norris of the Woods Hole Oceanographic Institution in Woods Hole, Massachusetts, found evidence of the catastrophic event in sediment cores from the Atlantic Ocean floor 480 kilometers (300 miles) off the northeast coast of Florida. The re-

searchers decided to gather samples in this area—1,600 kilometers (1,000 miles) from the crater—after concluding that a gigantic asteroid impact would have produced huge waves on the ocean surface, scouring bottom sediments throughout the Gulf of Mexico. Once in the Atlantic, the debris carried by the currents and winds would have settled to the sea floor. The scientists believed that they would uncover the region's geological history by studying layers of sediment off the Florida coast.

Norris and his team lowered a hollow drill through more than 2,500 meters (8,200 feet) of water and through as much as 750 meters (2,450 feet) of sea floor to collect the sediment. They extracted three cores—each about 1.5 meters (5 feet) long—containing materials from the time of the impact. The material was found in a muddy layer deposited at the time of the mass extinctions. Norris said this layer provided added proof of the asteroid impact. Sediments recovered at other locations from the same geological period have been found to contain traces of iridium, a metallic chemical element that is a telltale mark of extraterrestrial debris, but the findings off of the Florida coast were the first to clearly show a timeline of events.

The various rock layers immediately above and below the asteroid layer depict the violent impact in detail, with all three sample cores revealing the same chain of events. In the deepest and oldest layers, the fossil record shows an oceanic world teeming with life, mainly microscopic *plankton* (plants and animals that drift with the ocean currents). The next layer contains a band of tiny, glassy green pebbles thought to be molten rubble from the impact. On top of that is a thin, rust-colored layer about 2 millimeters (0.08 inch) thick—the apparent remains of the vaporized asteroid—topped by four inches of clay that is devoid of all signs of life. Norris said this lifeless period lasted about 5,000 years. The layer above the gray clay shows a reemergence of life in the area. This defines the beginning of the Cenozoic Era, the era in which we live today.

Ocean temperature study delayed. A four-year, $40-million underwater sound experiment, known as Acoustic Thermometry of Ocean Climate (ATOC), was delayed in March 1997 after an underwater cable was severed. The cable, located in 900 meters (2,950 feet) of water, may have been damaged by a fishing trawler or shark bite. Researchers said that the system, which measures the speed at which sound travels through the water, would not be operational again until late summer or fall 1997.

ATOC had been collecting data since it was activated in December 1995. The results show the feasibility of using measurements of underwater sound speeds to detect climate changes, said ATOC's chief scientist, Peter Worcester of the Scripps Institution of Oceanography in San Diego.

ATOC has a single sound source located 1,000 meters (3,300 feet) below the sea surface atop Pioneer Seamount, 30 miles (50 kilometers) west of northern California's Half Moon Bay. The ATOC transmitter broadcasts encoded sound signals across the North Pacific to an array of Navy listening posts shared with the scientific community.

In the ocean, the speed of sound varies with the depth of the water. Sound moves faster at greater depths because warm water transmits sound waves better than cold water. Sound also moves faster at greater depths, because sound speed increases with increasing pressure.

However, at a middle layer, about 900 meters (2,950 feet) deep, sound travels slowly. Because of that, sound emitted at middepth is confined between the shallow and deeper depths. Oceanographers call this channel the Sound Fixing and Ranging (SOFAR) channel because low-frequency waves travel long distances along it. Small changes in sound speed within the SOFAR channel are due mainly to changes in water temperature. By measuring the time it takes for sound pulses to travel from the transmitter to a receiver, ATOC scientists can monitor changes in the ocean's temperature along the sound wave's path and thereby learn about climate change.

Researchers were planning to install a second sound source in the sea near Kauai, Hawaii, during the summer of 1997. With multiple sound sources and crossing sound paths, ATOC scientists thought they would be able to monitor water temperatures over much of the northern half of the Pacific Ocean. Over time, the acoustic travel times could detail how changes in ocean temperature influence global climate. Knowing whether ocean temperatures are rising or falling over time would enhance the accuracy of computer models designed to predict climate change. Oceanographers said it would take until at least the year 2005, however, to gather sufficient data to draw any conclusions.

Some critics doubted whether ATOC could really detect changes in ocean temperature. Others opposed ATOC because they were concerned that the broadcast sounds might injure marine mammals, especially large baleen whales whose ears are tuned to hear ATOC's low-frequency sounds. However, data collected by ATOC's Marine Mammal Research Program provided evidence that the transmissions have had little effect on the healthy marine mammal population. Biologists conduct surveys in the vicinity of Pioneer Seamount both when the sound source is on and when it is off. They have found only a slight preference for animals to avoid the source during a transmission.

[Christina S. Johnson]

Lasers (beams of *photons*, or particles of light) are widely used for a variety of purposes, ranging from surgical procedures to the playing of compact discs. In 1996 a beam of sodium atoms that acted like a laser was created in a laboratory. Also in 1996, tiny structures made of carbon atoms were used to improve the world's best microscopes. United States physicists interested in subatomic particles learned they would have access to an advanced research facility in Europe, and the U.S. government announced plans to keep the American stockpile of nuclear weapons reliable and safe.

"Atomic laser." In January 1997, a team of physicists headed by Wolfgang Ketterle of the Massachusetts Institute of Technology (MIT) in Cambridge, Massachusetts, reported that it had developed an "atomic laser." Instead of emitting a beam of photons like an ordinary laser, the "atomic laser" produces a beam made up of sodium atoms.

The MIT team essentially produced a working demonstration of a theory that the German-Swiss physicist Albert Einstein developed in 1924, following up on ideas proposed by the Indian physicist Satyendranath Bose. This theory predicted the existence of an unusual state of matter that came to be called a Bose-Einstein condensate, or BEC.

To understand what a BEC is, it helps to know some of the basics of *quantum theory*, the branch of physics dealing with the behavior of atoms and subatomic particles. Part of quantum theory states that although atoms are physical objects, they also behave as waves. Each atom is a moving particle with a corresponding wave that carries energy in a series of crests and troughs. In a BEC, millions of atoms are confined in an extremely small area at temperatures near absolute zero, the lowest temperature possible—about –273 °C (–460 °F).

These extreme conditions cause the atoms to virtually stop moving. In addition, the waves of the individual atoms, though normally out of step with one another, all get in the same phase—that is, the crests and troughs of all the waves match up. When that occurs, the many waves merge into one wave, a property called *coherence*.

Buckyballs, molecules made up of 60 interlocking carbon atoms, lie in steps cut into a microscopic piece of copper. In November 1996, scientists at an International Business Machines Corporation laboratory in Zurich, Switzerland, announced that they had made this arrangement of buckyballs, which functions like an abacus, a device in which beads are moved along wires to perform arithmetic calculations. The researchers used an instrument called a scanning probe microscope to push the buckyballs off to the sides and create a diagonal furrow. Though this research was experimental, it may eventually lead to improved data-storage devices.

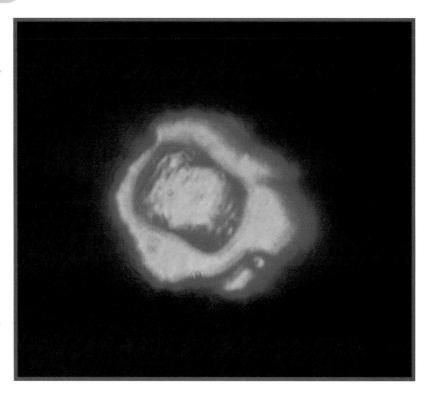

A square crystal of solid hydrogen is surrounded by a mass of liquid helium in the first X ray ever taken of solid hydrogen. In research reported in October 1996, a team of scientists at the Carnegie Institution of Washington (D.C.) and the University of Paris made this X ray after increasing the pressure on gaseous helium and gaseous hydrogen until the helium became liquid and the hydrogen solidified into a crystal. Although scientists had previously obtained indirect evidence that hydrogen becomes crystalline at high pressures, the X ray provided the first direct evidence of this altered state.

BEC's were first created in 1995 by three teams of researchers, including Ketterle's group at MIT. However, none of these teams was able to demonstrate that its BEC acted as a single wave—that is, until the MIT group succeeded in doing so in 1996.

The MIT researchers used sodium atoms to make their BEC because these atoms have metallic properties that enable them to be captured in *magnetic traps,* regions of confinement consisting of overlapping magnetic fields. The scientists created the BEC by confining a dense cloud of sodium atoms in a tiny magnetic trap within a vacuum and cooling the atoms to near absolute zero. They then focused a conventional laser on the center of the magnetic trap. The laser repelled the atoms in its path to each side, splitting the BEC into two BEC's. Lastly, the researchers turned off the magnets generating the magnetic trap, allowing the atoms—responding to gravity—to fall through the vacuum. As the atom clouds from the two BEC's fell, they overlapped each other and were photographed.

The photograph revealed a classic *interference pattern*—alternating dark and light bands—identical to the one produced when two beams of a photon laser, split from passing through two tiny slits, overlap each other. Each half of a split laser beam acts as a single wave, just as each atom cloud of a split BEC did. The interference pattern of alternating dark and light bands indicated that two waves were overlapping each other, with their crests and troughs alternatingly reinforcing and canceling each other.

When the researchers saw this pattern, they knew that each of their BEC's had indeed become a single wave, just like a regular laser beam. They had demonstrated the existence of an "atomic laser." However, unlike a standard laser, which can produce *amplification* of a wave—an increase in the wave's energy—by continuously producing more photons, an "atomic laser" cannot produce amplification because the number of atoms in a BEC stays constant.

The MIT research was considered unlikely to have immediate industrial applications, because the required low temperature and high vacuum would be difficult and expensive to maintain. However, one possible dividend might be in improving the atomic clocks that are currently the world standard for accuracy. These clocks employ ordinary incoherent beams of atoms, and the random motions of atoms within these beams limit the clocks' accuracy. A beam of coherent atoms would permit far more precise timekeeping.

Better microscopes. Among the most promising tools in nanotechnology, a growing field concerned with the creation of objects nearly the size of atoms, are *nanotubes,* tiny cylinders made up of molecules called buckminsterfullerenes, or buckyballs. A buckyball is a spherical arrangement of 60 carbon atoms in alternating pentagons and hexagons, similar to the panels of a soccer ball. Nanotubes are 100 times stronger than steel, yet it would take 50,000 of them laid side by side to equal the width of a human hair. In November 1996, a team of physicists at Rice University in Houston reported a new use for nanotubes— making the world's best microscopes even better. The team was led by Richard Smalley, one of the scientists who discovered buckyballs in 1985.

The world's most powerful microscopes are scanning probe microscopes, which can provide three-dimensional images of individual atoms. They are important research tools in physics, engineering, and chemistry, and they can be used to construct microscopic components of such small devices as computer chips. The key to their operation is a tiny, sharp point, called a probe, that can be maneuvered above the surface of a specimen. By monitoring the strength of an electric current or force that passes between the probe's tip and the specimen's surface, a computer keeps the probe at a constant distance—usually just a few times the diameter of an atom—above the surface. The computer then constructs a contour map of the specimen based on the movement of the probe. To build microscopic structures, a probe can be made to move atoms about on a surface.

The Houston scientists reasoned that nanotubes would make good probes for scanning probe microscopes because they are good conductors of electricity

and are stronger and thinner than conventional probes, which are cone-shaped crystals of silicon and other materials. By manipulating nanotubes and conventional probes under an optical, or light, microscope, the scientists were able to attach the nanotubes to the probes with a type of resin, or glue. After gluing the nanotubes in place, the scientists tested the ability of the nanotube probes to study specimens. The nanotubes were able to reach down into crevices that were too narrow for conventional probes. They also bent rather than broke when they were made to hit the specimens. Conventional probes rarely survive such "tip crashes," which accidentally happen from time to time.

The results of this study indicated that nanotube probes would be able to make more precise contour maps of specimens, study rougher surfaces, and last longer than conventional probes. The study also raised expectations that nanotubes would enhance the role played by scanning probe microscopes in nanotechnology.

Accelerator project accelerated. *Particle accelerators,* machines that boost electrically charged atoms and subatomic particles to extremely high speeds, are probably the most important tools in particle physics, the branch of physics that studies the behavior and properties of elementary particles. Particle accelerators have enabled scientists to learn much about subatomic particles and the forces that govern them and to create bizarre particles that previously existed only in theory. In December 1996, the governing council of CERN, the world's largest research center for particle physics, announced that construction of the world's most powerful accelerator, the Large Hadron Collider, or LHC, would be completed three years ahead of schedule, in 2005. The LHC was to be built on the border between Switzerland and France. CERN is located near Geneva, Switzerland, and is supported by 19 European countries.

The reason for the speeded-up schedule was that the United States, Japan, Russia, India, and Canada had agreed to make substantial financial contributions to the LHC. According to the agreement signed with CERN, the United States would contribute a total of $530 million to the project. The bulk of the money would be "payment in kind"—construction in the United States of accelerator components. Japan, Russia, India, and Canada together pledged nearly $170 million to the LHC, which had a total price tag of more than $5 billion.

The agreement did not make the United States a member of CERN. Membership would have required a far larger financial contribution than did commitment to the LHC. As of May 1997, the United States Congress had not yet appropriated funds for the project, but the funding was expected to be approved, because leaders from both political parties favored the project.

The agreement was great news for U.S. physicists, who were still recovering from the 1993 cancellation of the Superconducting Super Collider, or SSC, an even more powerful accelerator that was to be built in Texas. Congress canceled the SSC to reduce the federal budget deficit, plunging the future of particle physics in the United States into uncertainty. Though existing particle-physics facilities in the United States were being upgraded, none of them could compare with new facilities being planned by other nations. U.S. physicists feared being shut out of the forefront of research, where they had been since the end of World War II (1939-1945). Participation in the LHC was expected to help American physicists remain an important force in particle-physics research.

The LHC was to be built in an existing circular tunnel 27 kilometers (17 miles) in circumference. The tunnel had housed another accelerator, the Large Electron-Positron, or LEP, ring, which was to be taken out of service to make way for the LHC. Plans called for the LHC to produce two beams of protons—each beam with an energy of 7 trillion electron volts—moving in opposite directions. An electron volt is approximately the amount of energy gained by an electron as it moves through a flashlight battery. In 1997, the most powerful accelerator was the Tevatron at Fermi National Accelerator Laboratory, or Fermilab, near Batavia, Illinois. It produces beams that each have an energy of 0.9 trillion electron volts.

Oscillating beads
A thin layer of tiny bronze beads erupts into a peak, *right,* and then gets depressed into a crater, *below.* In research reported in August 1996, scientists at the University of Texas in Austin found that vibrations can cause granular material, such as tiny beads, to oscillate back and forth between these two features, which they called *oscillons.* The research showed how orderly structures can result from chaotic events.

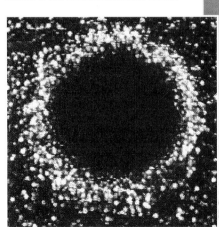

The SSC would have produced beams that each had an energy of 20 trillion electron volts.

At several points along the path of the LHC, the two proton beams will cross, producing violent, near head-on collisions. Particles created in the collisions will be studied by physicists. The highest scientific priority for the LHC will be to find the *Higgs boson,* a particle that is thought to be the source of the mass that most other particles carry. Physicists had been confident that the SSC would have had more than enough energy to produce the Higgs boson. They thought it likely that the LHC would also be able to produce it, but perhaps not in sufficient numbers to stand out from the background of other particle reactions.

Researchers also hoped to use the LHC to produce on a miniature scale the conditions that existed in the first instants after the *big bang,* the explosion of matter and energy that most astrophysicists believe created the universe. Scientists believe that at that time, subatomic particles such as protons and neutrons had not yet formed, and all matter consisted of an intensely hot "soup" of even smaller particles.

Even with the speedier construction schedule, some American physicists were still worried about maintaining the vitality of U.S. particle-physics research. All existing particle-physics facilities in the United States were scheduled to complete the bulk of their research programs by 2000. The long time commitment generally needed for particle-physics experiments was causing many young scientists to turn to other fields, and it was thought that the five-year gap between the scheduled end of existing research and the start-up of the LHC might accelerate that trend.

Virtual nukes. The Comprehensive Test Ban Treaty, signed by the United States and many other nations in September 1996, forbids all testing of nuclear weapons. Without testing, however, it is difficult to be sure if the thousands of nuclear weapons stockpiled by the United States and other nuclear powers are in working order and safe to handle. On December 19, 1996, United States Secretary of Energy Hazel O'Leary announced the adoption of a program designed to assure that the U.S. nuclear stockpile, which is to be re-duced to between 3,000 and 3,500 warheads by 2003 under the terms of the Strategic Arms Reduction Treaty, remains reliable and safe. The program was called the Stockpile Stewardship and Management Program, or SSMP.

Part of the SSMP involved simulating the operation of nuclear weapons with the aid of a new generation of supercomputers—a sort of "virtual nuclear testing" without actual testing. In early 1997, the first of three planned supercomputers began operation. This computer, an assemblage of 9,200 powerful Pentium processors of the sort used in desktop personal computers, could perform more than 1 trillion arithmetic operations per second. It was located at the Sandia National Laboratories in Albuquerque, New Mexico.

Another part of the SSMP was the National Ignition Facility, or NIF, at the Lawrence Livermore National Laboratory in California. Construction of this facility was scheduled to begin in mid-1997 and be completed in 2002. The NIF was to use clusters of high-powered lasers that would focus in unison on tiny pellets of hydrogen and other materials. The lasers would blast the pellets with enough energy to duplicate in miniature the conditions at the heart of a hydrogen bomb. Though the main purpose of these experiments would be to provide data to test the accuracy of the supercomputer simulations, scientists hoped that they would also prove useful in harnessing *nuclear fusion,* the process that releases energy in hydrogen bombs, for civilian energy production.

The SSMP was projected to cost about $4 billion per year through at least 2007. Because of the high cost, the program had a number of critics. Some opponents argued that it would be cheaper, easier, and safer to periodically remanufacture and replace entire warheads than to occasionally redesign and replace individual components of warheads, as was expected under the program. Other critics suggested that the money would be better spent on working toward eliminating all nuclear weapons from the Earth and on finding better ways to safely dispose of the enormous stockpiles of nuclear materials that were accumulating as the United States and Russia dismantled large numbers of weapons.　　[Robert H. March]

Advances in producing images of the body's nervous system are expanding scientists' ability to watch the human brain at work. In 1996, scientists at two research centers in the United States gained new insights into brain functioning in healthy people and those with psychiatric illness by using a new form of magnetic resonance imaging (MRI), called functional MRI (fMRI).

MRI has been used for several years to examine basic brain structure. An MRI unit consists mainly of a large magnet, devices for transmitting and receiving signals, and a computer. During an examination, the MRI unit surrounds the patient's body with a strong magnetic field. The machine induces changes in the energy emitted by the molecules that make up body tissues. The energy is emitted in weak electromagnetic signals, which are read by a computer and translated into an image.

Functional MRI provides an image of the brain's functioning in addition to its structure. For example, the device can detect energy changes in red blood cells in particular brain regions as a person performs specific actions or *cognitive* (thinking) tasks.

In July 1996, researchers at Yale University in New Haven, Connecticut, who had been experimenting with fMRI, reported that men and women used different brain regions while performing cognitive tasks. When comparing two words to see if they rhymed, for example, men used frontal brain regions on the left side only, while women used the frontal region on both sides of the brain.

A second study, at Harvard University in Cambridge, Massachusetts, used fMRI to study the brains of people with obsessive-compulsive disorder (OCD), a condition marked by intrusive, disturbing thoughts or ritualized behaviors. Compared to people without OCD, the Harvard investigators reported in July 1996, those with the disorder showed more activity in their frontal and middle brain regions.

Depression and AIDS. People show a dramatic, sustained rise in symptoms of depression as they develop AIDS, researchers at Johns Hopkins University in

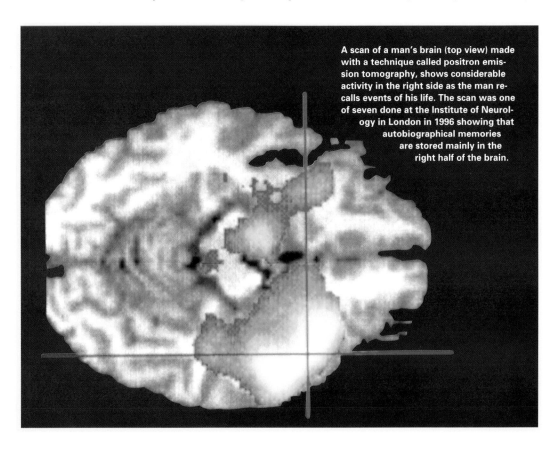

A scan of a man's brain (top view) made with a technique called positron emission tomography, shows considerable activity in the right side as the man recalls events of his life. The scan was one of seven done at the Institute of Neurology in London in 1996 showing that autobiographical memories are stored mainly in the right half of the brain.

Baltimore reported in November 1996.

Depression is common in people suffering from a chronic illness such as cancer, heart disease, or AIDS. Often, it is unclear whether the depression is an emotional reaction to the physical illness or the result of changes in the brain's biochemistry caused by the physical illness.

Physicians have found that about 1 out of 10 people infected with the human immunodeficiency virus (HIV), the cause of AIDS, also have symptoms of depression. Such symptoms include both psychological changes (excessive sadness, anger, hopelessness, helplessness, guilt, worry, and suicidal feelings) and physical changes (impaired sleep and loss of appetite and energy).

Depression can hinder patients' ability to function at work and in social situations. In some cases, it can lead to suicide. Depression can worsen physical illnesses—for example, by making patients less likely to continue treatment.

The Johns Hopkins study tracked 911 HIV-infected men in four American cities for five years before they were diagnosed with AIDS and two years afterward. The men's reports of depressive symptoms rose sharply about 1½ years before the diagnosis, and they remained high thereafter. The symptoms reached a plateau about six months before the diagnosis.

These findings show that there is a role for the intervention of mental-health-care providers in the treatment of HIV-infected people throughout the course of their illness.

The genetics of personality traits. The first evidence of an association between normal genetic variations and anxiety-related personality traits was reported in November 1996 by researchers at the National Institute of Mental Health (NIMH) in Bethesda, Maryland, and their colleagues at the University of Würzburg in Germany.

Since the discovery of the structure of DNA (deoxyribonucleic acid, the molecule genes are made of) in 1953, scientists have learned a great deal about how genes organize the chemical functioning and cellular structure of all life forms. Variations in genes are thought to contribute to many human diseases. Scientists have theorized that variations in genes may also contribute to differences in normal personality traits.

NIMH scientists studied a gene involved in regulating the level of a brain chemical called serotonin. Scientists believe that changes in the levels of serotonin in the brain play a role in the development of anxiety and depression.

After seratonin is released in the brain, a molecule known as a transporter removes excess amounts of the chemical from the *synapses* (spaces) between nerve cells. Doctors believe antidepressant medications may help depressed people in part by blocking the transporter and increasing serotonin levels. (The action of antidepressants is complex, however, and involves many other steps in addition to increasing the serotonin levels in the synapses.)

The researchers looked at variations in the gene for the serotonin transporter in the genetic material of 505 people. Some of the people had a shortened form of the gene that produced a less effective transporter. When the scientists compared these findings to the people's scores on personality measures, they found that people with the shortened gene had more anxiety-related traits.

The burden of minor depression. People with even mild symptoms of depression experience a greatly reduced ability to function normally in their work and social lives, researchers at the University of California at San Diego reported in November 1996.

Depression can have different meanings. For scientists and mental-health professionals, major depression is a syndrome, or collection of symptoms. These symptoms include both psychological and physical impairments that alter the way people perceive events, interact with others, and cope with daily challenges. When a person's symptoms are numerous or intense enough to seriously impair a person's everyday functioning, doctors say that person is suffering a major depressive episode. The San Diego study showed, however, that people with fewer or less intense symptoms—those with minor depression—also experience notable impairment.

The researchers studied 2,393 people, assessing their sense of well-being and their ability to function in their jobs and social situations. The scientists then di-

Mother mice—one mean, one nice
A mother mouse in which researchers have "knocked out" a gene called *fosB* ignores her pups, *top,* while a mother with an intact *fosB* cares for hers, *above.* This experimental result, reported in July 1996 by neuroscience researcher Jennifer Brown and her colleagues at Harvard Medical School in Boston, was one of the first bits of evidence that nurturing behavior in mammals is determined, or at least influenced, by genes.

vided the people into groups based on the severity of their depression. They found that more than 10 percent of the people were suffering from minor depression, more than twice as many as those with major depression.

Surprisingly, the people with minor depression were found to be experiencing as much disability as those with major depression. Both groups reported strained households and finances, social irritability, restricted activity, and poorer health.

These findings showed that minor depression is both a common problem and a serious one. They highlight the public-health importance of the illness and may prompt doctors to seek better treatments for this condition.

Mental illness in developing nations. Describing mental illness as "one of the last frontiers in the improvement of the human condition," an international group of scholars in March 1997 reported the results of a survey of mental illness in low-income societies in Asia, Africa, Latin America, and the Middle East. Led by Harvard Medical School researchers, experts from more than 30 nations recommended to the United Nations and the World Health Organization that health-care services in such countries be improved. They suggested that mental-health care should be integrated with primary care.

Priorities, they said, include programs for detecting and preventing mental illness in children and adolescents, the treatment and prevention of alcohol and drug abuse, and efforts to address the causes and effects of violence.

The survey revealed that although basic physical health—including infant mortality and life expectancy—had improved in low-income countries over the past generation, rates of clinical depression, schizophrenia, drug and alcohol abuse, and suicide had increased.

The researchers noted that many such illnesses were intricately related to economic, social, and political conditions in these societies. In most low-income countries, primary-care health services were inadequate, and mental-health clinicians, psychiatric medications, and psychosocial therapies were in especially short supply.

[Robert A. Lasser and
Richard C. Hermann]

The U.S. Centers for Disease Control and Prevention (CDC) in Atlanta, Georgia, reported in June 1996 that national homicide rates decreased by 1 percent a year from 1992 to 1994. This decrease followed a dramatic rise in homicides between 1985 and 1992, when the rates increased 4 percent annually. Firearms caused the majority of homicides—71 percent—in 1993 (the last year for which complete data were available), compared to 60 percent in 1985.

Over the years, homicide rates were strongly affected by rates for one specific age group: 15- to 24-year-olds. About 33 percent of homicide victims were between those ages. While homicide rates for persons younger than 15 or older than 24 remained stable from 1985 to 1992, rates among 15- to 24-year-olds increased by 16 percent each year during that time.

Foodborne illnesses. In January 1997, President Bill Clinton proposed a plan to battle foodborne illness. The plan, which would increase the number of food products certified for safety, required congressional approval and $43 million in funding.

Public-health officials applauded the proposal. Each year, according to the Council for Agricultural Science and Technology—a private association in Ames, Iowa—between 6.5 million and 33 million people suffer from a foodborne illness; as many as 9,000 die.

Of special concern to public-health authorities were illnesses caused by emerging *pathogens* (microorganisms that cause illness). One such pathogen was the parasite *Cyclospora cayetanensis*, which causes diarrhea, cramps, and fever. In June 1996, the CDC received 42 reports of cyclospora infections in New Jersey. This outbreak was part of some 850 cases of laboratory-confirmed cyclospora reported to the CDC from around the United States. Most of the ill people had eaten raspberries that public-health officials traced to Guatemala.

In April and May 1997, raspberries—this time from Chile as well as Guatemala—were again the suspected source of cyclospora infections. At least 90 confirmed cyclospora infections were reported in California, Florida, New York, Nevada, and Texas.

In March 1997, more than 150 children and teachers at schools in Michigan contracted hepatitis A, a viral infection that can lead to inflammation of the liver. Public-health officials determined that the source of the infection was frozen strawberries from Mexico that were processed in California and distributed to school lunch programs. Those exposed to the infection were treated with immunoglobulin shots, which can prevent hepatitis A if administered within 14 days of infection.

Airbag injuries. In November 1996, the National Highway Traffic Safety Administration (NHTSA) recommended ways to improve the safety of automobile airbags. From 1986 to early 1997, according to researchers, more than 60 people had died from injuries related to the force with which airbags inflated. Most of those killed—38—were children. However, airbags also saved the lives of more than 1,750 drivers and passengers during that time.

Airbags deploy at speeds up to 320 kilometers (200 miles) per hour. They were designed to protect an average adult male not wearing a seat belt. When children or short adults sit in the front seat of cars with airbags, the bags can strike them in the head or neck, causing injuries they might not have otherwise sustained. Although most of the 38 children killed by airbags were not properly buckled into safety seats, some died simply because the force of the airbag was too great for a child.

The NHTSA made the following recommendations: Infants in rear-facing child-safety seats should always ride in the back seat; children under age 12 should also ride in the back seat; all vehicle occupants should use shoulder and lap belts; and front seats should be moved as far back as possible from the steering wheel and dashboard.

The NHTSA also recommended that dealers or auto mechanics be allowed to disconnect airbags at the request of a vehicle owner; that airbags be made to deploy with 20 to 35 percent less force; that labels warning of airbag danger be posted in all new vehicles; that cutoff switches for deactivating airbags be provided in vehicles with no rear seat; and that "smart bags"—airbags that gauge a person's size and position on the seat and deploy with appropriate force—replace existing airbags.

In March 1997, the federal govern-

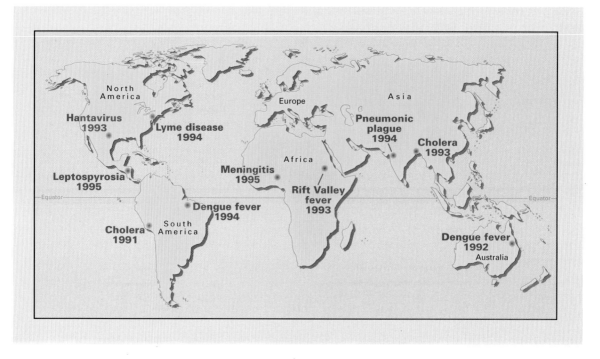

North
America

Hantavirus
1993

Lyme disease
1994

Europe

Asia

Pneumonic
plague
1994

Cholera
1993

Leptospyrosia
1995

Meningitis
1995

Africa

Equator

Rift Valley
fever
1993

Equator

Dengue fever
1994

Cholera
1991

South
America

Dengue fever
1992

Australia

Climate and disease

During the 1990's, health experts have documented the outbreak of many infectious diseases that have apparently been related to global warming. They speculated, for example, that a warmer, wetter climate may have caused the spread of mosquito-borne illnesses such as malaria and dengue fever. Scientists hope that further study of this climate-disease connection will help them predict—and prepare for—future disease outbreaks.

ment issued a rule allowing airbag manufacturers to "depower" airbags by up to 35 percent. Manufacturers planned to install such airbags on all new cars by the end of the 1998 model year.

Children and smoking. President Clinton in August 1996 approved regulations designed to cut youth smoking by one-half in seven years. The action, which placed nicotine under the regulation of the U.S. Food and Drug Administration for the first time, reflected the government's position that nicotine is an addictive drug. The new regulations required that vendors of tobacco products ask for identification from purchasers under the age of 27. The regulations also forbade the selling of tobacco products from most vending machines, the placement of tobacco ads on billboards within 305 meters (1,000 feet) of schools and playgrounds, and the advertising of tobacco products at sporting, musical, and cultural events.

Top 10 infectious diseases. In October 1996, the CDC reported that 5 of the 10 leading infectious diseases in the United States were sexually transmit-

ted. Chlamydia, gonorrhea, and AIDS ranked in order as the three most commonly reported infectious diseases of 1995. Those were followed by salmonellosis, hepatitis A, shigellosis, tuberculosis, primary and secondary syphilis, Lyme disease, and hepatitis B.

CDC's 50th anniversary. On July 1, 1996, the Centers for Disease Control and Prevention commemorated its 50th anniversary with the opening of an interactive museum called Global Health Odyssey. The museum, located at CDC headquarters in Atlanta, featured exhibits teaching people how to protect their health. Other exhibits highlighted the agency's efforts to monitor and improve public health since its establishment in 1946. The CDC led the effort to eradicate smallpox throughout the world and investigated the outbreak of such diseases as Ebola hemorrhagic fever. It also reported the first cases of AIDS and created a laboratory where dangerous viruses and other pathogens could be handled under maximum containment.   [Richard A. Goodman and Deborah Kowal]

In 1997, scientists cloned the first mammal from an adult animal, a scientific milestone that triggered the ethical concerns of scientists and laypeople alike. Other bioethical issues that received attention in 1996 and 1997 included the establishment of a Bioethics Advisory Commission, questions regarding the integrity and ethical conduct of scientists, and how budgetary and policy issues affect scientific research.

First mammal cloned from an adult. On Feb. 22, 1997, embryologist Ian Wilmut announced that he and his colleagues at the Roslin Institute in Edinburgh, Scotland, had created a clone from an adult sheep. A clone is an organism that is genetically identical to a parent organism. Animal cloning began in the 1960's with the splitting of frog embryos at early stages of development, which generally resulted in identical twins and triplets.

Wilmut created his clone from a mammary cell taken from a *ewe* (female sheep). He began by placing mammary cells in a laboratory dish and depriving them of nutrients, which put them into a nondividing state. He then removed the nucleus from an unfertilized sheep egg and replaced it with the nucleus from one of the mammary cells. The egg was electrically jump-started into behaving like a fertilized cell, and it grew and divided to form an embryo. The embryo was implanted into a surrogate mother ewe that gave birth in July 1996 to a lamb, which was named Dolly. Genetic tests confirmed that Dolly was genetically identical to the adult ewe from which the mammary cells were taken.

Wilmut's technique, which may allow scientists for the first time to replicate known characteristics—for example, intelligence, appearance, strength, or size—was developed from experiments underwritten by a Scottish biotechnology firm. The company was interested in developing animals that could produce substances of medical value to humans, such as the blood clotting factor used for treating hemophilia. In 1997, the company tested a protein, produced by genetically altered sheep, as a treatment for cystic fibrosis. Cloned animals capable of producing such substances would enable pharmaceutical companies to produce medicines more efficiently and at less expense.

Wilmut's announcement attracted worldwide attention and triggered widespread concern over the ethics of cloning animals and its implications for human beings. People wondered if the technique developed by Wilmut could be used to clone a human being—a notion regarded as little more than science fiction until the birth of Dolly. The news rocked many people's deeply held religious and ethical feelings regarding individuality and parenthood. The media explored the issue of whether human beings should ever be cloned, and the federal government and several state governments began considering legislation to ban human cloning.

As television crews from around the world converged on Dolly's pen, biologists, ethicists, and philosophers began to debate the implications of the development. Politicians began calling for new laws to regulate human cloning.

Within days of the announcement, President Bill Clinton asked the National Bioethics Advisory Commission to inquire into the ethical and legal implications of human cloning and to recommend government actions to prevent abuse. This commission, which was established by the president on July 19, 1996, with Harold Shapiro, president of Princeton University, as its chairman, was chartered to examine a variety of current bioethical issues: the rights of human research subjects; the uses to which genetic information should be put; discrimination against people shown to be susceptible to genetically based diseases; human embryo research; and the patenting of genes and genetically altered organisms.

In March 1997, President Clinton banned the use of federal funds for research on human cloning, and he asked that researchers voluntarily forego such research until its implications were explored. The ban was made before the advisory commission was able to respond to the president's request for advice.

Congress followed suit by introducing bills that would, if passed, ban the use of federal funds for human cloning experiments or even forbid such experiments altogether. In response, scientists cautioned politicians that laws affecting cloning should be carefully crafted to allow for exploration of benefits while restricting ethically repugnant work.

Radiation experiment victims. The National Bioethics Advisory Commission was created by President Clinton on the recommendation of the Advisory Committee on Human Radiation Experiments, which had been formed in January 1994 to investigate secret U.S. radiation experiments. The experiments were conducted by government scientists between 1945 and 1975 on U.S. citizens without their knowledge or consent.

In November 1996, Congress passed legislation that granted a total of $4.8 million in compensation to 12 people who had been injected with plutonium or uranium during the secret experiments. Only 1 of the 12 subjects of the experiments was still alive at the time the bill was adopted. The compensation money—approximately $400,000 per victim—was divided among surviving family members of the victims. Hazel O'Leary, secretary of the U.S. Department of Energy, said that further compensation would be provided to other people subjected to the experiments.

Misconduct charges overturned. Long-running cases of scientific misconduct were resolved in 1996 and 1997. Two prominent scientists, Thereza Imanishi-Kari and Bernard Fisher, were absolved of charges brought against them in separate cases by the Office of Research Integrity, a division of the U.S. Department of Health and Human Services.

In June 1996, an appeals board at Health and Human Services cleared Imanishi-Kari, an immunologist at Tufts University in Medford, Massachusetts, of charges that she had faked results of experiments in a paper published in 1986 in the scientific journal *Cell*. Imanishi-Kari coauthored the paper with Nobel laureate David Baltimore.

Baltimore, who was not accused of any misconduct, steadfastly defended his coauthor through a series of congressional hearings and administrative proceedings. Because of his involvement and strong support, the affair became widely known as the "Baltimore case." The appeals board in the case voided all sanctions against Imanishi-Kari, thereby effectively rebuking the Office of Research Integrity and its investigative procedures.

In March 1997, the same Office of Research Integrity dropped charges it had brought against Bernard Fisher, a cancer researcher at the University of Pittsburgh.

The case against Fisher involved his tenure as chairman of the National Surgical Adjuvant Breast and Bowel Project. This study, conducted between 1976 and 1984, had established *lumpectomy* (removal of just the tumor and surrounding tissue) as a standard treatment for breast cancer. The study had found that lumpectomy followed by radiation therapy is as effective in preventing recurrences of breast cancer as is mastectomy, the removal of the entire breast. In the years since the study, thousands of breast cancer patients have chosen lumpectomy over mastectomy, based on these results.

Fisher had learned in 1994 that a Canadian surgeon participating in the study had falsified documents in order to include women who did not meet study requirements. Fisher, however, did not disclose this information to the public for more than a year. When Fisher did make this information public, women who had chosen lumpectomy over mastectomy were greatly alarmed, and Fisher was harshly criticized in the press and in congressional hearings. Fisher, however, insisted that he had done nothing wrong.

His claim was eventually supported by independent reviews of the study's data made by the National Cancer Institute (NCI), the largest of the National Institutes of Health (NIH), a government agency that conducts and supports biomedical research. The NCI showed that the data, though falsified, did not affect the results of the study or conclusions regarding treatment that were based upon those results. Fisher, after being absolved of wrongdoing, sued the government for damage to his reputation.

Public funding of scientific research. Cuts in federal funding of scientific research proved to be far less severe in the proposed 1998 federal budget, released in February 1997, than was generally expected. In 1995 and 1996, members of Congress, exploring ways to balance the budget in seven years, projected that federal funding for nonmilitary research and development (R & D) would be cut by as much as 33 percent. The scientific community thus greeted the 14 percent funding cut projected in the 1998 budget for fiscal 1997 through 2002 with relief. President Clinton's strong defense of some programs, lobbying by scientists, and improving economic conditions helped protect R & D funding from the

How safe are airbags?

In 1996 and 1997, public attention focused on the safety of automobile airbags. According to the National Highway Traffic Safety Administration (NHTSA), more than 60 people, including 38 children, had died since 1986 from the impact of airbags.

A test with dummies conducted by the NHTSA shows that a rear-facing child seat, *left, top,* placed in the front seat of a car positions the head of an infant or small child within inches of an airbag inflating at up to 320 kilometers (200 miles) an hour, *left, bottom.*

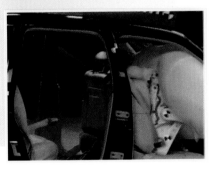

Another test, *above,* illustrates how the combination of an airbag and shoulder and lap belts can protect the life of an adult during a crash test with the vehicle moving at a speed of 55 kilometers (35 miles) per hour.

extreme projected cuts originally discussed in Congress.

A report released in March 1997 by the American Association for the Advancement of Science (AAAS), headquartered in Washington, D.C., revealed that by fiscal year 1997, federal funding for R & D, measured in inflation-adjusted dollars, had fallen 5 percent from its 1994 level. The AAAS also reported that funding trends varied between areas of research. In the 1990's, Congress gave high priority to biomedical research. As a consequence, budgets at the NIH increased by nearly 8 percent after 1994. The NIH was, however, the only federal research agency whose funding was increased significantly. Budgets at the Environmental Protection Agency, the Department of Energy, and the National Aeronautics and Space Administration were substantially reduced during the same period.

Federal funding for civilian R & D in the proposed 1998 budget was increased over the 1997 budget by slightly more than the anticipated rate of inflation. Funding for basic military research was also increased. In addition, a series of congressional proposals involving government funding of the sciences heartened scientists in 1997.

In the Senate, Republicans Connie Mack of Florida and Phil Gramm of Texas, conservatives known for their efforts to cut federal spending, introduced legislation in January 1997 advocating increases in civilian research budgets. The Mack bill called for doubling the NIH budget over the next five years. The Gramm bill proposed doubling R & D budgets at a number of federal agencies over the next 10 years.

In the House of Representatives, the science committee, led by Republican chairman James Sensenbrenner of Wisconsin, ended two years of partisan squabbling and sent a bipartisan "Views and Estimates" report to the House budget committee. The report advocated increased funding for all scientific agencies under the committee's jurisdiction. Scientists interpreted the proposed legislation and committee report as indications of a more positive attitude in Congress toward future funding of scientific research.   [Al Teich]

Mars missions and the international space station program were in the spotlight in late 1996 and throughout 1997. Not all of the news was happy, though. While two new robotic spacecraft were cruising to the red planet for arrivals in July and September 1997, the third and largest was lost in a launch failure. And while the United States and Russia continued to cooperate closely in human space flight, a small fire occurred on the aging Mir space station while a U.S. astronaut was aboard. Moreover, delays in work in Russia on a key component for the international space station led the U.S. National Aeronautics and Space Administration (NASA) to reschedule the beginning of construction in orbit.

Mars missions. Even before the autumn 1996 launches of three spacecraft to Mars, the planet was the subject of much excitement because of a startling assertion made by a group of scientists in August 1996. The scientists claimed to have found evidence of ancient microscopic life forms in a meteorite from Mars discovered in Antarctica in 1984. The discovery broadened interest in undertaking a mission to Mars in the near future that would collect samples of Martian rocks and return them to Earth.

The first of the new missions to the red planet, Mars Global Surveyor, was launched on a Delta 2 rocket from Cape Canaveral, Florida, on Nov. 7, 1996. The U.S. spacecraft carried many of the same kinds of instruments that were on the Mars Observer, which failed just as it was nearing the planet in 1993. The Surveyor was to orbit the planet for one Martian year—687 Earth days—mapping the topography and climate and relaying the information back to Earth.

The second mission, Russia's Mars 96 spacecraft, was the most ambitious. Like the others, it was launched during a periodic "window," when the positions of the planets are best for beginning months-long journeys from Earth to Mars. Lifting off from the Baikonur Cosmodrome in Kazakhstan on Nov. 16, 1996, Mars 96 carried instruments from several nations. It was to have split into one orbiter, two small science stations for studying the surface of Mars, and two penetrators for probing beneath the planet's surface. However, a malfunction caused the spacecraft and part of its booster rocket to plunge back to Earth.

The last to leave, also on a Delta 2 from Cape Canaveral, was Mars Pathfinder, the first U.S. mission to the planet's surface since the two Viking landers of 1976. Pathfinder, cushioned on all sides by airbags, was to land on a Martian plain called Ares Vallis on July 4, 1997. Once on the ground, Pathfinder was programmed to unfold and, if necessary, to right itself. Then Mars Sojourner Rover, a six-wheeled robot, was to roll off. The 10-kilogram (22-pound) vehicle, about the size of a child's wagon, was designed to move at a speed of 1 centimeter (0.4 inch) per second over the Martian soil for a range of up to 500 meters (1,640 feet). Its instruments were to gather data and send the information and images back to the lander, which in turn would relay them to Earth. Sojourner Rover was to travel over the Martian surface for about seven days, after which its systems would shut down.

Record flight. NASA biochemist Shannon W. Lucid set a record for the longest stint in space by a woman and the longest flight by any U.S. astronaut. Already a veteran of four shuttle flights, Lucid was launched on a fifth on March 22, 1996, to Russia's space station Mir. Lucid joined the Mir crew as a "cosmonaut researcher," working on three dozen experiments in life and physical sciences. By the time she landed at the Kennedy Space Center (KSC) on the east coast of Florida on Sept. 26, 1996, Lucid had spent 188 days in space. One of the six astronauts aboard Atlantis when it flew to retrieve Lucid, retired Air Force Colonel John E. Blaha, replaced Lucid and spent four months aboard the Russian station.

Trouble in space. The shuttle Atlantis was launched on Jan. 12, 1997, on the fifth U.S. mission to dock with Mir. The shuttle's six-member crew included physician astronaut Jerry M. Linenger, who replaced Blaha aboard the station.

Mir had been operating in low Earth orbit since 1986. New modules had been added over the years. But while Linenger was on board, the older systems began to show their age. Critical components—systems that provide oxygen for the crew to breathe, remove carbon dioxide from the station's air, cool the spacecraft, and allow it to communicate with the ground—failed. There were backup systems, and as a last resort

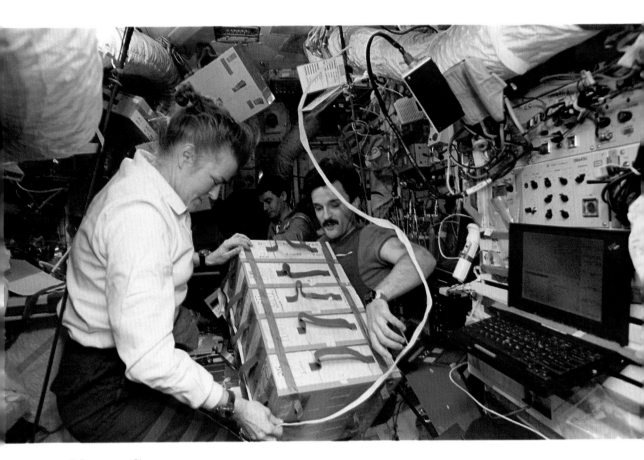

U.S. astronaut Shannon Lucid helps Russian cosmonaut Aleksandr Kaleri secure empty food trays aboard Mir, the Russian space station. Cosmonaut Valery Korzun works in the background. Lucid was sent into orbit March 22, 1996, and spent 188 days in space. By the time she returned to Earth on September 26, she had broken the U.S. space endurance record and the international space endurance record for women.

crews could abandon the station and return to Earth in the Soyuz capsules that are always docked to Mir. However, the problems worried both the Russian ground controllers and their NASA counterparts.

The most alarming incident occurred on Feb. 23, 1997. A canister containing chemicals that react to produce oxygen and generate heat caught fire. The fire burned for some 90 seconds before it was extinguished with foam. Smoke filled the station. No one was injured, and only a small area of the Kvant-1 module was damaged. But Linenger, the four Russians, and one German on board were forced to don oxygen masks. Then they had to wear filtration masks for two days, even while they slept.

A month later, Mir had been repaired and was deemed in good enough shape to allow Linenger and station commander Vasili Tsibliev to undertake a five-hour spacewalk. Linenger, directed by controllers in Moscow, was the first U.S. astronaut to conduct a spacewalk with Russian equipment. He wore a new, more flexible Russian space suit

and removed U.S. experiments from the station's exterior. Two U.S. astronauts had previously installed the experiments, but the pair had worked from a docked shuttle, worn U.S. suits, and been directed by flight controllers in Houston.

For a time, NASA debated whether to keep a U.S. astronaut aboard Mir. But eventually the agency decided it was safe to continue the shuttle-Mir program. Atlantis was launched for Mir on May 15 and replaced Linenger with C. Michael Foale, a NASA astronaut born in the United Kingdom. The Atlantis crew also included two non-U.S. members: France's Jean-François Clervoy of the European Space Agency (ESA), and Russia's Elena V. Kondakova. Both returned to Earth with the shuttle May 24.

Station delays. U.S. confidence in its Russian partner was further shaken by slow work in Moscow on a module for a new international space station. NASA, ESA, Japan, and Canada had been working on plans for such a station for more than a decade and hoped to launch the first components in late 1997. Russia

A Spaceship for Tomorrow

When the space shuttle was conceived in the 1970's, the dream of engineers was to create a new kind of spacecraft—one that could carry people and cargo into orbit, return to Earth, and then be used again repeatedly. They succeeded, but only partially.

In 1997, the National Aeronautics and Space Administration (NASA) and private aerospace companies were working to develop a space-launch vehicle that would operate more like an airplane. They envisioned a spacecraft that not only could be used repeatedly but would also be reliable and efficient enough to fly more frequently and at far less cost than the shuttle.

Of the shuttle's four major components, only one—the winged orbiter—is fully reusable. The large external fuel tank is jettisoned when empty, after eight minutes of flight, and it burns up as it reenters the atmosphere. The two booster rockets (at the sides of the external tank) are also jettisoned when empty, after only two minutes of flight. They then parachute into the ocean, where they are recovered. The rockets are later disassembled and refilled with solid propellant. But the recovery and refilling require so much special equipment and work that it would be nearly as economical to simply buy a set of throw-away rockets for each shuttle launching.

These and other difficulties make the shuttle an extremely expensive vehicle to fly—about $400 million per flight by the most conservative accounting. And that just covers the flight itself, not the satellites or laboratories that might be the cargo. So, more than 40 years after the dawn of the space age, single-use rockets remain cheaper to use than the shuttle.

Still, the idea of a single-use vehicle has always seemed wasteful. After all, what other mode of transportation throws away the vehicle with each trip? It has long been possible, in theory, to make a fully reusable, single-stage-to-orbit vehicle. But various factors, including the performance of engines and the materials available for fuel tanks and other structures, resulted in designs for vehicles that grew so big and expensive that they were impractical—at least if they were to carry any significant payload.

Some of these factors have changed in recent years, making the idea of a single-stage, reusable launch vehicle worth pursuing. Several key technologies have advanced since the shuttle was built. The development of certain composite materials (such as graphite-epoxy), stronger alloys (such as aluminum-lithium), and new ceramics make it possible to construct lightweight fuel tanks and better heat shields. Engines can be made lighter and more reliable. In addition, electromechanical flight-control systems are available to replace heavier, more troublesome hydraulic systems. And smaller, vastly more capable computers and more advanced navigational systems could streamline flight operations and maintenance.

Some of these technologies have already been applied in certain aircraft, including the B-2 bomber, the F-22 fighter, and the Boeing 777 jetliner. And some come from research begun in the 1980's to develop an aerospace plane, an airplane capable of flying into orbit.

By the early 1990's, enthusiasts for a completely reusable spacecraft had persuaded the U.S. Department of Defense to test a vehicle to demonstrate that a single-stage-to-orbit rocket could be practical and inexpensive. The McDonnell Douglas Corporation built the first such vehicle, dubbed the Delta Clipper Experimental, or DC-X.

With its conical shape and its tail-first landings on a column of flame, the DC-X looked like something straight out of Buck Rogers. A ground crew of several dozen demonstrated that, after a flight, the DC-X could be ready to fly again the next day.

It will take just such "aircraftlike" operations to slash the costs of space transportation. Many space experts believe that lower costs will bring new customers, even tourists, into space. But many of these experts also believe that costs can never be cut drastically until government lets the private sector sit in the pilot's seat.

To a large degree, NASA agrees with this viewpoint. In 1995, it announced that it wanted to help private industry develop a new experimental spacecraft, to be called the X-33. The hope was that this vehicle would demonstrate that space travel could be economically efficient. The target was to reduce the cost of launching a payload by 90 percent, to about $1,000 a pound. If this target could be reached, NASA speculated, perhaps private industry would want to build and maintain a fleet of commercial reusable launch vehicles (RLV's) on its own.

Although the RLV is sometimes portrayed as a replacement for the shuttle, that is not the goal for the vehicle. There is no urgency to replace the shuttle, because it was designed to easily fly another 15 years. With upgrading, it could fly until 2030. The goal for the RLV is simply to slash launch costs.

Three large aerospace companies were interested in developing the X-33. McDonnell Douglas proposed an enlarged version of its DC-X, called the DC-XA, or Clipper Graham. Rockwell International (teamed with Northrop Grumman) proposed a vehicle based on the shuttle orbiter, with

The VentureStar

In an artist's conception, the planned reusable launch vehicle VentureStar, *left,* deploys a satellite from its cargo bay. Expected to be flying by 2004, the VentureStar, *above, center,* was to be 38 meters (125 feet) long, considerably shorter than the space shuttle (including booster rockets), right. A smaller prototype, the X-33, left, was scheduled to fly by 1999.

many improvements. But in July 1996, NASA selected a plan by the Lockheed Martin Corporation because the plan used many technological innovations, and the company had promising ideas for an RLV to follow the X-33. Lockheed Martin's plan called for an RLV powered by a new engine called a linear aerospike engine. Instead of having the conventional cluster of cone-shaped rocket nozzles, this design has several nozzles arranged linearly along the edges of rectangular wedges. An automatic flight control system would independently adjust the throttles on each of the vehicle's seven engines. The plan also included a "lifting body" design, in which the vehicle is mostly body, with small wings. The large surface area of the X-33 would distribute the heat encountered upon reentry into Earth's atmosphere in such a way that a new type of metallic heat shield can be used.

The X-33 was to be 20.4 meters (67 feet) long and 20.7 meters (68 feet) wide. It was to fly 17,000 kilometers (11,000 miles) per hour—not fast enough to reach orbit. The first flight was expected in March 1999.

Lockheed Martin calls its concept of the RLV that would follow the X-33 the "VentureStar." It would be similar to the X-33 but about twice as long and wide. It could carry up to 18,160 kilograms (40,000 pounds) in a large cargo bay. The first flight of the VentureStar could come as early as 2004.

Plans called for the VentureStar to be completely automated—the spacecraft would not car-

ry a flight crew. Directions for each flight's mission would be programmed into the vehicle's onboard computer system. This automatic flight control system would control everything from engine operations to craft orientation to flight paths. People on the vehicle would be simply passengers. A separate capsule with a life-support system would carry them inside the RLV's cargo bay.

NASA already had flights to the International Space Station in mind for the RLV. Even if the RLV only took over the shuttle's role of carrying cargo to and from the station, it would be a big help, because it would make the station less dependent on the shuttle. That would, in turn, make the station cheaper to operate and free the shuttle to make only flights requiring astronauts. The space station was scheduled to be assembled in space between 1998 and 2002, during more than 40 missions involving the shuttle and Russian and European Space Agency vehicles.

Since its first flight in 1981, the space shuttle, despite its limitations, has been a very useful vehicle. The shuttle's crews have launched commercial and military satellites into space, repaired broken satellites (including the Hubble Space Telescope), and conducted a number of important scientific experiments. But in the future, the VentureStar or some other design for a fully reusable launch vehicle may make space transportation much more reliable and affordable. And such a vehicle may be the best way to maintain a vigorous presence in, and to expand the uses of, the final frontier.   [James R. Asker] joined the effort in 1993. Work proceeded smoothly on the first element of the station scheduled for launch, the FGB Energy Block or "space tug." The FGB, built in Russia but paid for by the United States, was to serve as a base for other station elements. The next component to be launched, a U.S.-built "node," was to connect several other modules.

It was the third component scheduled for launch, a Russian unit called the service module, that caused the problems. The service module was to be one of Russia's contributions to the station program. But Russia had been suffering financial problems since the breakup of the Soviet Union in 1991. These problems prevented government-authorized payments for the module from reaching the contractors doing the work.

By the spring of 1997, construction of the service module had barely begun. NASA rescheduled the start of the orbital assembly of the station to 1998. And while NASA still hoped to use the Russian module as the third component, the agency began a costly effort to build a backup module in the United States.

Service call. The space shuttle Discovery took off from KSC on Feb. 11, 1997, for a rendezvous with the Hubble Space Telescope. The optics of the telescope, famously flawed when it was launched in 1990, had been corrected on a similar shuttle mission in 1993. And the Hubble had become one of the most productive instruments in the history of science.

By 1997, it was again time to replace some of the orbiting observatory's instruments with more advanced ones. First, the crew of seven, led by Navy Commander Kenneth D. Bowersox, snared Hubble and mounted it in the shuttle's cargo bay. Then two pairs of astronauts conducted spacewalks to install the new science instruments and make needed repairs.

The new instruments, both the size of a telephone booth, were the Near Infrared Camera and Multi-Object Spectrometer (NICMOS), and the Space Telescope Imaging Spectrograph (STIS). Together, astronomers hoped, the units would give them their farthest look yet into the universe—and thus the farthest look back in time.

Mission to Mars

In an artist's conception, Mars Sojourner Rover, a small six-wheeled robot, moves across the Martian landscape, *right*. The rover was launched on Dec. 4, 1996, aboard the Mars Pathfinder spacecraft, which was due to make a landing on Mars on July 4, 1997. Sojourner Rover was designed to send pictures and data on Martian weather, rocks, and soil to Pathfinder for relay to Earth. Technicians test the inflatable airbags that were to cushion Pathfinder's landing, *below*.

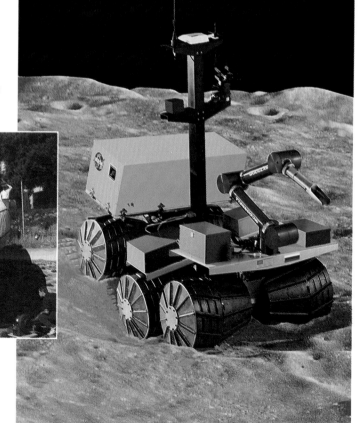

An unmanned Delta rocket explodes 13 seconds after liftoff at the Cape Canaveral Air Force Station in Florida on Jan. 17, 1997. The explosion rained flaming debris and propellant onto the air station and the Atlantic Ocean and resulted in the loss of the first of a new generation of Global Positioning System satellites. Investigators determined that the failure of one of nine motors on the booster rocket caused the blast. The accident was expected to delay the launch of several other communication satellites.

Alternating in daily rounds of spacewalks, two pairs of astronauts worked on the telescope for five days in the Discovery's cargo bay—one more day than planned. They installed the new instruments and other, smaller replacement parts. The astronauts spent part of the fourth and fifth days repairing damaged insulation that they discovered on the Hubble. The telescope was released on February 19.

Discovery landed at KSC two days later. On March 25, NASA announced that NICMOS was not focusing starlight quite as well as astronomers had hoped. In addition, its coolant was being used up faster than planned. Scientists feared that hundreds of projects using NICMOS would need to be rushed, while the instrument was still operational.

Columbia's missions. The space shuttle Columbia lifted off June 20, 1996, with a crew of seven, including an astronaut from France and one from Canada. The astronauts worked in the Spacelab module carried in the cargo bay, conducting experiments in life and *microgravity* (very low gravity) sciences. The orbiter landed July 7 at KSC.

On Nov. 19, 1996, Columbia carried five astronauts and two satellites into space. Both satellites were released to fly on their own for two weeks, retrieved using the shuttle's long robotic arm, and returned to Earth.

One, a German-built astronomy satellite, Orfeus-SPAS, was equipped with instruments that recorded ultraviolet data on deep space objects. The other, the Wake Shield Facility, had flown before. It is used to create an "ultra-vacuum" in space in which extremely pure materials can be formed. The satellite was used to make experimental wafers of thin films for advanced semiconductors. Columbia landed at Cape Canaveral on Dec. 7, 1996, completing a 17-day flight—a record length for a shuttle mission.

Columbia flew another Spacelab mission on April 4, 1997, again with a crew of seven. A 16-day flight was scheduled. Among the experiments planned were up to 200 involving small fires. Scientists hoped to advance their understanding of combustion by burning various materials and fluids in weightless conditions.

But when one of Columbia's three fuel cells malfunctioned early in the flight, controllers on the ground or-

Engineer Steven L. Smith works on the Hubble Space Telescope (HST), held securely in the space shuttle Discovery's cargo bay. The shuttle's manipulator arm hovers beside him. Discovery's flight, which began Feb. 11, 1997, was the second mission flown to upgrade the HST's scientific instruments and guidance systems. Astronauts on five space walks installed new instruments that were expected to improve the HST's sensitivity and wavelength coverage and patched the telescope's torn insulating cover.

dered it shut down. The units use oxygen and hydrogen to produce electrical power and water. The crew was able to conserve power and conducted a few experiments using flashlights. However, shuttle flight rules dictate that when one fuel cell is lost, the mission must be cut short. Columbia was ordered to land after just four days in space. It was only the third time in the 83 missions since Columbia conducted the first in 1981 that an orbiter had been ordered to land early because of a mechanical problem. With hindsight, engineers said the spacecraft should not have been allowed to fly. The fuel cell that malfunctioned had displayed unusual voltage changes during the countdown to liftoff.

Ariane 5, Europe's first heavy-lift launch vehicle, took off on its initial flight on June 4, 1996, only to explode half a minute later. Because the nearly 750-metric-ton (830-ton) rocket had begun to pitch and *yaw* (turn from a straight course) out of control, an automatic destruction system blew it up. Flaming debris rained down on the launch complex at Kourou, French Guiana. European space agencies and companies had spent nearly a decade and $8 billion to develop the launcher. Also destroyed in the accident were four science satellites known as Cluster. Worth $500 million, they were part of an international physics program to study the interaction of the *solar wind* (a stream of charged particles flowing from the sun) and Earth's magnetic field. Investigators concluded that errors in the computer software that controlled the launcher's guidance and flight control systems caused the accident. In the spring of 1997, the ESA decided to build replacements for Cluster.

New launch vehicle. In July 1996, NASA selected a partner in industry, and together they began to develop an experimental launch vehicle called the X-33. The United States hoped that new technologies and streamlined operations would lead to a new commercial launch vehicle soon after the year 2000 —one that would be fully reusable and drastically cheaper to fly than existing rockets or the space shuttle. (See CLOSE-UP.)   [James R. Asker]

See also ASTRONOMY. In the Special Reports section, see PROBING THE PLANETS.

SCIENCE YOU CAN USE

Topics selected for their current interest provide information that the reader as a consumer can use in understanding every-day technology or in making decisions—from buying products to caring for personal health and well-being.

Digital Video Discs Usher in a Sight and Sound Revolution

A new data-storage technology called DVD (digital versatile disc or digital video disc) may soon make your videocassette tapes and compact discs (CD's) as obsolete as your dad's old vinyl records. Some electronics companies in 1997 were staking their future on the hope that DVD's would revolutionize home entertainment by providing higher-quality video than a VCR (videocassette recorder), and better music than a standard stereo. They were also hoping that DVD technology would become the standard for delivering large *software programs* (operating instructions) for personal computers.

Two types of DVD were arriving on the market in 1997—DVD video and DVD-ROM (*read-only memory*). About two dozen brands of DVD video players were being manufactured, and many computer companies were expected by year's end to replace CD-ROM drives in their computers with DVD-ROM drives. The companies said the newly equipped computers would also be able to read and play DVD video, as well as CD's and CD-ROM's. Audio DVD's were still in development in 1997, as were DVD's on which people would be able to record their own audio, video, or data.

A DVD looks almost identical to an audio CD or a CD-ROM. All three are aluminum-coated plastic discs about 12.5 centimeters (5 inches) in diame-

Several companies in 1997 marketed DVD's, which outperform CD-ROM's and videocassettes in sound and picture quality and provide increased data storage capabilities.

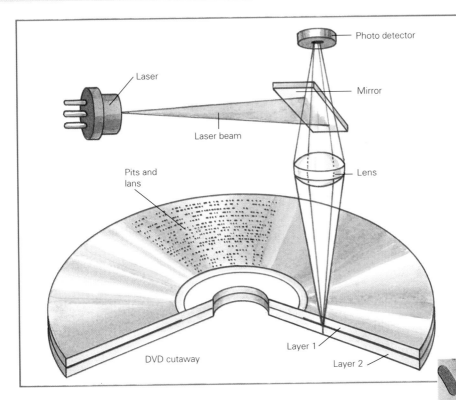

Photo detector

Laser

Mirror

Laser beam

Lens

Pits and
lans

Layer 1

DVD cutaway

Layer 2

DVD's contain at least two layers of data in digital form (a series of 1's and 0's), encoded in tiny *pits* (indentations) and *lans* (spaces). A lens focuses a laser beam on the DVD layer with the desired data. As the disc rotates, the pits and lans pass under the beam of laser light and reflect varying amounts of light to a photo detector. A microprocessor translates the light variations into words, sounds, or pictures.

ter. Even the technology used to create the devices is similar. However, DVD's differ in that they have two or more layers of densely encoded information, making them capable of storing a veritable ocean of words, music, and images—far more than a CD-ROM.

A CD-ROM stores about 680 *megabytes* (million bytes) of information. A byte is a group of 8 *binary digits*, or *bits*—data encoded as a series of 1's and 0's—that act as a single unit of information. A byte can represent, for example, a letter or numeral, the color of a minuscule portion of a photograph, or the tones in a fraction of a second of a musical arrangement. The numerical code for the letter A, for instance, is 1000001. A capacity of 680 megabytes limits a CD-ROM to about 20 minutes of video. In comparison, a single-sided, dual-layer DVD holds about 8.5 *gigabytes* (billion bytes) of data—enough

room to store a 4-hour movie.

This data is encoded in microscopic indentations, known as pits, etched in the surface of the disc. The smooth areas between the pits are called lans. The pits represent the 1's of digital code, and the lans represent the 0's. The pits and lans are arranged in spiral rings called tracks. The pits and lans on a DVD are about half the size of those on an audio CD or CD-ROM, and DVD tracks are narrower and bunched closer together.

To read the data, the player shines a small spot of laser light onto the disc as it rotates. The laser that reads DVD data has a shorter wavelength than the lasers used in CD technology. The shorter-wave-length laser has a finer focus, which is what enables it to make out the smaller pits and lans and narrower tracks in the DVD's layers.

The encoding of data in layers also

More data can fit on a DVD, *top*, than on a CD, *bottom*, because DVD's have smaller pits that are closer together. The tracks are also closer together to further boost DVD storage capacity.

Comparing data-storage technologies

Technology	Advantages	Limitations
CD-ROM	■ Capacity to hold text, graphics, video clips, animation, and sound. ■ Holds 680 megabytes of data.	■ Computer user cannot change the information put on the discs. ■ Single-sided, single-layered format limits storage capacity.
DVD	■ Holds 8.5 gigabytes of data—about 20 times more data than CD-ROM's. ■ Holds four hours of video, 16 hours of audio, or an entire library of text. ■ Stores a movie in versions for adults or children, and in a variety of languages and rated versions, screen formats, and camera angles. ■ DVD-ROM drives operate both DVD-ROM, DVD video, as well as audio CD's and CD-ROM's.	■ Players available in 1997 were not yet capable of recording videos or music. A recordable DVD player was expected to be on the market by the year 2000. ■ Players are two to three times as expensive as VCR's. ■ Movie studios have been reluctant to embrace DVD.
Laser disc	■ High quality sound and pictures. ■ Capable of storing up to eight hours of video.	■ Can play only prerecorded movies. ■ Can only be played on laser disc players. ■ Movie studios have released only a limited selection of movies on laser disc.

increases the information-storage capacity of DVD's. The upper layer (or layers) is *semitransmissive*—it permits some laser waves to pass through its surface to read the underlying data.

Even more information can be crammed onto a DVD with a technique known as data compression. This process reduces the amount of space needed to store video images by eliminating repeated information. Every second of a video image is made up of 30 still frames shown in rapid succession to create the illusion of movement. Most images, however, change little from one split-second frame to the next. With data compression, only the parts of the picture that have changed are encoded as new information on the disc.

The added storage space created by data compression allowed manufacturers to produce video DVD's with theater-quality surround sound, lush, high-definition images, and an array of special features. For example, not only can a DVD disc contain a full-length movie with exceptionally high-quality video, it can also store the movie soundtrack in up to eight languages as well as text subtitles in up to 32 languages. A DVD could even contain two versions of a movie—an R-rated version for parents

and a PG-rated version for children. The technology could also allow viewers to choose from a selection of movie endings, though no such films had yet been produced for DVD's in 1997.

An interactive mechanism on DVD's allows viewers to play at being a movie or TV director. With a click of a button, they can change the screen format from regular to widescreen or flip between different camera angles. For example, when watching a recorded football game, a viewer can watch the same play from the sideline, from a camera mounted on a goal post, or from an overhead view.

DVD video players can be hooked up to regular television sets, but the electronics industry hoped to develop a high-resolution digital television with high-fidelity speakers that would eventually replace standard sets. In the meantime, manufacturers recommended that DVD video players be wired to stereo speakers to enhance the video's sound quality.

The other type of DVD—DVD-ROM—offers even greater interactive features than CD-ROM. The multilayered discs provide breathing room to programmers whose graphics capabilities were restricted by the limits of the

CD-ROM. The added space allows for full-motion video, high-quality audio, and high-resolution pictures, games, and graphics.

DVD technology was developed in 1995, but industry infighting over distribution concerns kept the new devices off store shelves until 1997. Manufacturers had planned to unveil DVD's during the 1996 Christmas shopping season. That release date, however, was delayed while movie producers, software makers, and electronics-industry executives debated how they would prevent the *piracy* (illegal copying and selling) of their products and control their distribution.

The potential for the illegal reproduction of DVD's put a scare into people who are counting on making hundreds of millions of dollars from the sale of DVD software and videos. Hollywood studios were particularly reluctant to accept the new technology. Because a movie in digital form could be copied over and over again by electronic pirates, with every copy as perfect as the original, the studios delayed introduction of DVD's while strong copyright protections were hammered out.

The threat of piracy also caused filmmakers to fret over control of the international distribution of their motion pictures. Movies are released to theaters in other countries at later dates than in the United States. By the time an American film makes its debut in foreign theaters, the video version of the movie often has been released already in the United States. The movie industry feared that pirated DVD videos would hit foreign markets before the movies had made it to theaters in those countries. By early 1997, DVD manufacturers had agreed to a distribution plan drafted by film makers.

In an attempt to save box office dollars, filmmakers proposed dividing the world into five regions, and they asked electronics companies to market a slightly different DVD player for each region. Under this plan, DVD's produced for a particular part of the world will be specially coded for the players in that region. Thus, DVD players sold in one region will be unable to play DVD video released in another region. That will make it futile for someone in Italy, for example, to obtain a DVD copy of the latest *Die Hard* sequel from America for the purpose of making and selling pirated discs before the movie opens at Italian theaters.

Along with their other concerns, motion-picture producers, who were expected to release only about 100 DVD video titles in 1997, doubted that the public was willing to pay for the new gadgetry. Studio heads worried that consumers would be reluctant to dump their VCR's in favor of an unfamiliar technology. Americans had invested about $30 billion in VCR's by 1997, and there were thousands of movies available on videotape. Moreover, VCR owners can record movies and programs from their TV sets. By contrast, DVD players, which ranged in price from $500 to $1,000—twice the cost of a VCR—cannot record and can play only the limited number of titles released on DVD.

The computer industry was quicker to embrace the new technology, and companies were producing DVD-ROM drives in 1997. Drives manufactured as separate add-ons to older computers were priced between $200 and $400—a cost that might not turn off computer users, who are used to the expense of upgrading their machines.

DVD manufacturers were also hoping to generate interest among the movie buffs who enthusiastically embraced laser disc technology when it was first introduced in 1981. Laser discs far surpass VCR's in sound and picture quality. Many people in the electronics industry assumed that the laser disc would become the most popular system for playing movies at home, but that never happened. Industry analysts blamed the product's failure on its inability to record and on the limited selection of laser disc movies—the same problems that dogged DVD technology in 1997.

DVD manufacturers hoped to win over critics and ignite consumer interest when the discs finally hit store shelves. Industry insiders predicted that more than 10 million DVD-video players and 100 million DVD-ROM drives would be in American homes by the year 2000. The industry outlook was so sunny, in fact, that one DVD enthusiast advised that if you still haven't figured out how to program your VCR, don't bother learning now.

[Richard Sheffield]

Is Melatonin a "Miracle Cure" for Insomnia?

Health food stores in 1997 found it hard to keep pace with consumer demand for melatonin, a hormone that helps regulate the human sleep cycle.

It has happened to most of us. Instead of peacefully drifting off to sleep at night, we end up tossing and turning restlessly. Every sound disturbs us, and thoughts race through our minds making us feel uneasy or even panicky as we think about tomorrow and its problems.

The culprit is insomnia, the inability to sleep. Insomnia is recognized as a serious problem that affects people's productivity and happiness. The average person needs seven to eight hours of sleep a night, although sleep requirements and patterns of sleep vary from one individual to another. But whatever their particular needs, doctors say, many people today are not getting enough sleep.

People will try anything from counting sheep to popping pills in their quest for a good night's sleep. In 1997, millions of Americans ignored doctors' cautions and swallowed the newest "miracle cure" for insomnia—melatonin, a hormone supplement that may cause more problems than it relieves.

Sleeplessness has many causes. Physical ailments are sometimes involved, but in most cases stress or an irregular schedule that has tampered with the body's internal clock are at the root of the problem. The normal pattern of sleep and wakefulness is governed by a bodily mechanism known as a biological clock. Other animals have biological clocks that tell them when it is time to migrate, mate, or hibernate. One of the reasons for melatonin's popularity is its role in regulating the biological clock.

Many researchers point to the electric light bulb as the leading cause of sleep problems related to our biological clocks. When Thomas Edison, a well-known cat-napper, invented the light bulb, he also extended our "days," so that most activities no longer had to cease at nightfall. Work, social events, studying, and many other activities can now go on well into the night.

Our jam-packed days and shorter nights open the door to stress, another sleep stealer. Stress can set off a chemical reaction that causes our bodies to go into a "fight or flight" state. In this condition, a relic of our evolutionary past, the body is put on red alert, prepared to fight or run from a real or imagined foe. Moreover, insomnia itself can be a source of stress, as the fear of not being able to sleep replaces the original source of anxiety.

Not only are we dealing with more stress in our daily lives, we're also avoiding or ignoring the cues that our bodies need to get to sleep. Human beings are *diurnal* animals—we are biologically primed to sleep at night and be active during the day.

Our biological clocks respond to environmental cues that trigger physical responses that lead to sleep. The process begins when the retina of the eye senses darkness and relays that information to the brain. The brain then releases chemical messengers, such as hormones, that tell the rest of the body that it's time to sleep. The best known of these messenger hormones is melatonin.

Melatonin, the hormone that functions as the body's own sleeping potion, originates in the pineal gland, a tiny, pea-shaped gland located in the center of the brain. The gland produces the chemical from dusk until dawn. Babies begin producing melatonin when they are about 3 months old. Production gradually increases throughout childhood and peaks just before puberty.

After puberty, melatonin production gradually decreases. By the time most people are 70 years old, their pineal gland has hardened, and melatonin production has almost ceased.

Medical studies have shown that small doses of melatonin may ease the effects of *jet lag* (fatigue and irritability following long flights through several time zones). In addition, researchers at the Massachusetts Institute of Technology (MIT) in Cambridge, Massachusetts, found that the hormone may help night-shift workers sleep in the daytime.

In the mid-1990's, researchers in the United States linked declining melatonin levels to the aging process. Some researchers published those claims in books, leading people to believe that these preliminary findings proved that melatonin reverses the aging process. Soon, headlines were claiming that melatonin supplements not only aided

---

Getting a good night's sleep without drugs

- **Don't drink coffee, colas or other caffeinated beverages late in the day.**

- **Keep regular hours.** Awakening at more or less the same time each day is one of the best ways to keep the body's biological clock in order.

- **Exercise regularly to relieve tension.** A good time for a walk or workout is late afternoon or early evening, allowing the body to slow down and relax before it is time to go to bed.

- **Don't use alcohol as a sedative.**

- **Develop a sleep ritual** such as taking a bath, reading, or listening to music.

- **Don't bring work or worries into bed.**

- **Don't oversleep.**

- **Create a comfortable sleep environment** that is dark, and neither too hot nor too cold.

- **Don't assume that more sleep is always better.** The longer people stay in bed, the shallower and more fragmented their sleep becomes.

---

sleep but might also prevent the physical and mental decline that comes with aging and the cellular changes that lead to diseases such as cancer. More than 20 million Americans flocked to health food stores and pharmacies to buy melatonin pills.

This stampede prompted many physicians and other researchers to speak out against the casual use of melatonin and to dismiss the health claims about the product. Researchers warned that articles and books that touted the hormone as a "cure-all" based their claims on flimsy scientific evidence.

As of 1997, scientists had yet to study the long-term effects of melatonin on the human body. Although most researchers agreed that melatonin induces sleep and shifts the sleep cycle, no evidence supported claims that melatonin cures cancer, increases the human sex drive, or reverses the effects of aging. Scientists at MIT, Northwestern University in Evanston, Illinois, and Harvard University in Cambridge, Massachusetts, called these claims "irre-

Facts about melatonin

- Produced naturally in the human body by the pineal gland, located in the center of the brain. Darkness triggers the body to produce melatonin.

- Babies begin producing melatonin at 3 months old.

- The body ceases melatonin production at around age 70.

- Melatonin helps regulate the body's biological clock. Elevated levels in the blood lull the body into sleep.

- Melatonin sold in supplement form is made from synthetic chemicals or extracted from the pituitary glands of cows.

- Low-doses of a melatonin supplement can hasten sleep and lessen the effects of jet lag.

- No one has ever studied the effects of long-term melatonin use in humans.

- The Food and Drug Administration does not regulate melatonin, which is classified as a dietary supplement.

- Pregnant women are advised not to take melatonin since doctors do not know how it will affect a fetus.

- Children, whose pituitary glands produce the hormone in abundance, are advised not to take melatonin supplements.

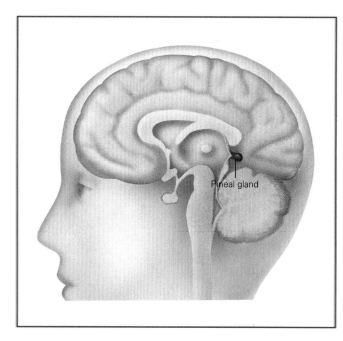

The pineal gland, the source of melatonin, is located near the center of the brain. Melatonin is believed to play an important role in a person's sleep patterns, but there is little evidence to support the many other claims being made for the hormone.

sponsible," "seriously flawed," "absurd," and even "wicked." A researcher at Northwestern accused some scientists of skewing results and misinterpreting data to promote sales of the hormone.

Doctors cautioned that melatonin makes the human body react in a variety of ways. They pointed out that some people are highly sensitive to melatonin and either should not ingest the hormone or should take doses much smaller than those offered in the over-the-counter supplement. (An average dose of over-the-counter melatonin increases the hormone to 30 times its normal level in the bloodstream.) Taking too much melatonin, or taking it at the wrong time of day, physicians warned, may bring on sleep at an inconvenient or even dangerous time, such as while driving.

Doctors were also concerned that no agency regulates the quality of the over-the-counter supplement. The Food and Drug Administration (FDA) does not monitor commercial production of melatonin because the hormone is sold as a dietary supplement and is thus not subject to FDA scrutiny. The FDA has collected complaints from people who have suffered from disrupted sleep, genital pain, and nausea after taking melatonin. Nonetheless, the FDA said it would not control the compound until research clearly shows that it can be harmful to health.

Anyone concerned about the strength or purity of the supplement must either trust the manufacturer's claims on the label or hire a lab to perform a chemical analysis. Most melatonin sold in the United States is made from synthetic chemicals and is probably free of contaminants. However, some U.S. and foreign manufacturers extract melatonin from the pineal glands of cows.

Scientists caution against using melatonin derived from cow brains. In 1996, British researchers established a possible link between eating beef from cattle infected with bovine spongiform encephalitis ("mad-cow disease") and developing a new form of Creutzfeldt-Jakob disease (CJD), a rare and deadly degenerative disease of the human brain. The investigators feared that melatonin from infected cattle could transmit CJD. Although the United

Kingdom placed a ban in 1989 on the sale of any product made from a cow's nervous system, in 1997 melatonin made from cows was still produced in other European countries. Doctors advised consumers to purchase only synthetic melatonin.

Researchers also warned that children and adolescents, whose melatonin levels are already high, should not take the hormone. Doctors were concerned that melatonin supplements might delay the onset of puberty in adolescents.

In 1997, most doctors and scientists agreed that extensive research must be conducted on the hormone before they could approve of its use as a sleeping aid. Doctors advised people who are desperate for some shut-eye to try sleeping aids that don't come out of a bottle.

Fortunately, overcoming insomnia is not that difficult for most people. In many cases, simple sleep-inducing techniques or changes in personal habits will restore normal sleeping patterns. Many doctors who specialize in sleep medicine prefer this approach to the use of sleeping pills, which may cause dependence or have other unwanted side effects.

To help the body know that it is time to sleep, physicians suggest making one's bedroom as dark as possible, which should trigger the brain to release the chemical messengers that induce sleep. Sleep experts also recommend that people do their television viewing in other rooms so that the bedroom is more strongly associated with sleep.

People can also help themselves get to sleep by cutting back on alcohol, cigarettes, and caffeine, all of which can contribute to insomnia. Although alcohol initially relaxes the body, it can disrupt normal sleep patterns. It is also important to note that alcohol combined with sleeping pills can be fatal. Cigarettes, which contain nicotine, a drug that stimulates the body, and food and drinks containing caffeine, another stimulant, can also disturb sleep patterns.

Relaxation techniques can bring an agitated body and mind to the sleep-ready state. One such technique involves tensing and releasing the muscles of the body one at a time, starting with the toes and moving up to the scalp.

If insomnia persists despite such efforts, sleeping pills may be necessary,

Avoiding jet lag without drugs

Before leaving:
- Beginning several days before departure, gradually shift sleeping and eating patterns, as much as possible, to coincide with the time zone of your destination.
- Avoid overeating and the consumption of alcohol.

While traveling:
- Avoid alcohol.
- Do not smoke.

At your destination:
- Adopt local time immediately upon arrival.
- Get as much sleep as you can in the first couple of days.
- After flying east, get out in the morning light.
- After flying west, stay outside in the late afternoon.

Source: U.S. Food and Drug Administration.

but experts caution that they should be used only as a last resort. Some sleeping pills, such as Sominex and Nytol, are available "over-the-counter" without a doctor's prescription. The active ingredient in these drugs is diphenhydramine, an antihistamine commonly used in allergy medications. Because antihistamines tend to cause drowsiness, pharmaceutical manufacturers use them in sleeping pills. While antihistamine sleeping pills do help bring on slumber, they tend to cause a "hung over" feeling the next day.

More potent sleeping pills are available through a doctor's prescription. However, most prescription pills are effective for only two to three weeks at a given dose, after which increasingly larger doses are needed to get the same effect. The American Sleep Disorders Association warns that the use of sleeping pills can lead to fatal overdoses, harmful interactions with other medications, interference with breathing, and damage to the kidneys, liver, and lungs.

Sleep experts maintain that behavior modification and relaxation techniques remain the safest and most effective methods of curing insomnia.

[Bonny Hart]

Reducing the Dangers of Hazardous Household Waste

Americans toss out more than 180 million metric tons (200 million tons) of garbage every year. In addition to the mountains of chicken bones, newspapers, and plastic wrappers that pile up in the trash, people annually dispose of an estimated 1.45 million metric tons (1.6 million tons) of hazardous household waste. Although the bulk of household garbage can be recycled, incinerated, or dumped in a landfill, hazardous waste needs special handling and should not be mixed in with the rest of the trash.

About 60 different hazardous chemical materials—ranging from flammable liquids to aerosols containing a form of nerve gas—can be found in the average household. These chemicals, which are ingredients in such products as paint, flea collars, and drain cleaners, can pose environmental and health hazards.

The Environmental Protection Agency (EPA) has defined four major types of hazardous waste: corrosive, toxic, ignitable, and reactive. A corrosive waste—battery acid, for example—causes a chemical action that eats away materials or living tissue. Toxic wastes, found in such things as pesticides, cleaning products, paints, and photographic supplies, can cause poisoning or even death in small concentrations.

Ignitable wastes, found in lighter fluid, gasoline, kerosene, nail polish remover, and oils, burn easily and can catch fire spontaneously. Reactive wastes, such as acids in drain cleaners, react chemically with air, water, or other substances, generating heat or even exploding.

The EPA regulates the disposal of hazardous waste generated by business-

More than a million tons of hazardous household waste is discarded in the United States each year. Most of it ends up in landfills not equipped to handle such material.

es and industry. However, the agency does not have a big enough staff to monitor the disposal of household hazardous waste. The agency counts on people in every household to use proper methods of disposal. According to the EPA, products that should not be casually tossed into the trash include the following items:

Solvents: These chemicals, used to remove grease or strip paint, contain numerous hazardous compounds including toluene and xylene. Both chemicals are flammable and poisonous, and can cause damage to the liver, kidneys, and bone marrow and interfere with the action of the nervous system.

Paint: Oil-based and latex paints are flammable and can contaminate the water supply if flushed into a sewage system. Substances in paint can cause health problems if ingested.

Pesticides: When heated, most pesticides emit toxic fumes. Many pesticides that have been banned by the EPA can still be found around the house or in the garage. Substances purchased before the ban that contain chlordane and silvex can cause kidney damage and cancer. Diazinon, a chemical in many pesticides that interferes with the nervous system, is a threat to birds and animals as well as to humans.

Automotive products and supplies: Motor oil, which contains poisonous and cancer-causing substances, can pollute ground water if disposed of improperly. Motor oil dumped into a sewer system can damage the sewage treatment plant.

Gasoline is flammable and contains benzene, a known cancer-causing chemical. Gasoline can also irritate skin, and its fumes can damage the eyes, nose, and brain.

Most antifreeze contains ethylene glycol, which can damage the heart and kidneys. As little as 45 milliliters (1½ ounces) of antifreeze can kill a child. It can also be fatal to dogs and cats, which are attracted by its smell and taste. Antifreeze also contains heavy metals, which have been linked to nerve and kidney damage.

Batteries: Three heavy metals—cadmium, lead, and mercury—are commonly found in batteries. Cadmium is a probable *carcinogen* (cancer-causing substance). It can also damage the liver and

cause kidney failure. Mercury can produce birth defects and damage nerves, impairing hearing, walking, and talking. Lead, used in large quantities in automobile batteries, can cause blood disorders and harm the nervous system.

In 1996, the United States outlawed the manufacture of batteries containing mercury. However, many mercury batteries were still stored on household shelves when the law took effect.

Computers: Personal computers, which contain lead and mercury, are a growing source of hazardous waste. A 1991 study by Carnegie Mellon University in Pittsburgh, Pennsylvania, predicted that by the year 2000 more than 150 million home computers would be discarded worldwide.

Everyday items: Many products around the house that may not seem dangerous are far from harmless. For instance, most people do not use caution when handling glue or nail polish, but both emit toxic fumes and contain chemicals that are hazardous to the environment. Everyday items such as thermostats, thermometers, and fluorescent lamps, all of which contain some mercury, pose a hazard if people do not properly dispose of them. Oven, toilet bowl and drain cleaners, mothballs, and even smoke detectors—which contain small amounts of radioactive material—also can present hazards to health and the environment.

Most people dispose of hazardous household products by simply throwing them in the trash or pouring them down a drain. Others may burn them or dump them on a vacant lot. But these disposal methods can wreak havoc on the environment.

Hazardous waste from household products can contaminate lakes, rivers, streams, and groundwater. It takes only a small amount of a hazardous material to cause significant contamination. For example, according to the EPA, 3.8 liters (1 gallon) of motor oil is enough to make 3.8 million liters (1 million gallons) of water undrinkable.

When hazardous household products are poured down a sink or flushed down a toilet they enter either a septic system or a municipal sewer system. In a septic system, wastewater travels to a drain field where bacteria in the soil help break down the waste. Toxic mate-

Potentially hazardous household trash

Product	Possible hazards	Precautions	Disposal suggestions
Aerosols	Contents may be toxic and are easily inhaled. Cans may explode or burn if exposed to heat.	Store cans in a cool place.	Do not put cans in the trash unless they are completely empty. Do not burn cans or put them in a garbage compactor.
Antifreeze	A very poisonous substance. Has sweet taste that attracts children and pets.	Clean up any leaks or spills.	Never pour any amount down a sink with drainage to a septic system.
Auto batteries	Contain strong acid, very corrosive, and a danger to eyes and skin.	Old batteries can leak, so don't leave them lying around.	Most batteries can be recycled.
Auto motor oil and transmission fluid	Poisonous. Used oil and fluid may be contaminated with lead and other toxic substances. Skin and eye irritant.	Don't let drained oil or fluid spill onto the ground or run into the street.	Most oil and transmission fluid can be recycled.
Lacquer, lacquer thinner, and paint	Extremely flammable and poisonous.	Use only in a well-ventilated area. Do not use in a room with pilot light, open flame, electric motors, or spark-generating equipment. Do not smoke while using these products.	Use up according to label instructions or take remainder to a waste collection center.

rials in the wastewater can kill the helpful bacteria and damage the system. Some toxic materials can move through the soil without being broken down and contaminate ground or surface waters.

Hazardous household material that travels with wastewater to a central sewage system may end up in rivers, lakes, and streams. Hazardous waste dumped into ditches and fields can also pollute groundwater and streams as well as poisoning plants and wildlife and contaminating the soil.

Hazardous household wastes in trash containers can pose a threat to sanitation workers. Workers have been seriously burned, lost their eyesight, or suffered lung damage while handling hazardous materials that had been mixed in with ordinary trash. And people who have tried to burn hazardous waste have sometimes been overcome by poisonous fumes.

Hazardous waste that is tossed out with the trash often ends up in a municipal landfill. Corrosive chemicals in the waste can destroy a landfill's protective plastic liner and leak out, contaminating the soil and groundwater below.

In order to limit the damage caused by hazardous household waste, the EPA recommends that people recycle potentially hazardous products whenever possible and dispose of them only as a last resort. Many businesses are equipped to recycle motor oil, car batteries, and transmission fluid.

The EPA is also lending a hand with recycling. By 1997, the agency had helped set up more than 3,000 collection programs across the country to help people dispose of hazardous waste.

Information on what products are considered a hazardous waste, and how to properly dispose of them can be obtained from your local or state environmental protection agency. For information on EPA hazardous waste collection programs, contact the EPA at (800) 424-9346.   [Harvey Black]

Digestive Aids—Soothing the Beast in the Belly

Shoppers taking a stroll down the aisles of their local pharmacy could easily conclude that the human race is plagued by digestive upsets—and to a large extent, they'd be right. Most people experience indigestion and heartburn from time to time, and for many the problem can be a persistent, even daily, affliction.

Fortunately, a variety of remedies offer relief to the millions whose stomachs churn and burn. These range from old stand-bys that neutralize acid or break up gas bubbles in the stomach, to newer medications that temporarily switch off the secretion of stomach acid.

The new acid suppressors are over-the-counter versions of potent acid-fighting drugs that were once available only by prescription. In prescription form, the medications—called histamine H_2-receptor antagonists (also known as H_2-blockers)—were long used for the treatment of ulcers. The over-the-counter products, containing lower doses of those drugs, had become popular aids by 1997. The drugs relieve heartburn and heal *esophagitis* (inflammation of the esophagus).

Heartburn, indigestion, and a sour, acid, or upset stomach are catchall terms that people use to describe a variety of symptoms in the stomach and upper abdomen brought on mainly by eating. Symptoms of heartburn and indigestion include pain or pressure, bloating, burping, or a searing sensation behind the breastbone.

In many cases, these symptoms are due to a condition called *gastroesophageal reflux disease* (GERD), in which digestive acids in the stomach back up into the esophagus, the muscular tube that carries food from the mouth to the stomach. Normally, a muscular ring of tissue called the lower esophageal sphincter prevents acid backsplash. Sometimes, however, the sphincter fails to do its job and allows some of the stomach's acidic contents to squirt up into the esophagus.

If the result is the all-too-familiar hallmark of heartburn—a burning sensa-

tion behind the breastbone. The chest pain caused by heartburn can be so severe that sufferers sometimes think they are having a heart attack. Other people experience a backflow of acid—or reflux—all the way into the mouth, causing an acid or bitter taste. Asthmatic wheezing, laryngitis, a sore throat, or a nagging cough may also indicate acid reflux, even in people who have no other heartburn symptoms.

When reflux is frequent and severe it

Acid suppressors called H_2-blockers are among the newest types of over-the-counter heartburn and indigestion remedies on drug store shelves. Before 1996, H_2-blockers were available by prescription only.

can damage the tissues lining the esophagus, causing *esophagitis* (open sores, bleeding, and scarring), which can narrow the opening and make swallowing difficult. Some people develop a rare but serious condition that can lead to cancer of the esophagus.

Eating habits and other factors can play an important role in increasing the likelihood of heartburn. Overindulging or eating too quickly can prompt the stomach to produce a lot of acid. Eating just before bedtime or a nap increases the chances of heartburn, because the corrosive acids rise from the stomach more readily when the head is no longer higher than the stomach.

Overweight people and pregnant women are also more prone to heartburn, because the extra pounds or growing fetus create pressure on internal organs and help force the reflux fluid upward. In addition, wearing tight clothing or bending over soon after eating puts upward pressure on the esophageal sphincter and contributes to reflux.

Heartburn is influenced not only by how you eat but also by what you eat. Various foods and beverages can slow the rate at which the stomach empties,

allowing stomach acids to linger. Certain foods can also cause the lower esophageal sphincter to relax or irritate the tissue of the esophagus. Foods and beverages that commonly cause heartburn include fried or fatty foods, coffee (including decaffeinated), tea, cola drinks, chocolate, alcoholic beverages, peppermint, acidic foods (such as citrus juices and tomato-based products), spicy foods, onions, and garlic. Smoking and certain medicines, such as aspirin and other painkillers, also promote heartburn by stimulating stomach acid production, relaxing the esophageal sphincter, or reducing the production of acid-neutralizing saliva.

For people suffering from digestive upsets other than heartburn, the cause of what ails them is more elusive. Doctors use the word *dyspepsia* to describe persistent or recurrent discomfort or pain in the upper abdomen, nausea, and feelings of fullness or bloating, particularly after eating. Although such symptoms sometimes signal an identifiable problem, such as a *peptic ulcer* (a raw area in the lining of the stomach), that is not always the case. When no such cause is found, doctors generally classify the condition as nonulcer dyspepsia (NUD).

Studies have suggested that people with NUD have hypersensitive stomachs. In 1991, researchers in Spain reported the results of an experiment in which they passed a balloon into the stomachs of volunteers, some with NUD and some without. Only those with NUD reported discomfort when the inflated balloon stretched the stomach's walls.

Another study was reported in 1991 by investigators in Scotland. These researchers found that after meals, the stomachs of some NUD patients seemed to contract more sluggishly and to empty their contents into the small intestine more slowly than normal. About half of the NUD patients said their symptoms were related to eating, and for some, specific items such as fatty foods or coffee tended to trigger an episode or worsen it. But most of the patients said their symptoms were not definitely linked to specific foods.

The best treatment for digestive ailments depends on the severity of the problem. For occasional indigestion and heartburn, over-the-counter reme-

Heartburn is a sensation of burning in the esophagus caused by acid rising up from the stomach. Indigestion is a feeling of discomfort and bloating caused by an irritation of the stomach lining.

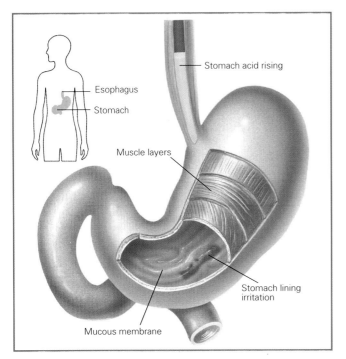

Esophagus

Stomach

Stomach acid rising

Muscle layers

Stomach lining irritation

Mucous membrane

Products for the relief of digestive upset

Drug	Brand name	Effects
Antacids ■ Aluminum (carbonate, hydroxide, phosphate forms)	Rolaids, Amphogel, Maalox, Mylanta	Neutralize stomach acid on contact. Provide fast but short-lived relief from heartburn and indigestion pain. Can constipate, cause diarrhea or gas.
■ Calcium (carbonate or phosphate forms	Tums and Alka-2	
■ Magnesium (carbonate, hydroxide, or other forms)	Gelusil, Maalox, Mylanta, Riopan, milk of magnesia	
■ Sodium bicarbonate	Alka-Seltzer and Bromo Seltzer	
Histamine H2-receptor antagonists (H2-blockers)	Tagamet, Pepcid, Zantac, Nizatidine	Suppress acid production in the stomach; promote healing of inflamed esophagus. May interact with asthma and blood-thinning drugs.
Proton-pump inhibitors	Prevacid, Prilosec	Suppress acid production in stomach; provide long-term relief. May interact with asthma and blood-thinning drugs.
Prokinetics	Urecholine, Reglan, Propulsid	Encourage movement of food through the digestive tract; speed emptying of the stomach; strengthen the lower esophageal sphincter. Can cause diarrhea.

dies can provide welcome relief. Persistent digestive woes may require stronger drugs that must be prescribed by a doctor. And in a small fraction of heartburn sufferers for whom medication fails to provide relief, surgery designed to place pressure on the esophageal sphincter to help keep it closed may be the solution.

The most frequently used over-the-counter products for digestive upset are antacids, available in both liquid and tablet form. Antacids contain chemical compounds called bases that neutralize excess stomach acid on contact. Liquids tend to be faster-acting, but tablets are already in recommended-dose form and are easy to carry. Antacids act quickly to douse the flames of heartburn, but their effects are short-lived.

There are four categories of antacids, based on their chemical makeup: products containing aluminum salts (such as ALternaGEL, Amphogel, and Rolaids), calcium salts (such as Alka-2, Calcium-Rich Rolaids, and Tums), magnesium salts (such as Gelusil, Maalox, and Mylanta), and sodium salts (such as Alka-Seltzer, Bromo Seltzer, and baking soda). All are effective at neutralizing

stomach acid, but each group has potential side effects. Each type can interact with other medications, which may make them unsuitable for people suffering from other medical conditions.

Sodium-based remedies, for example, can cause gas. And because they're high in sodium, they are not recommended for people on a salt-restricted diet, particularly those being treated for high blood pressure. The traditional home remedy of baking soda and water is out of favor, because baking soda is very high in sodium. Another problem with sodium-based remedies is that they can upset the body's acid balance, prompting the stomach to create more acid.

Antacids containing aluminum or calcium salts can cause constipation, and antacids with magnesium salts may cause diarrhea. (Some products combine aluminum or calcium salts with a magnesium salt to counterbalance the two effects.)

Aluminum antacids can also interfere with calcium absorption, and the overuse of aluminum antacids can weaken bones, especially in people with impaired kidney function. Kidney problems may result from extended and heavy use of either calcium- or magnesium-based antacids. The overuse of antacids with magnesium salts can also lead to serious heart problems.

Many commercial products aimed at calming digestive turmoil combine an antacid with other compounds. Some products, such as Mylanta, include an ingredient called simethicone that breaks up gas bubbles in the stomach.

Unlike antacids, which neutralize existing acid, the group of drugs called H_2-blockers are aimed at warding off heartburn and digestive upsets by suppressing acid secretion in the stomach. H_2-blockers take 30 minutes to an hour to kick in but offer 9 to 12 hours of protection, an advantage that makes them a good choice to keep reflux at bay through the night.

H_2-blockers attach to proteins called histamine-2 receptors on the stomach's acid-secreting cells. This action prevents the cells from being stimulated by a biochemical called histamine, thereby blocking acid production. Some H_2-blockers may interfere with drugs used to thin the blood or to treat asthma or seizures.

H_2-blockers—which include cimetidine, famotidine, nizatidine, and ranitidine—are available in liquid, tablet, or capsule form. All four can be obtained by prescription under the brand names Tagamet, Pepcid, Axid, and Zantac, respectively. Over-the-counter versions are also available at half the standard prescription dosage, under the names Tagamet HB, Pepcid AC, Axid AR, and Zantac 75.

Heartburn sufferers can combine the quick action of an antacid and the staying power of H_2-blockers by taking them together. Tagamet HB, Pepcid AC, and Axid AR may also be taken as a kind of antiheartburn insurance.

Because of possible side effects and the risk of interactions with other drugs, however, doctors caution against the overly casual use of acid-controlling drugs. They also warn that frequent use of the drugs can mask some serious medical conditions.

Moreover, even though H_2-blockers are more effective than antacids, some people who take them still have recurrent episodes of heartburn. For such patients, doctors may prescribe a full-strength H_2-blockers or a drug called a proton-pump (or acid pump) inhibitor, which in 1997 was one of the newest advances in heartburn treatment.

Proton-pump inhibitors, which include the drugs lansoprazole (Prevacid) and omeprazole (Prilosec), were the most powerful suppressors of acid secretion available in 1997. They work by deactivating a key substance needed by stomach cells to secrete acid. Side effects from proton-pump inhibitors are rare, though they may interact with blood-thinning drugs and some medications used to treat asthma, mood and sleep disorders, and seizures.

Other drugs used to do battle with digestive problems include compounds known as promotility, or prokinetic, agents. These drugs strengthen the esophageal sphincter, help move food through the digestive tract, and speed the emptying of the stomach, making them potentially useful remedies for some patients with heartburn or NUD. Researchers have found that cisapride (Propulsid), a member of this group of drugs, given alone or in combination with other drugs such as H_2-blockers, is the most effective and causes the fewest side-effects. It may cause diarrhea, however, and can interact with alcohol and with other medications.

In general, physicians say, when it comes to digestive upsets, it's a good idea to see your doctor if your symptoms last more than a few days or if you're having difficulty swallowing. Severe symptoms, such as extreme discomfort or pain in the digestive tract, frequent vomiting or diarrhea, vomiting blood or material that resembles coffee grounds (digested blood), or blood in the stool require immediate medical attention. Problems like these may signal a serious medical condition— such as a peptic ulcer, gall bladder disease, or, rarely, cancer—which could be masked by prolonged self-treatment. For this reason, experts caution against using digestive aids for extended periods of time unless under the supervision of a physician.

For digestive upsets caused by occasional indulgences, however, acid controllers and other digestive aids can help us cope with the consequences of giving in to temptation. But, simple lifestyle changes can go a long way toward alleviating the problem for many people.

[Joan Stephenson]

Carbon Monoxide Detectors: Tracking "the Silent Killer"

Most people already have at least one smoke detector inside their house. But hardware and housing supply stores are now offering another type of detector that should also be essential equipment in houses and apartments. These devices are designed to detect carbon monoxide, a gas that has been dubbed "the silent killer."

Carbon monoxide is an invisible, odorless, and tasteless gas, and when it is present in an enclosed area in sufficient quantities it can cause death by poisoning within minutes. It is the leading cause of gas poisoning deaths in the United States.

Carbon monoxide poisoning kills about 250 Americans in their homes annually, according to the National Fire Protection Association, and the danger is increasing because of several trends in house-building and heating technologies. For example, tightly sealed "energy efficient" houses are more likely to accumulate harmful levels of carbon monoxide than older houses that are not so well insulated. And some of the newer high-efficiency gas- or oil-burning furnaces can also contribute to the problem. According to fire fighters, these appliances are vulnerable to *backdrafting*, a phenomenon in which carbon-monoxide-rich combustion fumes get sucked back into a house instead of being vented up the chimney.

Any living environment contains some levels of carbon monoxide, which is a normal by-product of the *combustion* (burning) of natural gas, oil, wood, coal, and other fuels. The gas, which has the formula CO, is made up of one atom of carbon and one of oxygen.

The burning of fossil fuels usually releases mostly harmless carbon dioxide (CO_2) and water vapor. The proportion of carbon monoxide produced by combustion can become much greater than normal and can gradually build up indoors if there is not a rich supply of oxygen. This can occur if the fuel and air mixture in a furnace is improperly adjusted. Even if a heating appliance is adjusted properly, however, carbon monoxide can accumulate indoors if the combustion gases are prevented from leaving the house by a blocked chimney or a dislodged or broken flue pipe.

The most frequent causes of carbon monoxide poisoning in the home are blocked or clogged chimneys, malfunctioning wood-burning stoves, broken or damaged flue pipes from gas or oil furnaces, cracked furnace heat exchangers, and malfunctioning burners inside furnaces, water heaters, and gas clothes

Kitchens and fireplaces can be sources of carbon monoxide. A carbon monoxide detector can warn when dangerous levels of the gas are circulating in the home.

Type of detector	How it works
 Electric-powered plug-in sensors	These detectors can be plugged into a wall outlet or wired directly into a house's electrical system. A heated metallic sensor reacts with CO in a way that changes the electrical conductivity of a wire. A computer chip in the detector converts these conductivity changes into a CO concentration reading. Many plug-in detectors have a numerical display that continually tracks the CO concentration and can show the previous high level. The devices emit a loud, continuous alarm when they detect CO levels that are rising into the danger zone.
 Battery-powered sensors	Most battery-powered detectors use a *biomimetic* (life-mimicking) sensor, a disk coated with a chemical that absorbs and combines with CO in much the same way that the blood protein hemoglobin does. As the disk absorbs CO, its surface grows darker in color. A light-sensitive detector measures the degree of darkening and converts it into a concentration reading. The device sounds an alarm when the detector measures a dangerous level of CO.
 Carbon monoxide detection cards	These cards have a dot containing a chemical that combines with CO. The dot changes color when the card is exposed to a high level of CO.

dryers. Inadequately vented fireplaces and attached garages that permit automobile exhaust to enter a house can also cause carbon monoxide poisoning. Activities that can lead to a dangerous buildup of carbon monoxide include operating kerosene space heaters with inadequate ventilation, using charcoal grills indoors, or running a gas range to heat a room.

Regardless of how carbon monoxide is released into the air of a home, even tiny quantities of it can be extremely poisonous. That is because the gas is about 250 times more likely than oxygen to combine with *hemoglobin* (the red oxygen-carrying pigment inside red blood cells).

When carbon monoxide is inhaled, it combines with hemoglobin to form a compound called carboxyhemoglobin. Unlike ordinary hemoglobin, carboxyhemoglobin is unable to absorb oxygen from the lungs and thus cannot transport oxygen to the body's cells. As a result, the cells are gradually starved of oxygen.

The first symptoms of carbon monoxide poisoning resemble the flu. As little as 200 parts per million (ppm) of carbon monoxide in the air (0.02 percent by volume) can cause a headache, fatigue, nausea, and dizziness after two or three hours. A concentration of 800 ppm can produce a headache after one hour, unconsciousness, convulsions, and heart failure in two hours, and death within three hours. A nonfatal poisoning may result in brain or heart damage.

Poisoning can occur in as little as three minutes after exposure to high levels of carbon monoxide. Infants, the elderly, and individuals with heart disease are likely to show symptoms of poisoning more quickly than other people.

The best way to avoid carbon monoxide poisoning is to keep your furnace, water heater, fireplace, and chimney clean and well maintained. However, in the event that one of these appliances or devices malfunctions, carbon

Effectiveness

Most plug-in detectors will sense very low levels of CO, and will sound an alarm when levels reach 100 parts per million. Some models are equipped with a back-up battery in case of power outage.

Most battery-powered sensors are as effective as AC-powered devices. However, batteries must be checked and changed regularly.

Underwriters Laboratories, Inc. (UL), an organization that sets safety standards for appliances, says cards give inaccurate CO readings, and thus it does not recommend them.

monoxide detectors can provide a crucial early warning if the gas begins to build up in the air. These devices, which sell for $30 to $95, are available under such brand names as First Alert, Nighthawk, Lifesaver, S-Tech, American Sensors, Enzone, Emerson, and Macuro.

The devices emit a loud, continuous alarm when they detect carbon monoxide levels that are rising into the "danger zone"—a minimum concentration of about 100 ppm. Some devices also emit an intermittent alarm or a chirping sound or flash a warning light when they detect concentrations slightly below the danger zone. Other models provide a digital readout of carbon monoxide concentrations.

Electronic detectors should not be confused with carbon monoxide detection cards, which contain a chemical dot that changes color when the card is exposed to high levels of the gas. These cards do not sound an alarm and so must be checked frequently for signs of

high carbon monoxide concentration.

The concentration of carbon monoxide in the air determines how soon an electronic detector sounds its alarm. According to standards set by Underwriters Laboratories, Inc. (UL), a non-profit organization that conducts safety tests on products, a carbon monoxide detector should sound an alarm in less than 90 minutes when 100 ppm of the gas is present. The UL standards require a detector to sound in less than 35 minutes for carbon monoxide concentrations of 200 ppm and in less than 15 minutes for a level of 400 ppm or higher. Most carbon monoxide detectors that were on the market in 1997 met or exceeded those standards.

Detectors come in several varieties. AC house current powers some detectors. These units can be plugged into a wall outlet or wired directly into a house's electrical system. Other units are battery operated. Both the plug-in and battery-operated detectors are reliable, but each has certain advantages and disadvantages.

With a plug-in unit, you never have to worry about changing the battery. On the other hand, such devices become inoperative if the electric power in your house fails. Some of the more expensive plug-in detectors include a battery backup for extra security. Battery-powered detectors are easy to install and move, and they operate during power outages. But their batteries require monitoring.

Detectors use several methods to measure carbon monoxide concentrations in the air. The AC-powered models usually employ a sensing device made of a metal wire that changes its electrical *conductivity* (ability to conduct a current) when exposed to carbon monoxide. A computer chip in the detector converts these conductivity changes into concentration readings.

Most battery-operated detectors use a *biomimetic* (life-mimicking) sensor, which consists of a disk coated with a chemical that absorbs and chemically combines with carbon monoxide in much the same way that hemoglobin does. As the disk absorbs the carbon monoxide, its surface grows darker in color. A light-sensitive detector measures the degree of darkening and converts it into a concentration reading.

The effects of carbon monoxide on the body

Concentration (parts per million)	Symptoms
35	No adverse effects within 8 hours.
200	Mild headache after 2 to 3 hours.
400	Headache and nausea after 1 to 2 hours.
800	Headache, nausea, and dizziness after 45 minutes; collapse after 2 hours.
1,000	Loss of consciousness after 1 hour.
1,600	Headache, nausea, and dizziness after 20 minutes; unconsciousness after 30 minutes.
3,200	Headache, nausea, and dizziness after 5 to 10 minutes; unconsciousness after 30 minutes.
12,800	Unconsciousness and danger of death after 1 to 3 minutes.

When carbon monoxide drops to an acceptable level, the sensors return to their original state.

Of course, the devices are not able to detect carbon monoxide levels if they are not plugged in or if their batteries are dead. For this reason, detectors come equipped with lights that indicate whether they are receiving power. Most detectors also feature a mechanism that allows you to test the alarm to ensure it is in working order.

The alarm test button often doubles as a reset button that allows you to turn the alarm off after the device detects hazardous levels of carbon monoxide. If the detector continues to measure high levels of gas, the alarm will sound again several minutes after someone pushes the reset button. Once the carbon monoxide concentration falls below the level that triggered the alarm, the alarm should shut off automatically.

The U.S. Consumer Product Safety Commission recommends installing at least one carbon monoxide detector per household, preferably near the sleeping quarters. However, because a detector's alarm may not be loud enough to be heard throughout the house, safety experts suggest installing additional units in frequently used parts of the house.

Some rooms, though, are not good places to install detectors. Installing a carbon monoxide detector too close to a gas range or near any gas or oil heating appliance may produce false alarms. Also, high humidity and water vapor can damage the sensor inside a detector, so it is not advisable to install the devices in bathrooms.

When buying a carbon monoxide detector, look for a model that has the UL label on it, indicating that the unit meets the minimum Underwriters Laboratories performance standards for such devices. Installing the detector is easy—either plug it into a wall outlet or insert batteries and screw it onto a wall. You can place the detector anywhere on a wall or on the ceiling. (Because carbon monoxide has nearly the same density as air, it does not accumulate in either high or low places.) The services of an electrical contractor may be needed to wire a detector directly into the house current.

Once the detector has power, its sensor will take a few hours to adjust to the atmosphere in the house. Typically, a red light will flash on and off during this warm-up period and will stop flashing when the unit is ready for operation.

After the detector has been installed, test it at least once a month by pushing the test/reset button. If the alarm sounds when you push this button, the unit is working properly. Testing the detector by placing it close to an automobile exhaust pipe, which emits extremely high levels of carbon monoxide, will permanently damage the unit's sensor. Maintain your detector by keeping it free of dust, grease, and humidity.

If the alarm on your detector sounds continuously and members of your household are experiencing headaches, drowsiness, or other symptoms of carbon monoxide poisoning, the National Fire Protection Association urges you to evacuate the premises immediately and call 911 or your local fire department.

However, the association says, if nobody is showing any ill effects, try opening the windows and doors to ventilate the house and see if that silences the alarm. If the fresh air stops the alarm, ask your heating contractor or appliance service center to send a specialist who can locate and eliminate the source of the carbon monoxide.

[Gordon Graff]

WORLD BOOK

Supplement

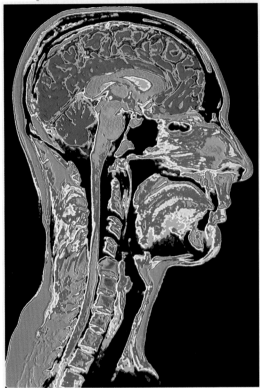

Twelve new or revised articles reprinted
from the 1997 edition of
The World Book Encyclopedia

Dinosaurs ruled the earth for millions of years. Although these creatures died out long ago, they still fascinate people. Many museums have exhibits that reconstruct what dinosaurs may have looked like. The exhibit above shows a skeleton and a model of the dinosaur *Herrerasaurus. Herrerasaurus* was one of the earliest meat-eating dinosaurs.

Dinosaur

Dinosaur is the name of a group of prehistoric reptiles that ruled the earth for about 160 million years. These animals died out millions of years ago, but they have fascinated people ever since they were first described in the early 1800's. The name *dinosaur* comes from the term *Dinosauria,* which means *terrible lizards.* But dinosaurs were not lizards, only distantly related to them, and most were not very terrible.

Some of the best-known dinosaurs were terrifying, however. Many were of enormous size. Some dinosaurs towered above and weighed more than any other animal ever to live on land. The largest dinosaurs may have grown as long as 150 feet (45 meters) and weighed as much as 85 short tons (77 metric tons). Such giants would have been more than 10 times as heavy as a full-grown elephant. The only animals that grow to this size today are a few kinds of whales, and they live only in the water. Size was not the only characteristic that made some dinosaurs terrifying. Many large dinosaurs were fierce and deadly meat-eaters.

The first dinosaurs appeared on the earth about 230

David B. Weishampel, the contributor of this article, is Associate Professor of Cell Biology and Anatomy at the Johns Hopkins University School of Medicine. He coedited The Dinosauria and coauthored The Evolution and Extinction of the Dinosaurs. Unless otherwise credited, the paintings and diagrams were prepared for World Book by Alex Ebel.

million years ago. They lived in nearly all natural settings, from open plains to forests to the edges of swamps, lakes, and oceans. Then about 65 million years ago, the dinosaurs died out.

Dinosaurs varied greatly in how big they grew, how they looked, and where they lived. Some of the most famous were such gigantic animals as *Apatosaurus, Diplodocus,* and *Tyrannosaurus*—pronounced *uh PAT uh SAWR uhs, duh PLAHD uh kuhs,* and *tih RAN uh SAWR uhs. Apatosaurus* (formerly called *Brontosaurus)* grew about 70 feet (21 meters) long. *Diplodocus* reached an even greater length—about 90 feet (27 meters). Both *Apatosaurus* and *Diplodocus* were plant-eaters. Each had a small head and an extremely long neck and tail. *Tyrannosaurus* was a fierce meat-eater. It stood almost 12 feet (3.7 meters) tall at the hips and had an enormous head and long, pointed teeth. But not all dinosaurs were giants. The smallest kinds were approximately the size of a chicken.

In certain ways, dinosaurs were like many modern reptiles. For example, some dinosaurs had teeth and skin much like those of alligators living today. Many were probably about as intelligent as crocodiles and alligators. However, dinosaurs also differed from present-day reptiles in many ways. For example, no modern reptiles grow as large as the biggest dinosaurs. In addition, many kinds of dinosaurs were *bipedal*—that is, they walked on their hind legs. Dinosaurs also had a different kind of leg posture. Lizards, turtles, and most other modern reptiles hold their legs out to the sides of their body in a low, sprawling posture. But dinosaurs held their legs under their body, much like those of a bird, a horse, a dog, or a person. This upright posture enabled dinosaurs to walk on all four legs without dragging their bellies on the ground.

Dinosaurs lived during most of the Mesozoic Era. This period in the earth's history lasted from about 240 million to 65 million years ago. The Mesozoic is sometimes called the *Age of Reptiles* or *Age of Dinosaurs* because dinosaurs and other reptiles were the largest animals during that time. Dinosaurs belonged to a group of closely related animals called *archosaurs (AHR kuh sawrs,* meaning *ruling reptiles).* However, not all archosaurs were dinosaurs. Other well-known members of this group included *crocodilians* (alligators and related animals) and *pterosaurs (TEHR uh sawrs,* meaning *winged reptiles).* By about 65 million years ago, nearly all archosaurs and many other creatures had died out, and the Mesozoic Era came to an end.

Scientists do not know why dinosaurs died out. For many years, scientists thought that dinosaurs had left no

descendants (offspring). But since the 1960's, dinosaur research has indicated that birds descended from particular kinds of small, meat-eating dinosaurs. This research has led many scientists to classify birds as living dinosaurs.

Scientists learn about dinosaurs by studying their fossils, which include preserved dinosaur bones, teeth, eggs, nests, tracks, skin imprints, and waste material. Scientists also study living animals that resemble dinosaurs in some ways.

The world of the dinosaurs

When dinosaurs lived, the earth was much different than it is today. For example, the Alps, the Himalaya, and many other surface features had not yet formed. The first flowering plants did not appear until late in the Mesozoic Era. Mammals, which evolved at about the same time as dinosaurs, were extremely small during the Mesozoic. In addition, many plants and animals that are now extinct or rare were common then.

Land and climate. Scientists believe the earth's continents have not always been arranged as they are today. About 250 million years ago, they formed a single land

Interesting facts about dinosaurs

WORLD BOOK illustrations by Tim Hayward, Bernard Thornton Artists

Tyrannosaurus rex, whose name means *king of the tyrant lizards,* was one of the most frightening meat-eaters of its time. It grew about 40 feet (12 meters) in length and had teeth about 6 inches (13 centimeters) long.

Dinosaurs and birds are closely related. Many dinosaurs looked much like modern birds. For example, the dinosaur *Ornithomimus, below right,* resembled the modern ostrich, *above right.*

The huge head of *Styracosaurus* had many spikes on top of its bony frill. The animal also had a parrot-like beak and a large horn over its nose.

Seismosaurus was one of the largest of all dinosaurs. It may have weighed 85 short tons (77 metric tons), more than 10 times as much as a full-grown elephant.

mass surrounded by an enormous sea. During the Mesozoic Era, this land mass began to break apart to form the continents and oceans that we know today. The continents slowly drifted away from each other toward their present locations.

As the continents moved, their surface features and climate changed. For a time, huge, shallow seas covered portions of North America, Europe, Africa, and Asia. Thick forests bordered drier plains, and swamps and deltas lined the seacoasts. Later in the Mesozoic, the seas drained from the continents and the Rocky Mountains began to form.

Throughout the Mesozoic, dinosaurs lived in a climate that was milder and less changeable than the climate today. Areas near the seas and along rivers and lakes may have had mild, moist weather all year. Inland regions were drier and, in some cases, desertlike. Toward the end of the Age of Reptiles, the climate grew cooler and drier and the change of seasons became more distinct.

Plant and animal life also changed during the Mesozoic Era. During the first half of the era, primitive forms of *conifers* (cone-bearing trees), *cycads* (palmlike trees), and ginkgoes were among the most common plants. Other plant life included ferns, giant horsetails, and mosses. Land animals, in addition to dinosaurs, included crocodilians, frogs, insects, lizards, turtles, and a few kinds of small mammals. Many reptiles lived in the seas, including *ichthyosaurs (IHK thee uh sawrs),* which resembled porpoises, and *plesiosaurs (PLEE see uh sawrs),* which had long necks. Other Mesozoic sea creatures included clams, corals, jellyfish, snails, sponges, squids, and starfish, as well as sharks and many other primitive varieties of fish. Flying pterosaurs dominated the skies.

During the second half of the Mesozoic Era, the first flowering plants began to appear. Forest trees included the first modern conifers as well as primitive magnolias, oaks, palms, and willows. Birds had evolved from small meat-eating dinosaurs, and the first snakes appeared. The dominant sea animals were gigantic lizards called

mosasaurs (MOH suh sawrs). These animals had flippers instead of legs. Other sea creatures included huge turtles and the first modern bony fish.

Kinds of dinosaurs

Dinosaurs lived throughout most of the Mesozoic Era, which is divided into three periods—Triassic, Jurassic, and Cretaceous. The Triassic Period lasted from about 240 million to 205 million years ago. The Jurassic lasted from about 205 million to 138 million years ago, and the Cretaceous from about 138 million to 65 million years ago.

Dinosaur ancestors. Dinosaurs probably evolved from the same ancestors as crocodilians and other archosaurs. Scientists believe the ancestors were small, meat-eating reptiles. These agile predators hunted prey by chasing after it on their hind legs and sometimes on all four legs. Scientists have discovered fossils of several kinds of archosaurs that lived at the beginning of the Mesozoic.

One possible dinosaur ancestor is *Lagosuchus,* whose name is pronounced *luh GAHS uh kuhs* and means *rabbit crocodile. Lagosuchus* was a small reptile from the Triassic Period whose fossils have been found in what is now Argentina. It was one of the most active predators of its time, and it had many of the characteristics of fully developed dinosaurs. For example, its long neck curved in an S-shape, a feature typical of many dinosaurs. True dinosaurs probably evolved from *Lagosuchus* and other early archosaurs.

True dinosaurs. Scientists divide true dinosaurs into two major groups: (1) ornithischians *(AWR nuh THIHS kee uhns)* and (2) saurischians *(saw RIHS kee uhns).* The two groups differed mostly in the structure of their hips and other skeletal features. Ornithischians, whose name means *bird-hipped,* had a birdlike hip structure. Saurischians, whose name means *lizard-hipped,* had a hip formation much like that of lizards. Both groups consisted of several recognizable kinds of dinosaurs.

Ornithischians were plant-eaters. They had a beaklike

WORLD BOOK illustrations by George Fryer, Bernard Thornton Artists

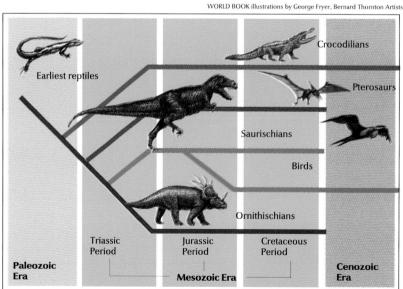

Crocodilians

Earliest reptiles

Pterosaurs

Saurischians

Birds

Ornithischians

Triassic Period
Jurassic Period
Cretaceous Period

Paleozoic Era

Mesozoic Era

Cenozoic Era

Dinosaur family tree. The ancestors of all dinosaurs were small, lizardlike reptiles. These early reptiles first appeared about 330 million years ago, during the Paleo- zoic Era. The two major kinds of dinosaurs—ornithischians and saurischians—lived throughout most of the Meso- zoic Era (240 million to 65 million years ago). The Mesozoic is divided into three periods— the Triassic, Jurassic, and Cretaceous. Dinosaurs died out at the end of the Cretaceous. Birds, which descended from saurischians, survived into the Cenozoic Era, which began 65 million years ago and continues today.

bone in front of their lower jaw, and many had bony plates in their skin. During the Cretaceous Period, ornithischians became the most important plant-eating dinosaurs. There were five basic kinds of ornithischians: (1) stegosaurs, (2) ankylosaurs, (3) ornithopods, (4) pachycephalosaurs, and (5) ceratopsians. Each group included many different species.

Stegosaurs *(STEHG uh sawrs)* were large plant-eaters with huge, upright bony plates or spines along the back. They lived from the middle of the Jurassic to the middle of the Cretaceous. One of the best-known stegosaurs is *Stegosaurus,* which lived in what is now North America. Other stegosaurs lived in Africa, Europe, India, and China. Stegosaurs walked on four legs. The largest stegosaurs measured about 30 feet (9 meters) long and about 6 feet (1.8 meters) tall at the hips. They had a small head and a short neck. Stegosaurs' front legs were much shorter than their back ones. Because of the difference in leg length, stegosaurs walked with their head close to the ground, making them look bent over.

Some stegosaurs had two rows of spines along their back, while others had two rows of stiff, vertical plates. The tail was armed with pairs of bony spikes. Some scientists believe that the plates and spikes may have helped protect the animals from enemies. Other scientists also suggest that the plates helped control the animal's body temperature. According to this theory, overheated blood was pumped through the thin plates and returned to the rest of the body. Air moving around the stegosaur's back would have cooled the blood as it flowed through the plates. The plates could also have warmed the blood by absorbing heat from the sun.

Ankylosaurs *(AHNG kuh luh sawrs)* were the most heavily armored of all dinosaurs. They were low, broad animals and walked on four legs. Most kinds of ankylosaurs grew 15 to 30 feet (5 to 9 meters) long and had a skull 2.5 feet (80 centimeters) long. Heavy, bony plates

covered the body and head of most ankylosaurs. Many of the plates had ridges or spikes. In some ankylosaurs, large spikes also grew at the shoulders or at the back of the head. Some kinds of ankylosaurs had a large mass of bone at the end of the tail. This bone could be used as a powerful club against enemies.

Ankylosaurs lived in many parts of the world from the middle Jurassic to the end of the Cretaceous. These tank-like animals were some of the most successful plant-eating dinosaurs. They most frequently ate the leaves of ferns and low-growing flowering plants.

Ornithopods *(AWR nuh thuh pahds)* could walk either on four legs or on their two hind legs. One of the first dinosaur fossils ever discovered was that of an ornithopod's tooth. This animal, called *Iguanodon (ih GWAN uh dahn),* measured about 30 feet (9 meters) long. *Iguanodon* had a bony spike on the thumb of each forelimb. Other ornithopods, such as *Heterodontosaurus (HEHT uhr uh DAHN tuh sawr uhs),* grew only about 4 feet (1.2 meters) long.

Ornithopods lived throughout the Mesozoic. But they reached their greatest development in hadrosaurs *(HAD ruh sawrs),* also known as duckbilled dinosaurs. Hadrosaurs lived at the end of the Cretaceous, mostly in what are now Asia and North America. They also inhabited Europe and South America. Hadrosaurs had a broad, ducklike beak at the front of the mouth. They also had jaws with hundreds of teeth farther back in the mouth, which they used to chew tough plant leaves. Their hind legs were strong, and they carried their tails stiffly outstretched and parallel to the ground. Some hadrosaurs were 9 feet (2.7 meters) tall at the hips and more than 30 feet (9 meters) long.

Hadrosaurs such as *Prosaurolophus (proh SAWR uh lahf uhs)* and *Edmontosaurus (ehd MAHN tuh SAWR uhs)* had skulls that were either flat or arched into a bony crest. Other kinds of hadrosaurs, such as *Corythosaurus*

Text continued on page 300.

Kinds of dinosaurs

Scientists divide dinosaurs into two major groups—ornithischians and saurischians—according to the structure of the hips. Ornithischians, such as *Corythosaurus,* had a birdlike hip structure. Saurischians, such as *Allosaurus,* had hips like those of lizards. The two groups differed in the three bones that made up the hipbone—the *ilium, ischium,* and *pubis.*.

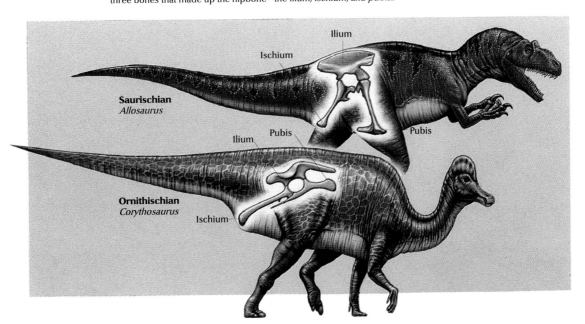

Ilium

Ischium

Saurischian
Allosaurus

Pubis

Ilium

Pubis

Ornithischian
Corythosaurus

Ischium

When dinosaurs lived

Dinosaurs lived during most of the Mesozoic Era, which is divided into three periods—the Triassic (240 million to 205 million years ago), the Jurassic (205 million to 138 million years ago), and the Cretaceous (138 million to 65 million years ago). The illustrations that appear below and on the next page include dinosaurs from each of these periods.

Plateosaurus
20 feet (6 meters) long
Late Triassic

Procompsognathus
3 feet (0.9 meter) long
Late Triassic

Heterodontosaurus
3½ feet
(1.1 meter) long
Early Jurassic

Stegosaurus
25 feet
(7.6 meters) long
Early Jurassic

Scelidosaurus
12 feet
(3.7 meters) long
Late Jurassic

Brachiosaurus
70 feet
(21 meters) long
Late Jurassic

Apatosaurus
70 feet
(21 meters) long
Late Jurassic

Ornitholestes
6 feet (1.8 meters) long
Late Jurassic

Camptosaurus
15 feet (4.8 meters) long
Late Jurassic

Compsognathus
2½ feet
(0.8 meter) long
Late Jurassic

Allosaurus
30 feet (9 meters) long
Late Jurassic

Iguanodon
30 feet (9 meters) long
Early Cretaceous

Deinonychus
9 feet (2.7 meters) long
Early Cretaceous

Ornithomimus
14 feet (4.3 meters) long
Cretaceous

Tyrannosaurus
40 feet (12 meters) long
Late Cretaceous

Ankylosaurus 30 feet (9 meters) long
Cretaceous

Velociraptor
6 feet (1.8 meters) long
Late Cretaceous

Corythosaurus
30 feet (9 meters) long
Late Cretaceous

6 feet
(1.8
meters)

Pentaceratops
25 feet
(7.6 meters) long
Late Cretaceous

Dinosaurs of the Jurassic Period (205 million to 138 million years ago) included the huge
Diplodocus and the meat-eating *Allosaurus, shown at center.* Another Jurassic dinosaur,
Stegosaurus, in the background, had stiff bony plates along its back. *Camptosaurus, pictured in the
lower left corner,* could walk on its two hind legs.

(kaw RIHTH uh SAWR uhs) and *Parasaurolophus (PAIR uh SAWR uh LAHF uhs),* had a showy crest on the top of the head. This crest housed air passages from the animal's nose. Some scientists think that hollow-crested hadrosaurs could have made loud honking sounds when they exhaled through the air passages. These honks may have resembled sounds made by modern elephants and whales. Scientists also believe hadrosaurs took care of their young, tending the nests and providing the babies with food and protection. Most modern reptiles do not care for their young.

Pachycephalosaurs *(PAK uh SEHF uh loh sawrs)* were the dome-headed ornithischians. They lived mostly in western North America and Asia during the second half of the Cretaceous Period. Pachycephalosaurs walked on their hind legs, and most measured from 6 to 25 feet (1.8 to 8 meters) long. These dinosaurs had extremely thick skulls, often covered with bumps and spikes. Scientists believe that pachycephalosaurs used their heads in butting matches, much as male bighorn sheep do today.

Ceratopsians *(SEHR uh TAHP see uhns)* are known as the horned dinosaurs because most of them had horns. Most walked on four feet, resembled rhinoceroses, and ranged in length from about 6 to 25 feet (1.8 to 8 meters). Ceratopsians' heads were often enormous. They typical-ly had a parrotlike beak and a bony frill extending across the neck from the back of the skull. One ceratopsian, *Torosaurus (tawr oh SAWR uhs),* had the largest head of any animal ever to live on land. This head measured about 8.5 feet (2.6 meters) long. In another kind, *Styracosaurus (sty RAK uh SAWR uhs),* the margin of the frill had many spikes. Most ceratopsians had horns on the face, usually one on the nose and one over each eye. *Centrosaurus (SEHN troh SAWR uhs),* for example, had one large horn on the nose and two smaller ones over the eyes. *Triceratops (try SEHR uh tahps)* had horns over the eyes that grew up to 3 feet (90 centimeters) long. Earlier ceratopsians, such as *Psittacosaurus (SIHT uh koh SAWR uhs), Protoceratops (PROH tuh SEHR uh tahps),* and *Leptoceratops (LEHP tuh SEHR uh tahps),* were hornless. Ceratopsians lived during the Cretaceous Period in what are now Asia and North America.

Saurischians included both the largest and the fiercest dinosaurs. There were two basic kinds of saurischians: (1) sauropodomorphs *(SAWR uh PAHD uh mawrphs)* and (2) theropods *(THUR uh pahds).* Each of these groups included many different kinds of dinosaurs.

The earliest sauropodomorphs, such as *Plateosaurus (PLAT ee oh SAWR uhs),* lived during the late Triassic

Dinosaurs of the Cretaceous Period (138 million to 65 million years ago) included hadrosaurs, *center,* which had wide, ducklike bills. Other dinosaurs included the fierce, meat-eating *Tyrannosaurus rex* and the horned *Triceratops, both upper left.* Flowering plants appeared during this period, and opossums, snakes, and lizards were common.

Period. These dinosaurs had a long neck and a small head and grew almost 30 feet (9 meters) long. Animals like *Plateosaurus* were the first diverse and widespread plant-eating dinosaurs. They fed on the tall trees of the period. Early sauropodomorphs could walk on their two hind legs as well as on all four legs.

Sauropods, the later sauropodomorphs, were the giants of the dinosaur world. The largest ones included *Seismosaurus (SYZ muh SAWR uhs),* which may have grown to a length of 150 feet (45 meters), and *Supersaurus (SOO pur SAWR uhs),* which was about 98 feet (30 meters) long. Most sauropods were 30 to 60 feet (9 to 18.3 meters) in length. Adults usually weighed from 10 to 30 short tons (9 to 27 metric tons). Sauropods walked on four stout, strong legs, much like those of an elephant. All sauropods had a long neck, a small head, a long tail, and a huge, deep chest and stomach region. Sauropods were the largest plant-eaters, feeding on the tops of tall trees such as conifers. During the Cretaceous Period, they declined in importance in the Northern Hemisphere. But they remained the dominant plant-eaters in what are now South America, India, and Africa. These regions were almost completely in the Southern Hemisphere at that time.

One of the best-known sauropods is *Apatosaurus.*

More than any other dinosaur, *Apatosaurus* brings to mind the image of a dinosaur for many people. Its front legs were shorter than its hind legs, and its back sloped down toward the base of its neck. *Diplodocus* looked much like *Apatosaurus* but was slimmer and longer. Both *Apatosaurus* and *Diplodocus* lived during the Jurassic Period in what is now North America.

Brachiosaurus (BRAK ee uh SAWR uhs), another kind of sauropod, lived in Africa and North America at the same time as *Apatosaurus* and *Diplodocus.* With its neck stretched upward, *Brachiosaurus* stood about 50 feet (15.2 meters) tall. It weighed about 85 short tons (77 metric tons). The animal's front legs were longer than its hind legs, and its back sloped down toward the tail. These features gave *Brachiosaurus* a stance much like that of a giraffe.

Theropods were the only meat-eating dinosaurs. These powerfully built animals walked upright on their two hind legs. Their short, slender forelimbs ended in hands that could grasp objects fairly well. Nearly all theropods had a long, muscular tail, which they carried straight out behind them for balance. Large theropods had a short neck and a large, long head. Small theropods had longer necks and a smaller head. Some theropods were toothless. Others had sharp teeth and strong

Text continued on page 303.

A World Book special feature

Working with dinosaur fossils
Scientists called *paleontologists* learn about dinosaurs by studying dinosaur fossils.

Ken Abbott, University of Colorado at Boulder

Ken Abbott, University of Colorado at Boulder

Paleontologists find fossils in areas where deep, fossil-bearing layers of rock are exposed. After locating fossil material, scientists begin to remove the rock around the fossil. In many cases, they dig out the portion of the rock that contains the fossil. They then ship the rock and fossil to a laboratory.

At the laboratory, scientists carefully study the fossils. Fossil remains can tell scientists many things about dinosaurs. A dinosaur tooth, for example, may indicate whether the animal ate meat or plants. Other dinosaur remains can show how large the creature grew, how fast it ran, or how it killed prey.

John Weinstein © The Field Museum, Chicago (Neg#GN86807.10)

A museum display of a dinosaur skeleton, such as this *Brachiosaurus,* consists of fossilized bones mounted on a metal or plastic framework. Missing bones may be replaced with pieces made from fiberglass, plaster, or plastic. Scientists rarely discover all the bones of a large dinosaur, and so they estimate the animal's length based on the bones that were found.

jaws, which helped make them the fiercest predators of the Mesozoic.

Two important groups of theropods were the allosaurs *(AL uh sawrs)* and ceratosaurs *(suh RAT uh sawrs)*. Allosaurs were the main meat-eating dinosaurs during the Jurassic Period. Most were about 30 to 40 feet (9 to 12 meters) long. Allosaurs had forelimbs with three fingers on each limb. In contrast, most ceratosaurs were small. One example, *Coelophysis (see loh FY sihs)*, was about 10 feet (3 meters) long. These animals were fast, active predators. By studying them, scientists have learned much about the early evolution of theropod dinosaurs. Many ceratosaurs lived about 230 million years ago, as the Age of Dinosaurs was just beginning.

The best known of all theropods are the tyrannosaurs *(tih RAN uh sawrs)*. They ranked among the most frightening meat-eaters of their time. One famous kind is known by its scientific name, *Tyrannosaurus rex*, which means *king of the tyrant lizards*. This giant predator stood nearly 12 feet (3.7 meters) tall at the hips and grew about 40 feet (12 meters) long. Its head measured up to 4.5 feet (1.4 meters) in length, and its teeth were about 6 inches (15 centimeters) long from the base to the sharp tip. The animal had short forelegs with only two fingers, but extremely powerful hind legs. Tyrannosaurs roamed what are now western North America and east-central Asia. They lived during the second half of the Cretaceous Period.

Other dinosaurs of the Cretaceous Period included small but ferocious theropods, such as *Deinonychus (dy NAHN ih kuhs)* and *Velociraptor (vuh LAHS uh RAP tuhr)*. Both grew to about 20 inches (50 centimeters) tall at the hips and 6 feet (1.8 meters) long. On each of the hind feet, there was a large, curved, razor-sharp claw used to slash, kill, and cut apart prey.

A more peaceable theropod, *Ornithomimus (awr NIHTH uh MY muhs)*, looked much like a featherless ostrich with a long tail. This dinosaur was about the size of a modern ostrich and may have been just as fast a runner. Scientists think that *Ornithomimus* sprinted as fast as 30 to 40 miles (48 to 64 kilometers) per hour. These ostrich-like theropods lived during the Cretaceous Period in North America and Asia. They probably ate small fruits, the cones of certain trees, and the seeds of flowering plants, as well as eggs, insects, mammals, and lizards.

One of the most intelligent dinosaurs was a small, bipedal theropod called *Troodon (TROH uh dahn)*. It lived during the late Cretaceous in North America. *Troodon's* brain was as large, compared with its body weight, as that of many modern birds and small mammals. It had excellent vision and probably hunted for mammals and other prey at night. *Troodon* grew to about 6 feet (1.8 meters) in length. Theropods also included one of the smallest known dinosaurs, *Compsognathus (kahmp SAHG nuh thuhs)*. This animal was about the size of a chicken.

How dinosaurs lived

For many years, people thought that dinosaurs were clumsy, slow-moving, unintelligent creatures that lived much like modern reptiles. However, fossil evidence suggests that some dinosaurs—especially small theropods—were much more active and intelligent than previously thought. In addition, scientists generally agree that

small theropods are the closest known relatives to birds. Thus, scientists can learn much about the life of dinosaurs by studying birds and other modern animals that have some similarity to dinosaurs.

How dinosaurs lived depends partly on whether they were *ectothermic* (cold-blooded), like modern reptiles, or *endothermic* (warm-blooded), like birds and mammals. The body temperature of ectothermic animals changes with the temperature of their surroundings. For example, a lizard's body temperature rises as the air becomes warmer or the sun shines. When the air cools or the sun disappears, the lizard becomes cooler. Lizards become active when they are warm, but they are sluggish when cool. In contrast, endothermic animals generate their own heat and have a constant, fairly warm body temperature. Such animals tend to be more active than their ectothermic counterparts.

Traditionally, dinosaurs were considered ectothermic. People believed they were merely large versions of cold-blooded lizards and crocodilians. Later, scientists argued that some dinosaurs were more active and thus maintained a more constant body temperature than previously believed. However, they continued to think dinosaurs were ectothermic. Scientists pointed out that large animals, particularly gigantic dinosaurs, lost their body heat slowly. Their great size would enable them to keep a more constant body temperature even if they were cold-blooded.

Since the mid-1970's, growing numbers of scientists have argued that many, or even all, dinosaurs were probably endothermic. They point out that not all dinosaurs were gigantic, especially the babies. Smaller dinosaurs could not rely on their size to keep them warm. Other dinosaur features, such as the internal bone structure and the chemistry of the bone, also suggest that dinosaurs were endothermic.

Reproduction and growth. Scientists do not know how all dinosaurs reproduced. Fossil dinosaur eggs show that at least some dinosaurs laid hard-shelled eggs, as do modern alligators. The female may have dug a nest in the soil and deposited eggs in it. Some dinosaurs, particularly hadrosaurs, may have cared for their young from the time the babies hatched until they left the nest. Others probably left the young to survive as best they could.

Scientists can only guess how long dinosaurs lived. But they can estimate the time it took for dinosaurs to grow to adult size. The growth rate depends on whether dinosaurs were ectothermic or endothermic. Endothermic animals grow more rapidly than do ectothermic ones. If sauropods were endothermic, it probably took them about 30 years to reach their average adult weight of 30 short tons (27 metric tons). If the animals were ectothermic, however, it may have taken them 200 years or longer to grow that large.

Group life. Fossil evidence shows that more than 20 kinds of dinosaurs may have occupied a particular area at the same time. Many dinosaurs, including ceratopsians, ornithopods, sauropodomorphs, and perhaps stegosaurs, probably lived in herds the year around. Other kinds, such as ankylosaurs and tyrannosaurs, may have spent most of their life alone or in small groups.

Some scientists think that dinosaurs were brightly colored, like many modern birds, snakes, and lizards. Cer-

Text continued on page 305.

A World Book special feature

Changing interpretations of dinosaurs

Our understanding of dinosaurs has changed dramatically over the years. Scientists once thought these animals were slow-moving, unintelligent creatures that did not adapt well to changing environments. Today, however, scientists believe that dinosaurs were among the most adaptable and diverse animals that ever lived.

Tyrannosaurus rex is one of many dinosaurs about which opinion has changed greatly. People first thought this giant meat-eater was primarily a scavenger, feeding only on the decaying bodies of dead dinosaurs. They also thought it lived a sluggish life, sleeping or basking in the sun between meals.

However, scientists gradually came to believe that *Tyrannosaurus* had a much more dynamic lifestyle. Scientists now argue that it was an active predator as well as a scavenger. *Tyrannosaurus* probably stalked its prey. When close enough, it caught the victim by running toward the creature on its powerful hind legs. *Tyrannosaurus* killed the prey by clamping its strong jaws on the victim's neck. It then stripped the meat from the prey's body and swallowed it.

Today, scientists are still trying to discover more about *Tyrannosaurus.* For example, they do not know exactly how the predator used its extremely small arms. Some regard the arms as strong limbs that helped the animal grab prey. Others believe the limbs were weak and virtually useless. New research and fossil discoveries will help solve such mysteries.

© The Field Museum, Chicago (Neg#CK9T)

An early view of *Tyrannosaurus rex* showed the giant meat-eating dinosaur as a slow, rather sluggish creature. The picture above was painted in the 1930's. It depicts *Tyrannosaurus* with heavy limbs and loose-fitting skin, somewhat like the limbs and skin of an elephant. The bulky *Tyrannosaurus* confronts a *Triceratops,* but it does not attack the horned dinosaur.

A modern illustration of *Tyrannosaurus, left,* shows a faster and more active creature. *Tyrannosaurus's* skin is tight and scaly, making its body look athletic and limber. It is shown attacking two small ceratopsians.

© Jan Sovak

tain dinosaurs perhaps attracted mates by displaying colorful body parts. For example, the crested head of a hadrosaur and the neck frill of a ceratopsian may have been vividly colored. If dinosaurs also made noises, both sounds and colors may have served to attract mates.

Getting food. Most dinosaurs were plant-eaters. They probably fed on a wealth of leaves, small fruits, and seeds from Mesozoic plants. Sauropodomorphs browsed on the leaves of tall trees, while hadrosaurs chewed on the foliage of lower branches, shrubs, and ferns. Pachycephalosaurs, ankylosaurs, ceratopsians, and stegosaurs fed on low vegetation that grew along the edges of streams and rivers or on open plains.

Nearly all theropods, large and small, were hunters. They preyed on a wide variety of plant-eating dinosaurs and possibly on each other. Some of the small theropods probably ate insects, eggs, mammals, and lizards. All theropods, and particularly the smaller ones, were extremely active and could run quickly when attacking. Such fierce animals as *Deinonychus* may have hunted their prey in packs as wolves do today. Other theropods may sometimes have been *scavengers* that picked up meat from dead animals they found.

Protection against enemies. Plant-eating dinosaurs had many forms of protection against predators. The huge size of sauropods probably kept them safe from most enemies, but their smaller offspring had to stay alert to danger. Ankylosaurs had bony plates for protection, and ceratopsians and stegosaurs probably used their horns and spikes to fight off predators. Ornithopods, ceratopsians, and other dinosaurs probably gathered in herds to discourage enemies.

Why dinosaurs died out

For about 160 million years, dinosaurs were the largest and most successful animals on land. Then about 65 million years ago, these huge archosaurs died out along with pterosaurs, mosasaurs, and many other reptiles. Mammals then became the dominant animals on the earth.

Scientists have developed many theories to explain dinosaur extinction. The two major theories involve (1) gradual climate changes and (2) the collision of an asteroid with the earth. The first theory argues that, toward the end of the Cretaceous Period, the shallow seas dried up and the climate became more varied everywhere around the globe. Winters became too cold and summers too hot for dinosaurs to survive. Dinosaurs were too large to hibernate in dens, and they had no fur or feathers for protection against the cold. They also probably had difficulty cooling off in hot weather. Thus, death and extinction came as a result of gradually colder winters and hotter summers.

The other major extinction theory claims that a large asteroid hit the earth at the end of the Cretaceous. This asteroid impact would have thrown billions of tons of dust and debris into the atmosphere. Heat from the impact may have caused huge fires worldwide. Together the clouds of smoke and debris would have blocked sunlight from reaching the surface of the earth for many months. Although the seeds and roots of plants had a good chance of surviving this lightless period, the plants themselves stopped growing and died. If the catastrophe was severe and widespread enough, plant-eating di-

nosaurs would have starved to death. As the plant-eaters died, so did the meat-eating dinosaurs that fed on them. In addition, the darkened skies caused land temperatures to drop below freezing for 6 to 12 months in many parts of the world. Such low temperatures further damaged the dinosaur populations.

According to the asteroid theory, small mammals and birds survived because they were protected from the cold by fur or feathers. Mammals and birds also could feed entirely on seeds, nuts, and rotting vegetation. Other survivors may have escaped extinction because they could live at the bottom of lakes or burrow underground.

Most scientists, however, feel that no single theory completely explains why dinosaurs suffered extinction. They argue that a combination of causes contributed to the dinosaurs' disappearance. In fact, experts now believe that not all dinosaurs became extinct at the end of the Cretaceous. Many scientists regard birds as living dinosaurs that survived extinction.

Dinosaur discoveries

Before the 1800's, no one knew that dinosaurs had ever existed. People who found a dinosaur tooth or bone did not know what it was. Then, two important events happened. Around 1818, an English scholar, William Buckland, obtained a large lower jaw that contained a number of sharp teeth. After studying this jaw, Buckland came to the conclusion that it was unlike any fossil previously discovered. So he gave it a new name, *Megalosaurus* (great lizard), in 1824.

At nearly the same time Mary Ann Mantell, an English amateur naturalist, found a large tooth partly buried in a rock. She showed the tooth to her husband, Gideon, a physician who collected fossils. He decided that the tooth came from a huge, iguanalike reptile, which he named *Iguanodon* (iguana tooth) in 1825.

Within a few years, the remains of several kinds of large, extinct reptiles had been discovered. In 1841, Sir Richard Owen, an English scientist, suggested that these creatures belonged to a group of reptiles unlike any living animals. In 1842, he called this group *Dinosauria* (terrible lizards). Its members later came to be known as dinosaurs.

During the late 1800's and early 1900's, large deposits of dinosaur remains were discovered in western North America, Europe, Asia, and Africa. Today, most dinosaur discoveries are made in China, Mongolia, Argentina, and Australia. Some also occur in the United States and Canada. During the late 1900's, extensive research and fossil discoveries greatly increased the number of known dinosaurs. Scientists discover and describe an average of seven new kinds of dinosaurs every year.

David B. Weishampel

Related articles in *World Book* include:

Allosaurus	Hadrosaur
Ankylosaurus	Paleontology
Apatosaurus	Prehistoric animal
Brachiosaurus	Pterosaur
Diplodocus	Reptile
Earth	Stegosaurus
(The Mesozoic Era)	Triceratops
Eoraptor	Tyrannosaurus
Extinct animal	Velociraptor
Fossil	

Brain

Brain is the master control center of the body. The brain constantly receives information from the senses about conditions both inside the body and outside it. The brain rapidly analyzes this information and then sends out messages that control body functions and actions. The brain also stores information from past experience, which makes learning and remembering possible. In addition, the brain is the source of thoughts, moods, and emotions.

In such simple animals as worms and insects, the brain consists of small groups of nerve cells. All animals with a backbone have a complicated brain made up of many parts. Animals that have an exceptionally well de-veloped brain include apes, dolphins, and whales. Hu-man beings have the most highly developed brain of all. It consists of billions of interconnected cells and enables people to use language, solve difficult problems, and create works of art.

The human brain is a grayish-pink, jellylike ball with many ridges and grooves on its surface. A newborn baby's brain weighs less than 1 pound (0.5 kilogram). By the time a person is 6 years old, the brain has reached its full weight of about 3 pounds (1.4 kilograms). Most of the brain's nerve cells are present at birth. The increase in weight comes from growth of nerve cells, development and growth of supporting cells, and devel-opment of connections among cells. During this six-year period, a person learns and acquires new behavior pat-terns at the fastest rate in life.

A network of blood vessels supplies the brain with the vast quantities of oxygen and food that it requires. The human brain makes up only about 2 percent of the total body weight, but it uses about 20 percent of the oxygen used by the entire body when at rest. The brain can go without oxygen for only three to five minutes be-fore serious damage results.

The brain is at the upper end of the spinal cord. The spinal cord is a cable of nerve cells that extends from the neck about two-thirds of the way down the backbone. The spinal cord carries messages between the brain and other parts of the body. In addition, 12 pairs of nerves connect the brain directly with certain parts of the body. For more information about the nervous system and the brain's place in it, see **Nervous system.**

The brain works in some ways like both a computer and a chemical factory. Brain cells produce electrical signals and send them from cell to cell along pathways called *circuits.* As in a computer, these circuits receive, process, store, and retrieve information. Unlike a com-puter, however, the brain creates its electrical signals by chemical means. The proper functioning of the brain depends on many complicated chemical substances produced by brain cells.

Scientists in various fields work together to study the structure, function, and chemical composition of the brain. This field of study, called *neuroscience* or

Richard Restak, the contributor of this article, is Clinical Pro-fessor of Neurology at George Washington University Medical School and the author of The Brain *and* Brainscapes.

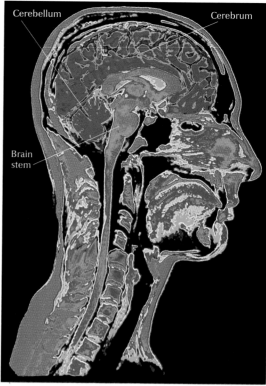

© Dan McCoy, Rainbow

The structure of the human brain is revealed in remarkable detail by magnetic resonance imaging (MRI). This image through the center of the head shows the brain's three main regions—the cerebrum, the cerebellum, and the brain stem.

Interesting facts about the brain

Your brain had reached its full weight of about 3 pounds (1.4 kilograms) by the time you were 6 years old.

All the nerve cells your brain will ever have were present within a few months after your birth.

The left side of your brain controls movements on the right side of your body, and the right side of your brain controls movements on the left side of your body.

Chimpanzees have the largest brains, in relation to their body weight, of any animals except for human beings.

The brain does not feel pain directly because it has no pain receptors. As a result, doctors can perform some types of brain surgery on patients who are conscious.

Brain cells begin to die if they are deprived of oxygen for three to five minutes.

Women have about 10 percent more of the brain cells called neurons than men have even though men, on the av-erage, are bigger than women and have larger brains.

Scientists do not completely understand why people dream. They think dreaming may help the brain restore its ability to focus attention, to remember, and to learn.

The brain requires about 20 percent of the body's oxygen supply though it makes up only about 2 percent of a person's total body weight.

Your brain is as individual as your face. Everyone's brain has the same physical features, but no brain looks exactly like any other brain.

neurobiology, is rapidly increasing our understanding of the brain. But much remains to be learned. Scientists do not yet know how physical and chemical processes in the brain produce much of the brain's activity.

This article deals chiefly with the human brain. The last section of the article briefly discusses the brain in various kinds of animals.

The parts of the brain

The brain has three main divisions: (1) the cerebrum, (2) the cerebellum, and (3) the brain stem. Each part consists chiefly of nerve cells, called *neurons,* and supporting cells, called *glia.*

The cerebrum makes up about 85 percent of the weight of the human brain. A large groove called the *longitudinal fissure* divides the cerebrum into halves called the *left cerebral hemisphere* and the *right cerebral hemisphere.* The hemispheres are connected by bundles of nerve fibers, the largest of which is the *corpus callosum.* Each hemisphere, in turn, is divided into four *lobes* (regions). Each lobe has the same name as the bone of the skull that lies above it. The lobes are (1) the frontal lobe, at the front; (2) the temporal lobe, at the lower side; (3) the parietal lobe, in the middle; and (4) the occipital lobe, at the rear. Fissures in the cerebral cortex form the boundaries between the lobes. The two major fissures are the *central fissure* and the *lateral fissure.*

A thin layer of nerve cell bodies called the *cerebral cortex* or *cortex* forms the outermost part of the cerebrum. Most of the cerebrum beneath the cortex consists of nerve cell fibers. Some of these fibers connect parts of the cortex. Others link the cortex with the cerebellum, brain stem, and spinal cord.

The cerebral cortex is folded into a surface with many ridges and grooves. This folding greatly increases the surface area of the cortex and the number of nerve cells it contains within the limited space of the skull. Some areas of the cortex, called the *sensory cortex,* receive messages from the sense organs as well as messages of touch and temperature from throughout the body. Areas in the frontal lobes called the *motor cortex* send out nerve impulses that control the voluntary movements of all the skeletal muscles. The largest portion of the cortex is the *association cortex.* Every lobe of the brain has areas of association cortex that analyze, process, and store information. These association areas make possible all our higher mental abilities, such as thinking, speaking, and remembering.

The cerebellum is the part of the brain most responsible for balance, posture, and the coordination of

Brain terms

Association cortex is any part of the cortex where information is analyzed, processed, or stored.

Axon, *AK sahn,* is the long extension of a neuron that carries nerve impulses away from the body of the cell.

Basal ganglia, *BAY suhl GANG glee uh,* are groups of neurons at the base of the cerebrum. They help control well-learned movement sequences such as walking.

Brain stem is the lowest part of the brain, connecting the spinal cord with the cerebrum.

Cerebellum, *SEHR uh BEHL uhm,* is the part of the brain below the back of the cerebrum that regulates balance and movement and coordinates the muscles.

Cerebral hemisphere is either the left or right side of the cerebrum, the main portion of the brain.

Cerebrum, *SEHR uh bruhm* or *suh REE bruhm,* is the largest and most complex portion of the brain. It controls thought and learning.

Corpus callosum, *KAWR puhs kuh LOH suhm,* is the largest bundle of nerve fibers connecting the left and right cerebral hemispheres.

Cortex is a deeply folded and ridged layer of neurons on the surface of the cerebrum.

Dendrite, *DEHN dryt,* is a branching structure at the receiving portion of a neuron.

Frontal lobe is the region at the front and top of each cerebral hemisphere. These two lobes are important for reason, emotion, and judgment as well as voluntary movement.

Glia, *GLY uh,* are cells that form a supporting network for the neurons in the brain.

Hypothalamus, *HY puh THAL uh muhs,* is a region in the upper part of the brain stem that controls body temperature, hunger, thirst, and the pituitary gland.

Medulla oblongata, *mih DUHL uh ahb lahng GAY tuh,* is the lowest part of the brain stem, at the top end of the spinal cord, that regulates heartbeat, breathing, and other automatic functions.

Midbrain is a middle area of the brain stem that contains many important nerve pathways.

Motor cortex is the part of both frontal lobes of the brain that controls voluntary muscle movements.

Myelin, *MY uh lihn,* is a fatty substance that surrounds and protects certain nerve fibers.

Neuron is a nerve cell. Neurons are the most important information-processing cells in the brain.

Neurotransmitters are chemicals that transmit nerve impulses between neurons.

Occipital lobe, *ahk SIHP uh tuhl,* is the region at the back of each cerebral hemisphere that contains the centers of vision.

Parietal lobe, *puh RY uh tuhl,* is the middle lobe of each cerebral hemisphere between the frontal and occipital lobes. The parietal lobes contain important sensory centers.

Pons, *pahnz,* is part of the brain stem that joins the hemispheres of the cerebellum and connects the cerebrum with the cerebellum.

Reticular formation, *rih TIHK yuh luhr,* is a network of nerve cells deep within the brain stem that plays a major role in maintaining sleep or wakefulness.

Sensory cortex is any part of the brain that receives messages from the sense organs or messages of touch and temperature from throughout the body.

Somatosensory cortex, *SOH muh tuh SEHN suhr ee,* is an area of the sensory cortex in the parietal lobes that receives messages of touch, temperature, and certain other bodily sensations.

Synapse, *sih NAPS,* is the structure where an impulse passes from one neuron to another.

Temporal lobe, *TEHM puhr uhl,* is the region at the lower side of each cerebral hemisphere. The temporal lobes contain centers of hearing and memory.

Thalamus, *THAL uh muhs,* is a structure at the top of the brain stem that serves as a relay center for sensory information.

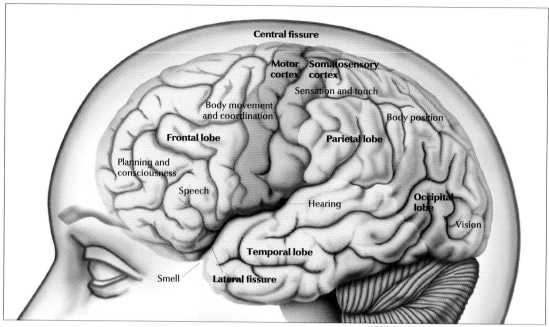

WORLD BOOK diagram by Colin Bidgood and Barbara Cousins

The cerebrum looks wrinkled because it is covered by a deeply folded layer of nerve cells called the *cortex.* The cerebrum is divided into left and right hemispheres. Each hemisphere is further divided into four lobes by *fissures* (grooves) in the cortex. This diagram shows the left hemisphere. Labels indicate the four lobes, the fissures that separate them, and some major functions of regions of the cortex.

movement. It lies below the back part of the cerebrum. The cerebellum consists of a large mass of closely packed *folia* (leaflike bundles of nerve cells). The cerebellum has a right and a left hemisphere, with a finger-shaped structure called the *vermis* in the middle. Nerve pathways connect the right half of the cerebellum with the left cerebral hemisphere and the right side of the body. Pathways from the left half connect with the right cerebral hemisphere and the left side of the body.

The brain stem is a stalklike structure that connects the cerebrum with the spinal cord. The bottom part of the brain stem is called the *medulla oblongata* or *medulla.* The medulla has nerve centers that control breathing, heartbeat, and many other vital body processes.

Just above the medulla is the *pons,* which connects the hemispheres of the cerebellum. The pons also contains nerve fibers that link the cerebellum and the cerebrum. Above the pons lies the *midbrain.* Nerve centers in the midbrain help control movements of the eyes and the size of the pupils.

At the upper end of the brain stem are the *hypothalamus* and the *thalamus.* There are actually two thalami, one on the left side of the brain stem and one on the right side. Each thalamus receives nerve impulses from various parts of the body and routes them to the appropriate areas of the cerebral cortex. The thalami also relay impulses from one part of the brain to another. The hypothalamus regulates body temperature, hunger, and other internal conditions. It also controls the activity of the nearby *pituitary gland,* the master gland of the body (see **Hypothalamus; Pituitary gland**).

A network of nerve fibers called the *reticular formation* lies deep within the brain stem. The reticular forma-

tion helps regulate and maintain the brain's level of awareness. Sensory messages that pass through the brain stem stimulate the reticular formation, which in turn stimulates alertness and activity throughout the cerebral cortex.

Brain cells. The human brain has from 10 billion to 100 billion neurons. All of these neurons are present within a few months after birth. After a person reaches about 20 years of age, some neurons die or disappear each day. In general, neurons that die are not replaced during a person's lifetime. Over a lifetime, however, this loss equals less than 10 percent of all the neurons.

The brain's billions of neurons connect with one another in complex networks. All physical and mental functioning depends on the establishment and maintenance of neuron networks. A person's habits and skills—such as nail-biting or playing a musical instrument—become embedded within the brain in frequently activated neuron networks. When a person stops performing an activity, the neural networks for the activity fall into disuse and eventually may disappear.

As in all other cells, a thin membrane forms the outermost layer of each neuron. However, a neuron's membrane is highly specialized to carry nerve impulses. Each neuron consists of a cell body and a number of tubelike fibers. The longest fiber, called the *axon,* carries nerve impulses from the cell body to other neurons. Short, branching fibers called *dendrites* pick up impulses from the axons of other neurons and transmit them to the cell body. The structure where any branch of one neuron transmits a nerve impulse to a branch of another neuron is called a *synapse.* Each neuron may form synapses with thousands of other nerve cells.

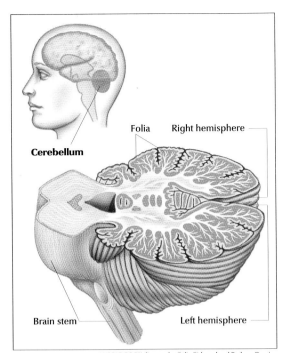

Folia   Right hemisphere

Cerebellum

Brain stem   Left hemisphere

The cerebellum is the part of the brain most responsible for balance and coordination. This cross section of the cerebellum shows the folia, which are leaflike bundles of nerve cells.

Some axons have a coating of fatty material called *myelin.* The myelin insulates the fiber and speeds the transmission of impulses along its surface. Myelin is white, and tightly packed axons covered with it form *white matter.* The neuron cell bodies and the axons without myelin sheaths make up the *gray matter* of the brain. The cerebral cortex is made up of gray matter, and most of the rest of the cerebrum consists of white matter.

The neurons are surrounded by *glia,* cells whose name comes from a Greek word for *glue.* Glial cells traditionally have been thought of as a supportive framework for the neurons. The glia also perform many other important tasks. For example, certain glia keep the brain free of injured and diseased neurons by engulfing and digesting them. Other glia produce the myelin sheaths that insulate some axons. Research using cells grown in laboratories also indicates that glia, like neurons, may transmit some nerve impulses.

How the brain is protected

The hard, thick bones of the skull shield the brain from blows that could otherwise seriously injure it. In addition, three protective membranes called *meninges* cover the brain. The outermost membrane is the tough *dura mater,* which lines the inner surface of the skull. A thinner membrane, the *arachnoid,* lies just beneath the dura mater. The delicate *pia mater* directly covers the brain. It follows the folds of the brain's surface and contains blood vessels that carry blood to and from the cerebral cortex. A clear liquid called *cerebrospinal fluid* separates the pia mater and the arachnoid. This fluid forms a thin cushioning layer between the soft tissues of the brain and the hard bones of the skull.

The *blood-brain barrier* safeguards brain tissues from the damage that could result from contact with certain large molecules carried in the bloodstream. Substances in the blood reach body tissues by passing through the thin walls of tiny blood vessels called *capillaries.* Much of this flow occurs through the spaces between the cells that make up the capillary walls. In brain capillaries, the cells are more tightly packed than in other capillaries, and the passage of substances from blood to brain cells is carefully restricted. The brain needs some kinds of large molecules for nutrition, however. The capillary walls have certain enzymes and other properties that enable these particular molecules to pass through.

The work of the brain

The structure of our brain determines how we experience the world. Our experiences, in turn, influence how our neurons develop and connect with one another. Individual brains can differ significantly, depending on a person's background and experience. The fingers activate the same general area of the sensory cortex in everyone's brain. But this area is larger in people who use their fingers particularly often—for example, people who play stringed instruments, or people who read *Braille* (an alphabet of small raised dots developed for the blind).

Scientists have also found evidence that the brains of men and women differ. The corpus callosum—the thick band of nerve fibers connecting the cerebral hemispheres—is larger in women. Careful examinations of brains after death have shown that women have about 10 percent more neurons in the cortex than men. Studies of men and women reading or thinking about words also show differences. These studies have found that men generally use only their left cerebral hemisphere for processing language, but women use both hemispheres.

Researchers are not sure if these physical differences in men's and women's brains mean that men and women think differently. Some evidence suggests that the sexes may have different mental strengths. Psychological testing consistently shows that men, on the average, perform better than women on spatial tasks, such as visualizing objects in three dimensions. Women, on the other hand, do better than men on tests involving writing, reading, and vocabulary. But this average difference in ability is small. Many individual men are better at language than the average for women, and many women have better spatial skills than the average for men.

Scientists have developed many methods to study how the brain works. Experiments with animals have revealed a great deal about the workings of various areas of the brain. Scientists have also learned much about the normal activity of the brain by observing injured brains. Damage to a specific part of the brain causes predictable problems in speech, movement, or mental ability.

Surgeons have mapped the functions of many areas of the cerebral cortex by electrically stimulating the brain during brain surgery. Surgical operations on the brain do not require that the patients be unconscious because the brain feels no pain directly. Thus, the patients can tell the surgeons what they experience when particular brain areas are stimulated.

Brain surgery has revealed that certain functions of the cerebrum occur chiefly in one hemisphere or the

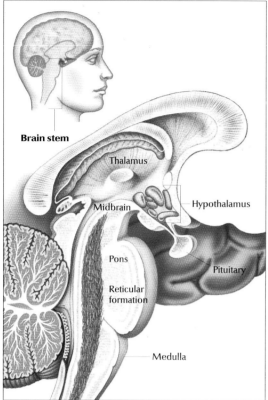

WORLD BOOK diagram by Colin Bidgood and Barbara Cousins

The brain stem is a stalklike structure that links the cerebrum with the spinal cord. The larger diagram shows a cutaway of the brain stem and the nearby pituitary gland.

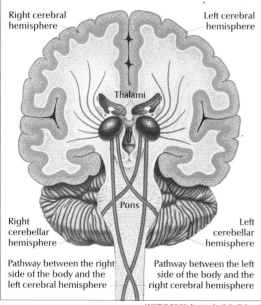

WORLD BOOK diagram by Colin Bidgood

Nerve pathways cross over as they pass through the brain stem. As a result, each cerebral hemisphere is linked with the opposite side of the cerebellum and controls the opposite side of the body.

other. Surgeons treat some cases of epilepsy by cutting the corpus callosum. This operation produces a condition called the *split brain,* in which no communication occurs between the cerebral hemispheres. Studies of split-brain patients suggest that the left hemisphere largely controls our ability to use language, mathematics, and logic. The right hemisphere is the main center for musical ability, the recognition of faces and complicated visual patterns, and the expression of emotion.

Positron emission tomography (PET) and *functional magnetic resonance imaging* (fMRI) are safe new technologies that enable scientists to study healthy, living brains at work. These technologies do not require any physical contact with the brain. They produce images similar to X rays that show which parts of the brain are active while a person performs a particular mental or physical task. PET shows the parts of the brain that are using the most glucose (a form of sugar), and fMRI shows the parts where high oxygen levels indicate increased activity.

In receiving sensory messages. Sensory messages are received and interpreted primarily in the cerebral cortex. Various parts of the body send nerve impulses to the thalamus, which routes them to the appropriate areas of the cerebral cortex. An area of the sensory cortex called the *somatosensory cortex* receives messages that it interprets as bodily sensations, such as touch and temperature. It lies in the parietal lobe of each hemisphere along the central fissure. Each part of the somatosensory cortex receives and interprets impulses from a specific part of the body.

Other specialized areas of the cerebrum receive the sensory impulses of seeing, hearing, taste, and smell. Impulses from the eyes travel to the visual cortex in the occipital lobes. Portions of the temporal lobes receive messages from the ears. The area for taste lies buried in the lateral fissure, and the center of smell is on the underside of the frontal lobes.

In controlling movement. Some reflex actions do not involve the brain. If a person touches a hot stove, for example, pain impulses flash to the spinal cord, which immediately sends back a message to withdraw the hand. However, the brain plays the major role in controlling our conscious movements as well as those we are unaware of. The *basal ganglia* are groups of neurons that lie at the base of the cerebrum. The basal ganglia help control well-learned movement sequences involved in such activities as walking or eating. Areas in the brain stem control the movements of the body's *involuntary muscles,* which line the walls of the stomach, intestines, and blood vessels.

The cerebral cortex and the cerebellum together largely regulate voluntary movements. The motor cortex in each cerebral hemisphere sends nerve impulses to the particular muscles used in an activity, such as writing or throwing a ball. The motor cortex lies in the frontal lobe in front of the central fissure. Each area of the motor cortex controls the movements of a specific part of the body. The largest areas control those parts of the body that make the most complicated and precise movements. Thus, a large area controls the lips and tongue, which make complex movements in speaking. Much smaller areas control the relatively simple movements made by such parts as the back and shoulders.

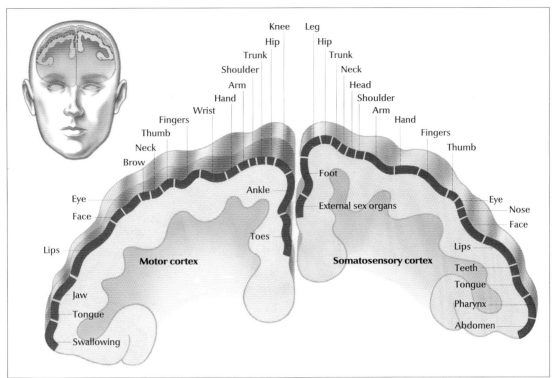

Regions within the motor and somatosensory areas of the cortex are linked to specific parts of the body. The largest areas within the motor cortex control the parts of the body that make the most complex voluntary movements. The largest areas within the somatosensory cortex receive sensory input from the most sensitive body parts.

The major motor pathways to the body cross over in the brain stem. The motor cortex of the left hemisphere thus controls movements on the right side of the body. Similarly, the right motor cortex directs movements on the left side of the body. More than 90 percent of all people are right-handed because the left motor cortex, which directs the right hand, is dominant over the right motor cortex, which directs the left hand.

The cerebellum coordinates the muscle movements ordered by the motor cortex. Nerve impulses alert the cerebellum when the motor cortex orders a part of the body to perform a certain action. Almost instantly, impulses from that part of the body inform the cerebellum of how the action is being carried out. The cerebellum compares the movement with the intended movement and then signals the motor cortex to make any necessary corrections. In this way, the cerebellum ensures that the body moves smoothly and efficiently.

In the use of language. In the late 1800's, scientists observed that damage to particular parts of the brain caused the same language disabilities in most patients. Damage to the left frontal lobe in *Broca's area*, named for French surgeon Pierre Paul Broca, destroyed the ability to speak. Damage to the left temporal lobe in *Wernicke's area*, named for German neurologist Carl Wernicke, caused difficulty understanding language. These observations led many scientists to think that the brain processed words in an orderly relay through a series of language-related areas. But new imaging technologies

such as PET and fMRI enable scientists to observe the brain directly while people speak, listen, read, and think. PET and fMRI studies show that language processing is extremely complex. Language areas are spread widely through the brain, and different types of language tasks activate these areas in many sequences and patterns.

In regulating body processes. The main control centers for body processes are in the brain stem. Nerve centers in the medulla regulate such body functions as breathing, heartbeat, and blood flow. Other areas within the brain stem control swallowing and the movements of the stomach and intestines.

The hypothalamus also has nerve centers that control certain body processes. Most of these centers maintain constant conditions within the body. For example, some centers regulate the amount of water in the body. Certain neurons detect changes in the level of water in the body's blood and tissues and relay this information to the hypothalamus. If the water level is too low, the hypothalamus produces the sensation of thirst, which causes the person to drink water. At the same time, the hypothalamus sends messages that cause the kidneys to reduce the amount of water they remove from the body. If the water level becomes too high, the messages from the hypothalamus eliminate thirst and increase the amount of water removed by the kidneys. Other centers in the hypothalamus operate on the same principle in regulating hunger and body temperature.

A slender stalk of tissue connects the hypothalamus with the master gland of the body, the pituitary. The hypothalamus indirectly regulates many body processes by controlling the pituitary's production and release of chemical messengers called *hormones*. Among other functions, these hormones regulate the body's rate of growth and its sexual and reproductive processes.

In producing emotions. The emotions we experience involve many areas of the brain as well as other body organs. A group of brain structures called the *limbic system* plays a central role in the production of emotions. This system includes portions of the temporal lobes, parts of the hypothalamus and thalamus, and other structures.

An emotion may be provoked by a thought in the cerebral cortex or by messages from the sense organs. In either case, nerve impulses are produced that reach the limbic system. These impulses stimulate different areas of the system, depending on the kind of sensory message or thought. For example, the impulses might activate parts of the system that produce pleasant feelings involved in such emotions as joy and love. Or the impulses might stimulate areas that produce unpleasant feelings associated with anger or fear.

In thinking and remembering. Scientists have only an elementary understanding of the extraordinarily complicated processes of thinking and remembering. Thinking involves processing information over circuits in the association cortex and other parts of the brain. These circuits enable the brain to combine information stored in the memory with information gathered by the senses. Scientists are just beginning to understand the brain's simplest circuits. Forming abstract ideas and studying difficult subjects must require circuits of astonishing complexity. Some aspects of human thinking— such as religious or philosophical beliefs—are still beyond scientists' understanding and may always be.

The frontal lobes of the cerebrum play a key role in many thinking processes that distinguish human beings from other animals. The frontal lobes are particularly important for abstract thinking, for imagining the likely consequences of actions, and for understanding another person's feelings or motives. Injury or abnormal development of the frontal lobes can result in the loss of these abilities.

Scientists also have much to learn about the physical basis of memory. Certain structures of the limbic system appear to play major roles in storing and retrieving memories. These structures include the *amygdaloid complex* and the *hippocampus*, both in the temporal lobe. Individuals who suffer damage to these structures may lose the ability to form new memories, though they may retain information about events occurring before the damage. These individuals can learn new physical skills, but when performing them do not remember having done the activities before.

Evidence suggests that memories may be formed through the establishment of new brain circuits or the alteration of existing circuits. Either process would involve changes at the synapses—that is, at the structures where impulses pass from one neuron to another. These changes may be controlled by *glycoproteins* or other large molecules at the synapses. Extensive research will be required to verify this general explanation of memory formation and to discover the specific details of the processes involved.

The chemistry of the brain

As in all other cells, many complex chemical processes occur within the neurons of the brain. However, some chemical processes occur only within and among neurons. Scientists are especially interested in gaining a fuller understanding of these processes and how they relate to the transmission of nerve impulses.

A nerve impulse is an electrical and chemical process controlled by the nerve cell membrane. The process involves *ions* (electrically charged atoms) of chemical elements, such as sodium and potassium. The membrane, which has pores, maintains varying concentrations of these ions inside the neuron and in its surrounding fluids. As the membrane selectively allows ions to enter and leave the cell, an electric charge—the nerve im-

Marcus E. Raichle, M.D., Washington University School of Medicine

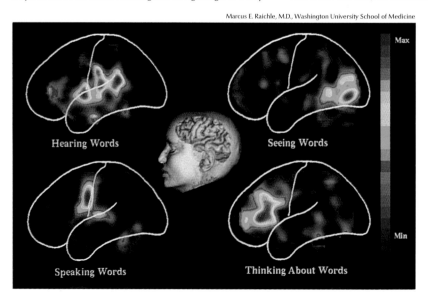

Hearing Words

Seeing Words

Speaking Words

Thinking About Words

Max

Min

Positron emission tomography (PET) images show brain activity. These PET scans show areas of the left cerebral hemisphere that are active while people perform language tasks. The white outline highlights the cerebrum and its central and lateral fissures. Neurons are most active where an image is red. Neuron activity decreases as the colors progress through the spectrum from red to violet.

pulse—travels along the neuron. For more details about this process, see **Nervous system** (How neurons carry impulses). The rest of this section discusses the chemicals that transmit impulses from neuron to neuron.

The brain's chemical messengers. Certain chemicals called *neurotransmitters* make it possible for a nerve impulse to travel from the axon of one neuron to the dendrite of another. An impulse cannot be transmitted electrically across the *synaptic cleft,* the tiny gap between the axon and the dendrite. Instead, when an impulse reaches the end of the axon, it triggers the release of neurotransmitter molecules from the cell. These molecules cross the synaptic cleft and attach themselves to sites called *receptors* on the dendrite of the other neuron. This action alters the electrical activity of the receiving neuron in one of two ways. Some transmitters stimulate the neuron to produce a nerve impulse. Others tend to prevent the neuron from producing an impulse.

Neurons may manufacture more than one neurotransmitter, and their membrane surfaces may contain receptors for more than a single transmitter. A neuron may "learn" from past experience and change the proportions of its various neurotransmitters and receptors. Thus, the brain has great flexibility and can alter its response to situations encountered over spans of time ranging from seconds to decades.

The brain produces many kinds of chemicals that are used as neurotransmitters. The most common ones include *acetylcholine, dopamine, norepinephrine,* and *serotonin.* The chemicals are not distributed evenly throughout the brain. Each is found only or primarily in specific areas. For example, the cell bodies of neurons that contain dopamine are in the midbrain of the brain stem. The axons of these cells reach into other areas, including the frontal lobes of the cerebrum and an area near the center of the brain called the *corpus striatum.* These dopamine pathways function in the regulation of emotions and in the control of complex movements.

During the 1970's, researchers discovered that morphine and related drugs relieve pain by attaching to receptors in certain regions of the brain. This discovery suggested that the brain produces its own painkillers that attach to these same receptors. Further research led to the discovery of *endorphins* and *enkephalins,* two neurotransmitters that bind to these receptors.

In the 1980's, researchers found that receptors exist in families. Each member or subtype of a family is responsible for a specific function. For example, scientists have discovered more than a dozen receptor subtypes for serotonin. This knowledge has led to development of drugs that affect specific serotonin receptors, such as migraine drugs and certain antidepressants. Scientists believe that the discovery of additional receptor subtypes will result in the development of drugs that work with increased precision in the treatment of thought, mood, and behavior disorders.

Brain chemistry and mental illness. All the brain's functions depend on the normal action of neurotransmitters. An excess or deficiency of a specific transmitter or group of transmitters may lead to a serious disorder in thought, mood, or behavior. For example, studies have suggested that chemical imbalances in the brain play a significant role in several types of mental illnesses. There is some evidence that the brain produces too much

dopamine in a severe mental illness called *schizophrenia.* This excess of dopamine may create emotional disturbances and cause a person to see things and hear sounds that do not exist.

Disturbances in brain chemistry may also be involved in *bipolar disorder,* also known as *manic-depressive disorder.* A person with this mental illness has alternate periods of *mania* (extreme joy and overactivity) and *depression* (sadness). Some research suggests that an excess of dopamine, norepinephrine, and serotonin causes mania and that a deficiency of the same chemicals causes depression.

How drugs affect brain chemistry. Psychiatrists treat some mental illnesses with drugs that restore the brain's normal chemical activity. For example, many tranquilizers that relieve the symptoms of schizophrenia block the brain's receptors for dopamine. However, it seems unlikely that a single neurotransmitter is responsible for schizophrenia or other complex mental illnesses, such as bipolar disorder and depression. These disorders probably result from chemical disturbances involving several neurotransmitters. For example, some drugs that have proved successful in treating depression influence norepinephrine, while others influence serotonin. Still others affect both of these neurotransmitters.

Certain drugs produce a feeling of well-being or reduce tension and worry by temporarily altering the normal chemistry of the brain. For example, *amphetamines* increase mental activity by causing brain cells to release an excessive amount of dopamine. Abuse of amphetamines can create mental disturbances like those that occur in some forms of schizophrenia.

A person's senses, emotions, thought processes, and judgment can be altered dramatically and dangerously by *hallucinogenic drugs.* These drugs include mescaline, psilocybin, and LSD (lysergic acid diethylamide). Each of these drugs structurally resembles one or more neurotransmitters. Mescaline resembles dopamine and norepinephrine, and LSD and psilocybin resemble serotonin. Scientists think a hallucinogenic drug may produce its effects by combining with the brain's receptors for the natural transmitter that it resembles. Hallucinogenic drugs may produce disturbances in brain chemistry that last long after their contact with the brain. For example, scientists believe that the drug called *MDMA,* commonly known as Ecstasy, may cause permanent damage to neurons that release serotonin. This damage may produce harmful effects on mood, thoughts, sleep, and motivation.

Disorders of the brain

Injuries, diseases, and inherited disorders can damage the brain. However, the seriousness of brain damage depends chiefly on the area of the brain involved rather than on the cause of the damage. Disorders that destroy brain cells are especially serious because the body cannot replace the lost cells. In some cases, however, undamaged areas of the brain may eventually take over control of some functions formerly carried out by the damaged areas.

Modern instruments and techniques enable physicians to diagnose brain disorders earlier and more accurately than in the past. For example, an instrument called an *electroencephalograph* (EEG) measures the patterns of electrical activity produced by the brain. Differences from

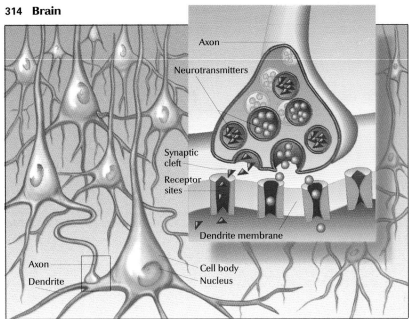

Axon

Neurotransmitters

Synaptic cleft

Receptor sites

Dendrite membrane

Axon

Dendrite

Cell body

Nucleus

Networks of neurons, *background,* form the brain's information-processing circuits. Information in the form of neurotransmitter chemicals travels from one neuron to another at the synapse, *inset.* Neurotransmitters leave the axon of the transmitting neuron and enter specific receptor sites in the membrane of the receiving dendrite.

WORLD BOOK illustration by Barbara Cousins

normal EEG patterns may indicate damage to the brain and also help locate the area of the damage. Computer-assisted EEG's can record and organize vast amounts of electrical data. The brain's responses to specific visual, auditory, and touch stimuli can be measured. Scientists can diagnose disorders by comparing the responses with average results obtained from large numbers of people. Another important technique is *computerized tomography* (CT). It involves X-raying the brain in detail from many angles. A computer then analyzes the X-ray data and constructs a cross-sectional image of the brain on a TV screen. *Magnetic resonance imaging* (MRI) uses magnetic fields and radio waves to produce images of the brain's structure.

Injuries are the leading cause of brain damage among people under 50 years of age. A blow to the head may cause temporary unconsciousness without permanent damage. Severe injuries to the head may cause more serious brain damage. Head injuries before, during, or shortly after birth may cause *cerebral palsy.* There are several types of cerebral palsy, all of which involve lack of control of muscle movements.

Stroke is the most common serious disorder of the brain. A stroke occurs when the blood supply to part of the brain is cut off. Nerve cells in the affected areas die, and the victim may lose the ability to carry out functions controlled by those areas. Many stroke victims suffer paralysis on one side of the body. Other symptoms include difficulty in speaking or in understanding language. Most strokes result from damage to the blood vessels caused by *hypertension* (high blood pressure) or *arteriosclerosis* (hardening of the arteries). Some victims of massive strokes die, but many other stroke victims survive and recover at least partially.

Tumors are abnormal growths that can cause severe brain damage. The effects of a tumor depend on its size and location. A tumor may destroy brain cells in the area surrounding it. As the tumor grows, it also creates pressure, which may damage other areas of the brain or at

least interfere with their normal function. Symptoms of a tumor include headache, seizures, unusual sleepiness, a change in personality, or disturbances in sense perception or speech.

Surgery cures some tumors. For cancerous tumors, physicians may combine surgery with drugs or radiation. One type of radiation, called *stereotactic radiosurgery,* is sometimes used as an alternative to traditional surgery. In stereotactic radiosurgery, doctors use computers and a CT scan or MRI to produce a three-dimensional image of the brain. Beams of radiation are then focused precisely on the target, which may be a tumor or a blood-vessel malformation. The individual beams are either too brief or too weak to harm areas of the brain in the path of the radiation. But their combined effect will destroy the target. These procedures are quick and painless and allow patients to resume moderate activity the same day.

Infectious diseases. A number of diseases caused by bacteria or viruses can damage the brain. The most common of these infectious diseases are *encephalitis* and *meningitis,* either of which may be caused by bacteria or viruses. Encephalitis is an inflammation of the brain. *Meningitis* is an inflammation of the meninges, the membranes that cover the brain and spinal cord. *Chorea* is a disease of the brain that mainly affects children from 7 to 15 years old. Most cases of chorea occur with rheumatic fever and may be caused by the same bacteria which cause that disease. A virus disease called *poliomyelitis* attacks the brain and spinal cord. Vaccines to prevent polio were developed in the 1950's.

Genetic disorders. Our *genes* (the hereditary materials in cells) carry instructions for the development of our entire bodies, including the brain. These instructions are extremely complex, and so errors occasionally occur. These errors can lead to serious defects in the structure and functioning of the brain. Some infants are mentally retarded at birth because genetic errors caused the brain to develop improperly during the

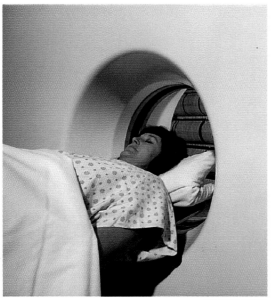

Dan McCoy, Rainbow

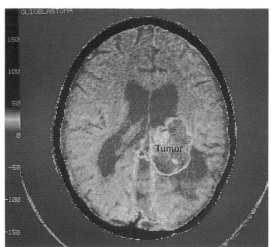

Dan McCoy, Rainbow

Computerized tomography (CT) aids in detecting brain tumors and other abnormalities. The CT scanner, *left*, X-rays the brain from many angles. From the X-ray data, the scanner's computer constructs images of the brain, *above*.

mother's pregnancy. In *Down syndrome,* for example, an extra *chromosome* is present. Chromosomes are structures in the cell nucleus that contain the genes. The extra chromosome causes mental retardation as well as physical defects. Another disorder that causes mental retardation is *fragile-X syndrome.* This disorder results from an abnormality on the X chromosome, one of the chromosomes that determine a person's sex.

Some children suffer severe brain damage after birth because of an inherited deficiency of an enzyme that the body needs to use foods properly. For example, a child who has *phenylketonuria* (PKU) lacks an enzyme needed to convert a certain *amino acid* (protein part) into a form the body can use. This amino acid, *phenylalanine,* accumulates in the blood and damages developing brain tissues. A diet low in phenylalanine can prevent brain damage in people who have PKU.

Some genetic errors damage the brain only later in life. *Huntington's disease,* for example, usually strikes during middle age. The disease causes various areas of the cerebrum and basal ganglia to wither away. Involuntary jerky movements are the main early symptoms of Huntington's disease. However, the disease eventually leads to incurable mental disintegration.

Scientists believe that genetic factors play an important role in most cases of *Alzheimer's disease.* This disease most commonly strikes after age 60. It is characterized by an increasingly severe loss of memory and other mental abilities. Most people with Alzheimer's disease eventually cannot care for themselves and become bedridden.

Heredity also plays a role in some types of mental illness. Many children of schizophrenics apparently inherit a tendency to develop schizophrenia. Studies have also revealed an inherited tendency to develop bipolar disorder. These tendencies may involve inherited defects in brain chemistry. Researchers continue to study these tendencies and how they interact with environmental conditions to produce mental illness.

Other brain disorders include (1) epilepsy, (2) multiple sclerosis (MS), and (3) Parkinson disease. Scientists do not know the cause of these disorders.

Epilepsy. Victims of epilepsy suffer seizures that occur when many nerve cells in one area of the brain release abnormal bursts of impulses. A seizure may cause temporary uncontrolled muscle movements or unconsciousness. Defects in genes cause some cases of epilepsy, but the cause of most cases is not known. Physicians treat epilepsy with drugs that reduce the number of seizures or prevent them entirely.

Multiple sclerosis develops when axons in parts of the brain and spinal cord lose their myelin sheaths. As a result, the axons cannot carry nerve impulses properly. Symptoms vary depending on what brain areas are affected, but they may include double vision, loss of balance, and weakness in an arm or leg. No cure is yet known. Drugs can relieve some of the symptoms. Some of these drugs help slow the loss of myelin.

Parkinson disease is characterized by slowness of movement, muscle rigidity, and trembling. These conditions result in part from the destruction of the nerve pathways that use dopamine as a transmitter. Treatment with the drug L-dopa replaces the missing dopamine and so can relieve the symptoms of Parkinson disease, though it cannot cure the illness. Some researchers have treated Parkinson disease by transplanting dopamine-producing brain tissue from fetuses into part of the basal ganglia, which help control body movement. This procedure is risky, and its usefulness has not yet been proved. In addition, it has aroused controversy on moral grounds because the fetal cells are obtained during abortions.

The brain in animals

Most *invertebrates* (animals without a backbone) do not have a well-developed brain. Instead, they have clusters of nerve cells, called *ganglia,* that coordinate the activities of the body. All *vertebrates* (animals with a backbone) have a complex brain. Scientific evidence suggests the complex brain in higher animals *evolved* (developed gradually) through the ages (see **Evolution**).

In invertebrates. The more advanced invertebrates, such as worms and insects, have some type of relatively simple brain. An earthworm, for example, has in its head region a large pair of ganglia that control the worm's behavior on the basis of information received from the sense organs. An insect has a more complex brain that consists of three pairs of ganglia. The ganglia receive information from the sense organs and control such complex activities as feeding and flying.

Octopuses have the most highly developed brain among invertebrates. Their brain is divided into several parts, the largest of which is the *optic lobe*. The optic lobe processes information from an octopus's eyes, which resemble the eyes of vertebrates in structure and function.

In vertebrates, the brain can be divided into three main regions: (1) the forebrain, (2) the midbrain, and (3) the hindbrain. The midbrain is the most highly developed region in primitive vertebrates, such as fish and amphibians. In contrast, the forebrain, or cerebrum, makes up only a small part of the brain in these animals. As increasingly complex vertebrates evolved, two major changes occurred in the brain. The size and importance of the cerebrum increased enormously, and the relative size and importance of the midbrain decreased. The hindbrain consists of the medulla and the cerebellum. Its structure and function is basically the same in all vertebrates, though the cerebellum is larger and more complex in advanced animals.

Among fish and amphibians, the midbrain consists chiefly of two optic lobes. These lobes serve not only as the center of vision but also as the major area for coordinating sensory and motor impulses. A fish's cerebrum is composed of two small, smooth swellings that serve mainly as the center of smell. In amphibians, the cerebrum is slightly larger and is covered by a cortex.

In reptiles, some functions of the midbrain have been taken over by the cerebrum. A reptile's cerebrum is larger and more complex than that of a fish or amphibian. Within the cerebrum are basal ganglia. These small bundles of neurons form a major area where information is analyzed, processed, and stored. Some advanced reptiles have a small area of cerebral cortex that differs from the cortex in lower vertebrates. This area, called the *neocortex,* functions as an important area for information processing and storage.

Birds have a cerebrum larger than that of fish, amphibians, and reptiles. But unlike some advanced reptiles, birds lack a neocortex. Instead, the dominant part of their brain consists of large, highly developed basal ganglia, which fill most of the interior of the cerebrum. The basal ganglia serve as the main center for processing and storing information and give birds an impressive ability to learn new behavior. The ganglia apparently also store the instructions for the many instinctive behavior patterns of birds. Birds also have a well-developed cerebellum, which coordinates all the sensory and motor impulses involved in flying.

The brain reaches its highest level of development in mammals. The neocortex forms nearly all the cerebral cortex of the mammalian brain, and the midbrain serves

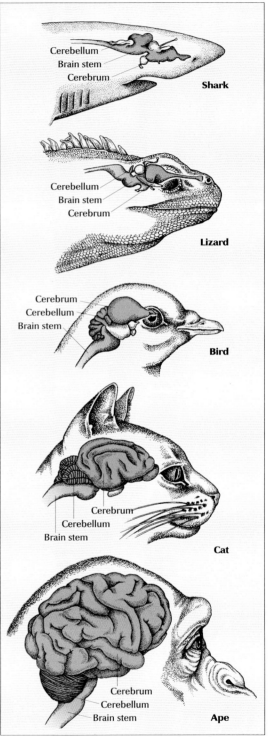

WORLD BOOK illustrations by Patricia J. Wynne

Brains of some vertebrates show the progression of brain development as animals evolved over millions of years. Sharks and other fish have a relatively simple brain with a small, smooth cerebrum. The cerebrum is larger but still quite smooth in reptiles and birds. The most advanced mammals, such as cats and apes, have a large, wrinkled cerebrum with billions of neurons.

mainly as a relay center. The most primitive mammals, such as moles and shrews, have a relatively small cerebrum with a smooth cerebral cortex. More advanced mammals, such as horses and cats, have a larger cerebrum covered by a cortex with many ridges and grooves. These indentations increase the surface area of the brain. Whales and dolphins have a large, highly developed brain. The brain in chimpanzees and other apes is even more highly developed. It resembles the human brain more closely than does the brain in all other species of animals.   Richard Restak

Related articles in *World Book* include:

Alzheimer's disease	Encephalitis	Phrenology
Aneurysm	Endorphin	Poliomyelitis
Aphasia	Epilepsy	Positron emission
Biofeedback	Huntington's disease	tomography
Cerebral hemor-	Mad cow disease	Psychosis
rrhage	Meningitis	Reflex action
Cerebral palsy	Mental illness	Schizophrenia
Cerebrospinal fluid	Mental retardation	Senility
Chorea	Multiple sclerosis	Skull
Concussion	Nervous system	Stimulant
Creutzfeldt-Jakob	Parkinson disease	Stroke
disease	Penfield, Wilder G.	Tay-Sachs disease
Electroencephalo-	Perception	
graph		

Cosmic rays are electrically charged, high-energy particles that travel through outer space. They are *subatomic particles,* units of matter smaller than an atom. Astronomers believe that cosmic rays fill our Milky Way Galaxy and other galaxies.

Scientists study cosmic rays because these particles are the only matter that reaches Earth from outside the solar system. Studies of cosmic rays reveal conditions in *interstellar space* (space between the stars). Scientists also learn about processes that occur when a star explodes as a *supernova.*

Physicists measure the energy of cosmic rays in units called *electronvolts* (eV). One electronvolt is the energy needed to move an electron between two points with a potential difference of 1 volt (see **Volt**). Most cosmic rays have energies between a few million and a few billion electronvolts. One million electronvolts is abbreviated 1 MeV, and 1 billion electronvolts is abbreviated 1 GeV. A proton with 1 GeV of energy can go through almost 2 feet (60 centimeters) of iron.

There are two kinds of cosmic rays: (1) *primary cosmic rays,* or *primaries,* which originate in outer space; and (2) *secondary cosmic rays,* or *secondaries,* which originate in Earth's atmosphere. Secondaries form when primaries collide with atoms at the top of the atmosphere. The collision changes the primary and the atom into a shower of secondaries. Many secondaries then collide with other atoms, making more secondaries.

Some secondaries reach the surface and even penetrate deep into the ground. No measurable amount of primaries reaches Earth's surface.

Primary cosmic rays

Primary cosmic rays move through space at almost the speed of light, which is 186,282 miles (299,792 kilometers) per second. Most primaries that reach Earth's atmosphere have traveled through the Milky Way for millions of years.

There are three main types of primary cosmic rays: (1)

galactic, (2) solar, and (3) anomalous component. *Anomalous component* means *peculiar part of a group.* Physicists gave anomalous component primaries this name when they were discovered in the early 1970's. The composition and behavior of these particles differed greatly from those of galactic and solar primaries, which had been identified by the late 1950's.

Galactic cosmic rays come from outside the solar system. Most primaries are galactic cosmic rays. About 98 percent of galactic cosmic rays are atomic nuclei, which carry a positive electric charge. Approximately 87 percent of the nuclei are single protons—nuclei of hydrogen atoms. Roughly 12 percent are helium nuclei, each consisting of two protons and two electrically neutral particles called *neutrons.* The remaining nuclear primaries include nuclei of all chemical elements heavier than helium.

The 2 percent of primaries that are not nuclei are electrons, which are negatively charged, and *positrons.* A positron is the antiparticle of an electron. A positron has the same *mass* (amount of matter) as an electron but carries a positive charge.

Energy sources. Scientists believe that galactic cosmic rays get their energy from shock waves produced by supernovae or from strong *magnetic fields* around *neutron stars.* A magnetic field is a region where magnetic forces can be felt. A neutron star is an extremely dense, rapidly rotating star that remains after some supernova explosions. Galactic primaries may also gain energy from weaker waves that travel along the weak magnetic fields of interstellar space.

The most powerful source of energy is supernova shock waves. However, the highest-energy primaries have more energy than even a supernova can provide. Scientists do not know how these particles get their extra energy.

Magnetic control. Magnetic fields control the travel of cosmic rays through space. A magnetic field can be thought of as a set of imaginary lines extending through space. No field line crosses another. In outer space, where magnetic fields are weak, a field line may be stretched many trillions of miles from its source. It is often not clear where these fields originate. See **Magnetism** (illustration: A magnetic field).

If a primary—or any other electrically charged object—moves across a field line, the field bends the path of the object at a right angle to the object's original path. Charged particles therefore can move easily along a magnetic field but have difficulty traveling very far across a field.

The travels of primary cosmic rays. After receiving their energy, primaries travel randomly along magnetic fields in the galaxy for an average of 10 million to 20 million years. Because of the randomness of this motion, the direction from which a primary comes gives scientists no indication of the source of the primary.

Some cosmic rays eventually leave the galaxy. Others strike so much interstellar matter that they lose almost all their speed and become particles of interstellar matter themselves.

Solar effects. A magnetic field carried by the *solar wind* prevents some galactic cosmic rays from entering the solar system. The solar wind is a continuous stream of *ions* (electrically charged atoms) flowing from the

**How cosmic rays
penetrate the
earth's magnetic field**

Primary cosmic-ray particles, even those with low energies, can enter the earth's atmosphere near
the poles by traveling along the field lines of the magnetic field. Only particles with extremely high
energies can cut across the field lines and reach the atmosphere near the equator. The magnetic
field there reflects most particles, including many with high energies. Secondary cosmic rays are
created in the atmosphere by collisions between the primary rays and atomic nuclei.

WORLD BOOK diagram

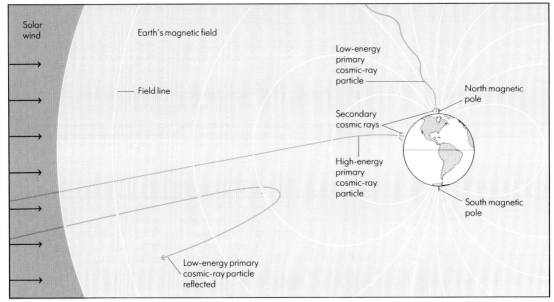

sun, typically at speeds of about 250 miles (400 kilometers) per second or more. These ions have too little
energy—only about 1,000 eV—to be cosmic rays.

Activity on the surface of the sun disturbs the solar
wind. Sunspots are one sign of solar activity (see **Sunspot**). The solar activity increases and decreases in an
11-year cycle called the *sunspot cycle.* As activity increases, the flow of the solar wind becomes more disturbed and the magnetic field therefore becomes more
complicated. As a result, the primary cosmic rays have
more difficulty reaching Earth. During a sunspot cycle,
the number of galactic primaries striking each square
inch (6 square centimeters) of the top of the atmosphere
ranges from two to six per second.

Solar cosmic rays are produced by the sun during
solar flares and other spectacular eruptions on the sun's
surface. Solar flares occur mainly during periods of high
activity in the sunspot cycle. Most solar cosmic rays are
protons with energies of only a few MeV. However,
large flares can produce particles with energies up to a
few GeV. Heavier nuclei and electrons also occur in
solar cosmic rays.

Anomalous component cosmic rays develop from
normal atoms in interstellar gas near the sun. Because
they have no electric charge, the atoms pass freely
through the solar wind and its magnetic field. Close to
the sun, some atoms absorb so much energy from the
sun's ultraviolet radiation that an electron leaves each of
them. Because electrons carry a negative charge, each
atom that loses an electron becomes a positive ion. Almost all ions produced in this manner are ions of hydrogen, helium, nitrogen, oxygen, and neon.

The solar wind picks up the new ions and carries
them to the edge of the *heliosphere,* the huge region of

space filled by the solar wind. The heliosphere extends
beyond the orbits of all the planets.

Scientists believe that there is a strong shock wave at
the edge of the heliosphere where the solar wind runs
into interstellar material and slows down. This shock
wave can accelerate the ions to energies of hundreds of
MeV.

After they are accelerated, the ions can re-enter the
heliosphere as anomalous component cosmic rays. During low points in the sunspot cycle, there are more
anomalous component primaries than galactic primaries
in the heliosphere at energies below about 100 MeV.

Anomalous component primaries are too weak to
produce many secondaries. Scientists therefore did not
discover them until the early 1970's, when spacecraft
carried instruments that could detect them.

Secondary cosmic rays

Secondary cosmic rays include all types of subatomic
particles. Most secondaries are *muons,* which are similar to electrons, but more massive. Physicists discovered
many types of subatomic particles in secondary cosmic
rays before building machines called *particle accelerators* to study high-energy particles.

Secondaries slow down in the atmosphere. Only a
small fraction of them reach Earth. Every minute, about
six secondaries strike each square inch of Earth's surface. Because of Earth's magnetic field, the concentration of secondaries is lower near the equator than near
the poles. Near the equator, low-energy primaries cannot reach the atmosphere because they cannot cross the
magnetic field lines. But primaries of all energy levels
can easily travel along the field lines that curve into the
poles.

Effects of cosmic rays

Cosmic rays do not produce enough radiation on Earth to harm living things. Above the atmosphere, however, the radiation reaches harmful levels. It is extremely dangerous in the *Van Allen belts,* regions that contain large numbers of particles. In addition, the radiation can be dangerous anywhere above the atmosphere during solar flares.

Galactic primaries consisting of heavy nuclei have caused problems in electronic circuits that are on spacecraft. If a heavy nucleus hits an ordinary computer chip, the chip may stop operating properly. As a result, engineers have developed chips that are less sensitive to cosmic rays.

Cosmic rays also produce *radiocarbon* in the atmosphere. Radiocarbon, or carbon 14, is a radioactive form of carbon. Scientists can use it to determine the age of ancient materials and to study solar activity. See **Radiocarbon.**

Cosmic ray research

During the late 1800's, physicists used *electroscopes* to study radioactivity. An electroscope stores electric charge and indicates the presence of the charge. Exposure to high-energy radiation causes a charged electroscope to lose its charge. Even when the electroscopes were shielded from the most powerful rays known to be given off by radioactive substances, they showed that radiation was still present.

In 1912, the Austrian physicist Victor F. Hess took electroscopes up in a balloon. He showed that the mysterious radiation increased with altitude. Hess concluded that the radiation must originate in the upper atmosphere or beyond. In 1936, he received the Nobel Prize for physics for discovering cosmic rays.

By the late 1950's, scientists had used many types of instruments on the ground and in balloons to determine that cosmic rays are electrically charged particles and that they consist mostly of hydrogen and helium nuclei. Researchers had also discovered that solar activity affects the intensity of cosmic rays.

Since the 1960's, scientists have used balloons and spacecraft to study low- and medium-energy primaries. They have used large instruments on the ground to study secondaries. Space probes far beyond the orbit of the outer planets continue to provide information on how the heliosphere affects cosmic rays.

R. B. McKibben

See also **Sun** (Flares); **Van Allen belts.**

Oyster is a type of shellfish that provides an important source of food and pearls. The soft, edible body of an oyster is protected inside a hard, two-piece shell, which is usually irregular in shape. An oyster spends all except the first few weeks of its life attached to rocks and other hard surfaces on the ocean bottom. Oysters are found in relatively calm waters of mild to tropical coastal oceans, where they often form large reefs.

People began eating oysters thousands of years ago. About 100 B.C., the ancient Romans raised oysters on "farms" along the coast of Italy. Later, Roman settlers in England collected oysters along the coast. In winter, they placed the shellfish in cloth bags filled with ice and snow and sent them to Rome. Today, oyster farms are common along parts of the United States and European coasts.

Oysters—like clams, scallops, and some other shellfish—are a type of *mollusk,* a group of soft-bodied animals that have no bones. Oysters are called *bivalve* (two valve) mollusks because their shell is made up of two parts called *valves.*

There are several different groups of oysters. One family of oysters includes pearl oysters, which produce high-quality pearls, and wing oysters. The oysters most often eaten by human beings belong to the family known as true oysters. They are the most abundant and well-known family and are found worldwide. This article chiefly deals with true oysters.

The body of an oyster

Shell. The valves of an oyster's shell are held together by an elastic ligament at the hinge. One valve is deeper, larger, and thicker than the other. This large valve is the one that the animal normally fastens to the ocean bottom.

The elastic ligament usually keeps the valves slightly apart. A strong muscle called an *adductor* closes the shell. When threatened or during long periods out of the water, oysters close their valves tightly. They can live with their shell closed for several weeks.

An oyster's shell is made of a hard, chalky material called *calcium carbonate.* The shell is produced by a skinlike organ called the *mantle,* which lines the inside of the shell. The mantle takes minerals from the food the oyster eats and uses them to produce the shell. Because the mantle makes shell in cycles, periods without shell growth leave a line. The distinct shell lines can be used like the rings of a tree to estimate the age of an oyster. The shell grows as long as the oyster's body grows.

The inside of the shell is white with colored highlights. The shell of a pearl oyster is lined with a smooth, shiny substance called *mother-of-pearl.* A scar inside the shell indicates where the adductor muscle was attached.

Sometimes a tiny piece of grit or other foreign substance can work its way between the mantle and the shell, irritating the mantle. The irritation stimulates the production of a pearl. Shell material is evenly laid down around the particle to stop the irritation. In this way, a pearl is formed. Pearl oysters can produce high-quality pearls and are the primary source of pearls. True oysters rarely produce pearls. When they do, the pearls are dull in color, irregular in shape, and of little value.

Body organs. An oyster, like all bivalves, does not have a head. A pair of W-shaped gills is located beneath the mantle. The oyster uses its gills, which are covered with fine hairs called *cilia,* to breathe and to trap small food particles. Water flow created by the cilia brings tiny, single-celled plantlike organisms called *phytoplankton* toward the gills. The cilia direct the food to the mouth. The food then moves into the oyster's stomach and final digestion takes place in the digestive gland.

The oyster's heart pumps blood to all parts of its body. A pair of kidneys removes chemical wastes.

An oyster has a simple nervous system made up of a few nerve bundles and connecting nerves. An oyster does not have eyes. However, it does have two rows of sensitive *tentacles* (feelers) along the mantle edge that can sense changes in light, chemicals in the water, and

Sakata Pearl Co. (U.S.A.), Ltd.

The Pacific pearl oyster,
above, has been cut to show
two gleaming jewels inside.

Young oysters, *below,* are
about as big as a needle
point. They swim in the sea.

U.S. Dept. of Interior

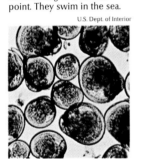

Joy Spurr, Bruce Coleman Inc.

Oysters fasten their shells to rocks or other hard objects on the ocean
bottom. Most species live in shallow coastal waters.

water currents. Any change will cause the tentacles to
contract (become smaller). In response, the adductor
muscle quickly closes the shell against possible danger.

The life of an oyster

Many kinds of oysters are *hermaphrodites* (pronounced *hur MAF ruh dyts*)—that is, animals with both
male and female reproductive organs. Certain oysters
begin their life as males but later develop into females.
Other kinds alternate between male and female several
times during their lives. During the female stage, various
oysters can produce as many as 500 million eggs each
year. Male oysters release sperm, which unite with and
fertilize the eggs. In many oysters, the eggs are fertilized
after the female releases them into the water. In others,
the sperm enter the female's body to fertilize the eggs.

Young. The earliest part of an oyster's life is spent
drifting in water as part of the mass of tiny organisms
called *plankton.* An oyster larva develops from the fertilized egg. After about 24 hours, the larva is called a
veliger (VEE luh juhr). Veligers use their cilia to move. A
tiny bivalve shell is visible.

Veligers remain floating in the water for about two
weeks. During this time, the animal continues to develop and forms a muscular "foot" that extends between
the valves. The animal is now called a *pediveliger
(PEHD uh VEE luh juhr).* The foot is used to test different

surfaces as the oyster searches for an appropriate site to
settle. An oyster usually chooses a hard surface, such as
a rock or the shell of another animal. It then attaches itself permanently to the surface using cement produced
by its body. Most pediveligers settle with adult oysters,
and together they often form crowded *beds* (groups) in
coastal inlets.

Young oysters grow quickly. They lose their foot
shortly after they settle. A month-old oyster is about the
size of a pea. A year-old oyster is approximately 1 inch
(2.5 centimeters) in diameter. Oysters usually grow at a
rate of an inch per year for three or four years. After this
time, their growth rate slows. Some North American
oysters grow as large as 14 inches (36 centimeters).
Most oysters live about 6 years, but some can survive
more than 20 years.

Enemies. An oyster has many enemies and no defense except its shell. Diseases caused by various viruses and *protozoa* (single-celled organisms) can kill
millions of oysters in a single year. Most newly hatched
oysters are eaten by fish.

Once settled, even adult oysters fall prey to many animals. Starfish use their tube feet to pull at the oyster's
valves, which eventually causes the adductor muscle to
weaken and the shell to open slightly. The starfish then
eats the soft oyster meat. Many crabs with powerful
claws and some fish with strong jaws are able to crack

The body of an oyster

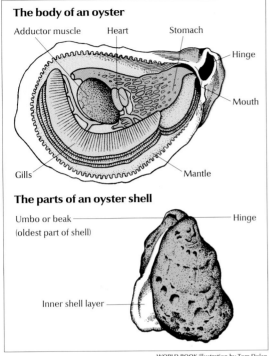

Adductor muscle   Heart   Stomach
Hinge
Mouth
Mantle
Gills

The parts of an oyster shell

Umbo or beak
(oldest part of shell)
Hinge
Inner shell layer

WORLD BOOK illustration by Tom Dolan

Where oysters are found

The blue areas of the map show the parts of the world where edible oysters are found. The map includes oyster farm areas.

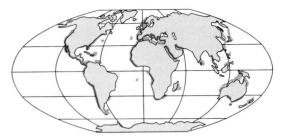

the shells of small oysters. An oyster-drill snail uses a combination of glandular chemicals and filelike tongue to make a hole in an oyster's shell. Once the hole is made, the snail sucks out the oyster meat. Some birds, such as the oystercatcher, can pry an oyster's shell apart with their strong beaks.

People are the greatest enemies to oysters. They collect and eat millions of oysters each year. Overfishing and pollution have reduced the stock of oysters.

The oyster industry

Oyster farming. The popularity of oysters as food—and the threat to their natural populations—has led to the growth of oyster farming. Most oyster farms are established in shallow, quiet coastal waters where there is a firm ocean bottom. Shifting sand or mud can cover and smother oysters. Floats mark a farmed area. Oyster farmers place old shells or tiles on the bottom to act as *cultch,* a surface to which the young oysters can attach themselves. Farmers often buy seed oysters to "plant" in the farming areas. Workers harvest the crop when the oysters are 2 to 4 years old and 2 to 4 inches (5 to 10 centimeters) in diameter.

Many oysters raised for market come from commercial oyster farms. Large oyster-farming centers include those along the southwest coast of France and the west coast of the United States. Oyster farmers raise and gather the shellfish along the entire coast of the United States. Louisiana, Maryland, Virginia, and Washington are the leading oyster-producing states. In Canada, the provinces of British Columbia and Prince Edward Island produce the most oysters. South Korea, Japan, the United States, and France are the leading oyster-producing countries.

Oyster harvesting is heaviest during fall and winter in most regions. Farmers use long tongs to collect oysters in shallow waters. In deeper waters, they gather the oysters with *dredges,* which are nets attached to metal frames. The dredges are attached to a boat by a line and dragged along the bottom.

Oysters are sold either in their shells or unshelled. Workers called *shuckers* remove the shell from the oyster. A shucker forces the valves apart and then cuts the adductor muscle. The workers remove the meat from the opened shell and pack the meat for shipment.

Oyster meat. People eat oysters fried, broiled, *scalloped* (baked in sauce), and prepared many other ways. Oysters are rich in protein and in several minerals and vitamins. But the U.S. Food and Drug Administration advises that people with diabetes, weakened immune systems, or other medical conditions should avoid eating raw oysters. People once believed that oysters were un-

© Don Gray, f/Stop Pictures, Inc.

Harvesting oysters with a dredge, oystermen watch the heavy net haul up their catch from the ocean bottom. The oysters are taken into port to be cleaned and packaged for market.

safe to eat during months without an *r* in their name—that is, from May to August. Scientists now know that European and North American oysters *spawn* (produce eggs) during summer. Oysters are less tasty when they are spawning, but they are safe to eat. Robert S. Prezant

Scientific classification. True oysters make up the oyster family, Ostreidae. The pearl oyster and the wing oyster belong to the family Pteriidae. An important source of pearls is *Pinctada margaritifera.*

Greenhouse effect is a warming of the lower atmosphere and surface of a planet by a complex process involving sunlight, gases, and particles in the atmosphere. On the earth, the greenhouse effect began long before human beings existed. However, recent human activity may have added to the effect. The amounts of heat-trapping atmospheric gases, called *greenhouse gases,* have greatly increased since the mid-1800's, when modern industry became widespread. Since the late 1800's, the temperature of the earth's surface has also risen. The greenhouse effect is so named because the atmosphere acts much like the glass roof and walls of a greenhouse, trapping heat from the sun.

The natural greenhouse effect. The atmosphere reflects toward space about 30 percent of the energy in incoming sunlight. The atmosphere absorbs about another 30 percent, and the remaining 40 percent or so reaches the earth's surface.

The earth's surface reflects about 15 percent of the solar energy that reaches it back toward space. The remaining energy heats the lands and seas. The warmed lands and seas then send most of the heat back into the atmosphere, chiefly as *infrared rays* and in evaporated water. Infrared rays are much like light waves but are invisible to the human eye.

When the rays from the lands and seas strike certain substances in the atmosphere, such as greenhouse gases and particles, those substances absorb the rays. As a result, the gases and particles are heated. They then are cooled by sending out infrared rays of their own. Some of the rays go into space. The remainder radiate back toward the earth's surface, adding to the warming of the surface layer of air. Without the natural greenhouse effect, the average temperature of the earth's surface would be about 59 Fahrenheit degrees (33 Celsius degrees) colder than it is now.

The chief greenhouse gases are made up of atoms of carbon (C), hydrogen (H), and oxygen (O). These gases are water vapor (H_2O), carbon dioxide (CO_2), methane (CH_4), and ozone (O_3). The greenhouse particles include cloud droplets, soot, and dust.

Increases in greenhouse gases. Since the early to mid-1800's, the amount of CO_2 in the atmosphere has increased by about 25 percent and the CH_4 concentration has risen by about 150 percent. Most of the increase has been due to human activities—chiefly the burning of *fossil fuels* (coal, oil, and natural gas) and the clearing of land. Fossil fuels contain carbon, and burning them creates CO_2. Trees and other plants absorb the gas through the process of photosynthesis. As land is cleared and forests are cut down, CO_2 levels rise.

The average temperature of the earth's surface has increased about 0.5 to 1.5 Fahrenheit degrees (0.3 to 0.8 Celsius degree) since the late 1800's. Scientists have not yet proved that an increase in atmospheric CO_2 has raised the surface temperature. But in the likely event that this relationship does exist, the eventual results could be severe. Many scientists estimate that, by about 2050, the amount of CO_2 in the atmosphere will have doubled from the preindustrial level. If this increase were to add to the natural greenhouse effect, the earth's surface temperature might rise between 3 and 8 Fahrenheit degrees (1.5 and 4.5 Celsius degrees) by 2100.

The increase in surface temperature, which is called *global warming,* could alter the ecology of many parts of the earth. For example, global warming could change rainfall patterns, melt enough polar ice to raise the sea level, increase the severity of tropical storms, and lead to shifts in plant and animal populations. Ocean currents and wind patterns could change, making some areas cooler than they are now. One remote possibility is that a warming of northern regions will result in more winter snowfall, causing some ice sheets to advance.

Studying the greenhouse effect. Researchers use high-speed computers to study how CO_2 concentration may affect surface temperature. The computers manipulate *mathematical models,* sets of equations that describe relationships between changeable factors. Scientists do not have enough data to prove that variations in CO_2 and other human-caused changes to atmospheric composition cause corresponding shifts in surface temperature. They may need until the 2010's to gather enough data. But some results of computer modeling suggest that the 2010's may be too late to avoid some damage from global warming.

Scientists have also examined evidence from the distant past to determine whether changes in CO_2 concentration cause temperature changes. Cores of ice drilled from great depths in Greenland and Antarctica provide a record for the past 160,000 years. During those years, the climate warmed and cooled several times. Researchers analyzed the gases and other substances that were trapped in the ice when it formed. During the cooler periods, the atmosphere contained about 30 percent less CO_2 and 50 percent less methane than during the warmer periods. Stephen H. Schneider

Penguin is a type of flightless bird that spends most of its life in the ocean. Penguins stand upright on land and walk with a waddle because they have short legs and tall, torpedo-shaped bodies. Although penguins appear awkward out of the water, they can walk about as fast as a human being. They also climb rocky slopes easily, sometimes hopping from rock to rock. Some penguins travel over ice and snow by *tobogganing* (sliding on their bellies).

Penguins lost the ability to fly millions of years ago. As they began to spend most of their time in the water, their wings started to look more like flippers. This major change helped make penguins excellent swimmers. They "fly" underwater using the same motion as birds that fly in the air.

The body of a penguin is specially suited to living in the sea. Penguins are covered with short, thick feathers that form a waterproof coat. Their feathers are black or bluish-gray, except on their underside, where the feathers are always white. Thick layers of blubber keep the birds warm in cold water. For additional warmth, penguins that live where the weather is extremely cold have

Peter Johnson, NHPA

Most species of penguins build their nests and raise their young in huge colonies called *rookeries.* This picture shows part of an enormous rookery of king penguins on South Georgia, an island in the South Atlantic Ocean.

William R. Curtsinger from Rapho Guillumette

Penguins are excellent swimmers. Adélie penguins, *above,* swim rapidly in leaps and dives along the surface of the water.

an extra layer of long, downy feathers below their waterproof feathers.

A penguin's beak can be black, red, bright purple, or orange. The feet are black, blue, or pink. Penguins use their feet to steer themselves when they are underwater. Some penguins have a crest of feathers on their head.

There are 17 *species* (kinds) of penguins. The largest is the *emperor penguin,* which stands about 4 feet (1.2 meters) tall and may weigh up to 100 pounds (45 kilograms). The emperor penguin ranks as one of the heaviest birds. The smallest penguin is the *little penguin,* sometimes called the *fairy penguin,* which stands about

1 foot (30 centimeters) tall and usually weighs about $1\frac{1}{2}$ pounds (3.3 kilograms). Most other species are $1\frac{1}{2}$ to 3 feet (45 to 90 centimeters) tall and weigh 5 to 15 pounds (2.3 to 6.8 kilograms).

Penguins can swim for many hours at about 8 miles (13 kilometers) per hour. In short bursts, they can reach three times that speed. Penguins swim below the surface, but they leap into the air for breath about once a minute. They can also dive much deeper than any other bird. Some species dive nearly 900 feet (275 meters) below the surface. The deepest divers can hold their breath for nearly 20 minutes.

Guy Mannering, Bruce Coleman Inc.

Michael C. T. Smith, NAS

Morton Beebe, DPI

A pair of Adélie penguins stand over the two eggs in their nest. A female penguin lays from one to three eggs, depending on the species, but most penguins lay two. The eggs hatch in one or two months.

Adult penguins provide food and warmth for their young. A small emperor penguin huddles under the warm body of an adult, *left.* An Adélie penguin feeds its young, *above,* by vomiting partially digested fish.

The life of penguins. Penguins eat fish, squid, and *crustaceans,* which include crabs and shrimp. The birds use so much energy swimming that they must consume huge amounts of food. As a result, they live in waters that contain large populations of prey. Animals that feed on penguins include seals, sea lions, and killer whales.

All penguins in the wild live south of the equator. They are not found in northern areas because they will not cross into warm ocean water from the cold seas they prefer. The *Galapagos penguin* lives the farthest north. This bird inhabits the cold waters around the Galapagos Islands, which lie almost on the equator in the eastern Pacific Ocean. Eight species of penguins make their home among the islands near New Zealand and Australia. Three species inhabit the coast of South America, and one lives near southern Africa. Six species live far south, in the icy waters near Antarctica.

Penguins seldom visit land except to raise their young. They make their nests in enormous gatherings called *colonies.* Most colonies occur on islands. Some lie in coastal areas, but only where there are no land mammals that might eat the penguin chicks or eggs. A penguin colony can have thousands of members. The colonies are noisy because the birds often call to one another with a braying sound like donkeys. Penguins recognize each other mostly by their voice.

Most penguins make their nests by digging shallow burrows under large rocks or bushes. Antarctic penguins build nests of pebbles on the ground because the frozen earth is too difficult to dig. The king penguin and emperor penguin build no nests at all. They keep their eggs or small chicks warm under a fold of their belly, holding them on the tops of their feet.

A pair of male and female penguins may nest together every year for many years. The female usually lays one or two eggs. Penguin eggs take from 30 to 65 days to hatch. Larger species take longer to hatch and to grow. Once laid, the egg must be *incubated* (kept at body temperature). Both parents take turns searching for food and caring for the eggs. The parent at the nest does not eat while the other parent is away, sometimes for a month at a time or longer.

When a chick hatches, the parents must guard it until it is strong enough to defend itself. It remains near the nest for the first 2 to 12 months of its life, depending on the species. The chick is covered by downy feathers that are slowly replaced by mature ones. It eats partially digested food fed to it by its parents. When young penguins are old enough, they leave the colony and learn to feed themselves at sea. They return to land only to *molt* (shed their feathers) and to *breed* (produce young). Penguins usually choose a mate and a nesting site close to where they were born. Though penguins sometimes travel thousands of miles or kilometers from their nesting place, they are able to return to their exact birthplace. Scientists believe penguins can navigate using the sun, stars, and geographical landmarks.

Some penguins kept in zoos have lived for more than 30 years. But in the wild, most species have a life span of about 20 years.

Conservation. Penguins are one of the oldest groups of birds. They have lived separately from land mammals, including human beings, for millions of years. Penguin populations are easily disturbed by human activity. For example, even a small amount of oil in the ocean is harmful to the birds. It robs their feathers of the ability to keep them warm. Also, commercial fishing in waters where penguins live makes it harder for them to find enough food. Because human activity has spread into areas where penguins live, some penguin species are in danger of dying out.   David G. Ainley

Scientific classification. Penguins belong to the family Spheniscidae. The scientific name of the emperor penguin is *Aptenodytes forsteri.* The king penguin is *A. patagonica.* The little penguin is *Eudyptula minor.* The Galapagos penguin is *Spheniscus mendiculus.*

Seal is a sea mammal that has a sleek, torpedo-shaped body and flippers in place of legs. Seals have adapted to living both on land and in the sea. They are excellent swimmers and are especially graceful in the water. On land, some seals walk on all four flippers, but others move by hunching their bodies with their powerful stomach muscles, somewhat like a caterpillar.

Seals generally live along the edges of continents and islands. Most *species* (types) of seals live in the earth's polar and temperate zones, where the fish populations are largest. Seals live mostly in the oceans or inland seas, but a few species live in fresh water. For example, the Baikal seal lives in Lake Baikal in Russia.

Seals belong to a group of animals called *pinnipeds.* This name comes from a Latin word meaning *fin-footed.* A seal's flippers look somewhat like fins. There are 34 different species of pinnipeds. They are divided into three main groups: (1) eared seals, which include fur seals and sea lions; (2) earless seals, including harbor seals and elephant seals; and (3) walruses.

Kinds of seals

Eared seals include fur seals and sea lions. They are called *eared seals* because they have ear flaps that cover their ear openings. Other seal species have uncovered ear openings. Another characteristic of these seals is that their hind flippers can be rotated forward and down, so that they can use all four flippers to walk on land. Fur seals and sea lions swim by using only their front flippers.

Eared seals live mainly in the northern Pacific Ocean and in coastal areas of the Southern Hemisphere. Fur seals have fur to insulate them from cold water, while sea lions rely on thick layers of blubber. Sea lions are larger than fur seals and have a broader, less pointy nose. Both species move well on land and often travel relatively far from shore.

Earless seals are different from fur seals and sea lions. These seals do not have ear flaps, but they do have ears. In fact, they have excellent hearing both above and below the water. Another important difference is that earless seals cannot use their rear flippers to walk on land. They pull themselves forward on their bellies, using their front flippers and powerful stomach muscles. On land, they do not move as fast as eared seals and cannot travel as far from shore. Earless seals use their hind flippers to swim using a side-to-side motion, like most fish. They can dive better than eared seals can.

Walruses are physically much different from other seals. For example, the walrus is the only seal with tusks. But walruses have features in common with both eared

Seals have sleek bodies with flippers in place of legs. This picture shows a mother seal, an Australian sea lion, protecting her *pup* (baby seal). Female seals almost always give birth to only one pup at a time. The pup is covered by a soft fur. Sea lion pups have brown fur.

Daniel Costa

and earless seals. Like eared seals, walruses use their hind flippers to walk on land. Like earless seals, walruses have small ear openings but no outside ears. For more information about walruses, see the **Walrus** in *World Book.*

The body of a seal

The largest pinniped is the southern elephant seal, which lives in the waters surrounding Antarctica. The male may grow 16 feet (5 meters) long and weigh up to 8,800 pounds (4,000 kilograms). This seal ranks second in size only to whales among all sea mammals. One of the smallest pinnipeds is the ringed seal. It usually grows about $3\frac{1}{2}$ feet (1.1 meters) long and weighs 110 to 200 pounds (50 to 90 kilograms).

Fur seals are the only seals that have fur. They rely almost entirely on their thick coats of fine fur for insulation against the cold. Other seals rely on a layer of blubber that is often 1 to 6 inches (2.5 to 15 centimeters) thick.

Head. All seals have slitlike nostrils, which they can close when they swim underwater. Some kinds of seals have small heads with short noses. Adult male elephant seals have a long, curved nose that helps them attract mates.

The nose of a male hooded seal has a pouch that extends to the top of his head. When a competing male approaches, the seal inflates this pouch as a threat, making his head appear larger. An additional pouch inside the nostril also inflates, forming a bright red "balloon" that adds to the display.

Seals have large eyes and can see well in the dark. This enables them to feed at night or in deep water where there is little light. All seals have whiskers on their upper lip. The whiskers are sensitive to touch and probably help the animal find food.

Flippers. Seals have four legs, but the leg bones above the ankles do not extend outside the body. The ankles and feet form large, paddlelike flippers. The front flippers of fur seals and sea lions are longer and flatter than those of earless seals. A fur seal's front flippers may

be more than 18 inches (45 centimeters) long and 6 inches (15 centimeters) wide.

The life of a seal

Seal rookeries. Seals go to their breeding grounds, called *rookeries,* to mate and to bear their young. More than 150,000 seals may gather at one rookery. The rookeries of earless seals can be on the shores of islands or continents. But all fur seal and most sea lion rookeries are on islands. Rookeries may occur on large sandy or rocky beaches.

Bull seals fight to establish territories within a rookery. They defend these territories and the cows within them. Young bachelors and older bulls without a *harem* (group of females) live apart from the others. Cow seals prefer to mate with the largest, most experienced males. Most cow seals bear their first young when they are 5 to 6 years old. They usually give birth every year after that. Some cow seals can give birth at 2 or 3 years of age. Some continue to bear young until they are about 25 years old.

Birth. In all seal species, the young are conceived during one mating season and are born during the next. In most species, the embryo undergoes a period of *delayed implantation*—that is, it does not begin to grow in the mother's body until six weeks to five months after conception. Actual development of the young occurs over a nine-month period. A seal almost always has one *pup* (baby seal) at a time. Twins are rare.

A newborn pup is covered by a fine soft fur. Sea lion pups have brown fur, and newborn fur seals, elephant seals, and monk seals have black coats. The fur of baby harp seals, leopard seals, walruses, and other seals that live on floating islands of ice is usually white or grayish in color.

All seal pups are born in an advanced stage of development. Their eyes are open and they can walk and vocalize within minutes of birth. Harbor seal pups can even swim within minutes of being born.

Raising young. Each seal species rears its pups differently. Most earless seal mothers remain at the rook-

The skeleton of a seal

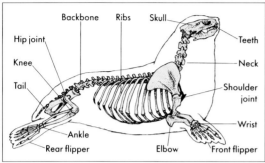

Backbone   Ribs   Skull
Hip joint
Teeth
Knee
Neck
Tail
Shoulder joint
Wrist
Ankle
Rear flipper   Elbow   Front flipper

WORLD BOOK illustration by John D. Dawson

Where seals live

The blue areas of the map show the parts of the world where seals are found. Most seals live in the Northern Hemisphere.

ery continuously from the birth of their pup until it is *weaned* (able to eat regular food). During this time the seal cows do not feed. Some other seals, including harbor, ringed, and Weddell seals, do eat while rearing their young. For these species, weaning occurs abruptly when the mother leaves the rookery, leaving the pup behind. In some species, such as northern elephant seals, the pup remains at or near the rookery, not eating or drinking, for months after weaning.

Eared seal mothers divide their time between feeding at sea and nursing their pups on land. A mother may stay at sea for several days and then return to nurse her pup for 1 to 3 days. This cycle lasts from at least four months up to three years. But in most species, pups are weaned within a year of their birth.

Mother seals find their pups out of the hundreds of others at the rookery by calling out to them. When a pup hears its mother, it begins to call back. Each mother and pup have a unique call, and the mother responds only to her own offspring. Once together, the mother recognizes her baby by its smell.

Food. Seals feed on various marine animals. They have sharp, pointed teeth. They cannot chew food because their teeth have no flat surfaces. They swallow small fish whole or grasp and tear off pieces of larger prey.

Fur seals and sea lions eat primarily fish and squid. Harbor seals eat mostly fish and octopuses. Crabeater seals feed mainly on small, shrimplike creatures called *krill.* Elephant seals prefer fish and squid. Leopard seals feed on fish, penguins, and sometimes other seals.

Diving. Seals are excellent divers. They can dive deeper and longer than most other mammals because their bodies store more oxygen. Fur seals and sea lions, for example, can store twice as much oxygen as human beings can. Earless seals can store three times as much oxygen as human beings can. Fur seals and sea lions feed on prey near the surface, while earless seals feed on prey in deeper water and on the bottom.

Elephant seals exceed all other seals and even most whales in diving ability. They can dive about as well as the sperm whale, which is the deepest diving whale. Northern elephant seals dive continuously, day and night, for two to eight months. They spend an average of 20 minutes underwater per dive.

Enemies. Seals have few enemies besides human beings. Large sharks and killer whales attack them in the water, and polar bears hunt seals on ice. A seal has few defenses against its enemies. In the water, it usually tries to escape an attacker. A frightened fur seal can swim as fast as 10 miles (16 kilometers) per hour for about five minutes. Some species swim among the strong waves and between the large rocks close to shore, where most

Daniel Costa

A male Northern fur seal guards his territory at a *rookery,* or breeding ground. The fur seal's thick coat provides insulation against the cold. Like sea lions and walruses, fur seals can rotate their hind flippers forward and down to walk on land.

of their enemies cannot go. Other species dive deep when an enemy approaches.

Many kinds of seals are so slow and clumsy out of the water that they have little chance of escaping an enemy. Crabeater seals are one of the fastest seals on land or ice. They can move about 15 miles (24 kilometers) per hour—almost as fast as a person can run.

People and seals

Seals in captivity. Fur seals and sea lions are the kinds of seals that most often perform in shows at circuses, zoos, and marine parks. These seals are more acrobatic and easier to train than other types of seals. Trained sea lions crave attention and enjoy performing. A strong bond often develops between sea lions and their trainers. Sea lions breed so well in captivity that many zoos and marine parks have had to control breeding to prevent overpopulation.

Hunting of seals. People have hunted seals for thousands of years. To the Inuit people of the Arctic, seals are an important source of food. Many peoples hunt seals for their fur, skin, and oil.

In many places, fur seals were hunted almost to the point of extinction. In 1911, Canada, Japan, Russia, and the United States signed an agreement to protect northern fur seals. Under the agreement, seals could be hunted commercially only on land.

Since the 1970's, the demand for seal fur has declined as people became more concerned about the welfare of the animals. A combination of the declining market for furs and pressure from environmental groups helped to end the commercial harvest of fur seals on the Pribilof Islands in 1986. However, thousands of young male fur seals are still harvested each year for food by residents of the Pribilofs.

Seals and fishing crews. In some cases, seals and fishing crews compete for the same fish. In the Ballard Locks near Seattle, for example, California sea lions have learned that salmon are easy to catch when the fish approach the artificial waterways called fish ladders. Salmon use these fish ladders when swimming around the locks. The sea lions eat so many of the salmon that the local salmon population has seriously declined. This decline has reduced the local salmon harvest.

However, seals are often blamed for reductions in fish harvests that may actually be due to overfishing. It is also possible that seal populations are shrinking because fishing by human beings is reducing the animals' food supply.

Threats to seal populations include the destruction of their habitats due to increased use of coastal resources and the expanded use of the ocean for recreation. Seals are often accidentally caught in fishing nets. Many seals also get entangled in discarded plastic packing straps and discarded or lost fishing gear. This problem grows worse over time, as many of these discarded products do not break down from the action of microbes in the water and so last for years. As human populations increase, people will likely disturb more seal rookeries.   Daniel P. Costa

Related articles in *World Book* include:
Alaska (Fur industry; picture: Northern fur seals)
Animal (How animals raise their young (picture)
Antarctica (Animal life)

Water pollution is one of the most serious environmental problems. It occurs when water is contaminated by such substances as human and other animal wastes, *toxic* (poisonous) chemicals, metals, and oils. Pollution can affect rain, rivers, lakes, oceans, and the water beneath the surface of the earth, called *ground water.*

Polluted water may look clean or dirty, but it all contains bacteria, viruses, chemicals, or other materials that can cause illness or death. Impurities must be removed before such water can be used safely for drinking, cooking, washing, or laundering. Some industries must clean the water before it can be used in their manufacturing.

Water pollution has become a serious problem in most countries. As a result, governments have passed laws limiting the amounts and kinds of wastes that can be dumped into water. Nations, states and provinces, cities and towns, and various industries have spent billions of dollars on research to reduce pollution and on the construction of water treatment plants. Nevertheless, pollution continues. In many parts of the world, cities and towns release untreated sewage into rivers, lakes, and coastal waters. Also, pollution that does not come from a direct point, such as a sewerage outlet or factory drain, is largely uncontrolled. These *nonpoint sources* of pollution include water that runs off construction sites and farmland, carrying soil particles and *nutrients* (nourishing substances) into streams and lakes. They also include water from lawns and gardens that may carry fertilizer and insecticide, and water from roads and parking lots that carries salt, oil, and grease.

Sources

There are three chief sources of water pollution. These sources are (1) industrial wastes, (2) sewage, and (3) agricultural chemicals and wastes.

Industrial wastes. United States industries discharge pollutants that include many toxic chemicals. Industries discharge much chemical waste directly into natural bodies of water. Also, the burning of coal, oil, and other fuels by power plants, factories, and motor vehicles releases sulfur and nitrogen oxides into the air. These pollutants cause *acid rain,* which enters streams and lakes.

High levels of mercury have been found in fish far from industrial areas. The main sources of the mercury appear to be emissions to the atmosphere from equipment such as coal-fired boilers, municipal incinerators, and smelters.

Some industries pollute water in yet another way. They use large quantities of water to cool certain equipment. Heat from the equipment makes the water hot. The industries then discharge the hot water into rivers and lakes, heating those bodies of water. Such heating that harms plants or animals is known as *thermal pollution.*

Sewage consists of human wastes, garbage, and water that has been used for laundering or bathing. Most of the sewage in the United States goes through treatment plants that remove solids and such dissolved substances as the nutrients nitrogen and phosphorus. About 25 percent of the households of the United States use *septic tank systems,* which pass the sewage through tanks and filter it through *leaching fields* into the land. Some sewage in the United States still goes untreated

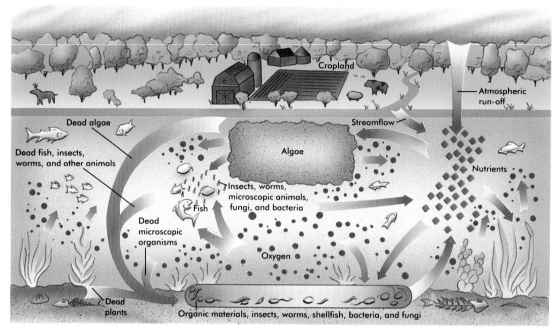

In a healthy water system, a cycle of natural processes turns waste material into useful substances. The bacteria of decay break down dead plants and animals and the body wastes of fish, releasing nitrates, phosphates, and other *nutrients* (chemicals needed for growth). Nutrients also enter the water from streams and other natural sources. Algae absorb the nutrients. Microscopic animals called *zooplankton* eat the algae, and fish eat the zooplankton. The fish produce body wastes and eventually die. Bacteria break down the wastes and dead fish, and the cycle continues.

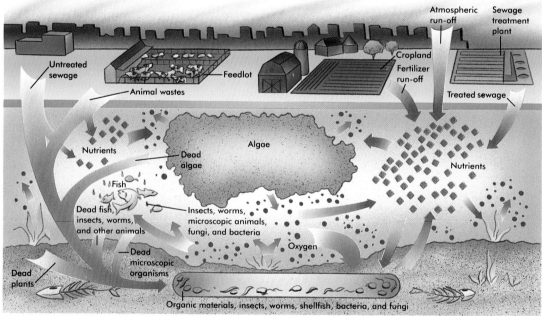

WORLD BOOK illustrations by Michael Yurkovic

Water pollution occurs when people upset the balance with excess nutrients from such sources as fertilizers and untreated sewage. This process is called *eutrophication.* The algae grow faster than the fish can eat them. As more algae grow, more also die. Bacteria in the water use up much oxygen consuming the excess dead algae. The oxygen level of the water drops, causing many aquatic plants and animals to die. As they decay, they consume still more oxygen. Without oxygen, the bacteria of decay can no longer function. Dead fish and other wastes sink to the bottom.

directly into waterways or the ocean. However, government regulations control the amount and the quality of the discharge.

Agricultural chemicals and wastes. Water from rain or melted snow flows from farmland into streams, carrying chemical fertilizers and pesticides that farmers have used on the land. Animal wastes also can cause water pollution, particularly from feed lots with large numbers of animals. Cattle, hogs, sheep, and poultry that are raised on feed lots do not distribute their wastes over widespread pastureland. Instead, much of their wastes runs off into nearby streams. Water used for irrigation also may be polluted by salt, agricultural pesticides, and toxic chemicals on the soil surface before it flows back into the ground.

Effects

Human illness. Water polluted with human and animal wastes can spread typhoid fever, cholera, dysentery, and other diseases. About 80 percent of the U.S. community water supplies are disinfected with chlorine to kill disease-causing germs. However, disinfection does not remove harmful chemical compounds such as polychlorinated biphenyls (PCB's) and chloroform, or harmful metals such as arsenic, lead, and mercury. The careless release of such toxic wastes, primarily into waste dumps, threatens ground water supplies. PCB's, chloroform, and pesticides have been found in some municipal drinking water. Scientists are concerned that drinking even small quantities of these substances over many years may have harmful effects.

Reduced recreational use. Pollution prevents people from enjoying some bodies of water for recreation. For example, odors and floating debris make boating and swimming unpleasant and the risk of disease makes polluted water unsafe. Oil spilled from ships or offshore wells may float to shore. The oil can kill water birds, shellfish, and other wildlife. In addition, water pollution affects both commercial and sport fishing. Fish can be killed by oil or by a lack of oxygen in the water, or they may die because of a reduction in the quantity and quality of their food supply. Industrial wastes, particularly PCB's, also harm fish.

Disruption of natural processes. Various natural processes that occur in water turn wastes into useful or harmless substances. These processes use oxygen that is dissolved in the water. Water pollution upsets these processes, mainly by robbing the water of oxygen.

Mineralization is a natural process by which *aerobic* (oxygen-using) bacteria break down organic wastes into simpler substances. Some of these substances, such as phosphates and nitrates, are nutrients for plants. Normal quantities of these nutrients help support normal quantities of life in the water.

When there are too many nutrients, however, a body of water may suffer from a process called *eutrophication.* The added nutrients may come from fertilizers draining off farmland or from detergents and other substances in sewage. An excess of nutrients causes the growth of higher-than-normal numbers of plants such as pondweeds and duckweeds, plantlike organisms called *algae,* fish and other animals, and bacteria. As more grow, more also die and decay.

Because the decay process uses oxygen, the addi-

tional decay uses up more of the oxygen in the water. Thus, less oxygen becomes available to support life in the water.

Some types of game fish—such as salmon, trout, and whitefish—cannot live in water with reduced oxygen. Fish that need less oxygen, such as carp and catfish, will replace them. If all the oxygen in a body of water were to be used up, most forms of life in the water would die.

Thermal pollution can also reduce the amount of oxygen dissolved in water. In addition, the warmer-than-normal water can kill some kinds of plants and fish.

Control

Sewage treatment. The most efficient sewage treatment plants use three processes—*primary, secondary,* and *tertiary* treatment. Primary and secondary treatment can remove up to 95 percent of the waste in sewage. Tertiary treatment removes even more impurities. Many plants use primary and secondary processes, and some use tertiary processes as well. However, most treated sewage still contains nutrients and toxic chemicals because secondary processes cannot remove them all.

Pretreatment of wastes. Industries can reduce pollution by treating wastes to remove harmful chemicals before dumping the wastes into water. Industrial wastes can also be reduced by using manufacturing processes that recover and reuse polluting chemicals.

Drinking water standards. In 1974, the U.S. Congress passed the Safe Drinking Water Act to help protect the nation's public water supply against pollution. This act authorized the Environmental Protection Agency (EPA) to establish uniform quality standards for more than 200,000 public water systems throughout the United States. The standards were designed to reduce the amount of harmful bacteria, chemicals, and metals in drinking water. The EPA and the state governments began to enforce the standards in 1977.

In 1979, the EPA issued rules to limit the amount of chloroform and other related organic chemicals called *trihalomethanes* (THM) in the drinking water of large cities. These chemicals form at treatment plants when chlorine is added to drinking water to kill disease-causing bacteria and viruses. Extended exposure to high levels of THM's, especially chloroform, is thought to increase the risk of cancer in people.

In 1986, Congress amended the Safe Drinking Water Act to ban the use of lead solder in public water systems. In 1988, further changes in the law lowered the amount of lead allowable in drinking water and banned the use of lead solder in drinking water pipes for new homes.   Gene E. Likens

Related articles in *World Book* include:

Acid rain	Mediterranean Sea (History of
Atlantic Ocean (Pollution)	the Mediterranean)
Environmental pollution	Ocean (Ocean
Environmental	pollution)
Protection Agency	Phosphate
Eutrophication	Polychlorinated
Giardiasis	biphenyl
Great Lakes (Water	Sanitation
quality)	Sewage
Tanker (Oil Spills)	Thermal pollution

See also *Environmental pollution* in the Research Guide/Index, Volume 22, for a *Reading and Study Guide.*

Jupiter is the largest planet in the solar system. Its diameter is 88,846 miles (142,984 kilometers), more than 11 times that of Earth, and about one-tenth that of the sun. It would take more than 1,000 Earths to fill up the volume of the giant planet. When viewed from Earth, Jupiter appears brighter than most stars. It is usually the second brightest planet—after Venus.

Jupiter is the fifth planet from the sun. Its *mean* (average) distance from the sun is about 483,600,000 miles (778,300,000 kilometers), more than five times Earth's distance. Ancient astronomers named Jupiter after the king of the Roman gods.

Astronomers have studied Jupiter with telescopes based on Earth and aboard artificial satellites in orbit around Earth. In addition, the United States has sent six *space probes* (crewless exploratory craft) to Jupiter.

Astronomers witnessed a spectacular event in July 1994, when 21 fragments of a comet named Shoemaker-Levy 9 crashed into Jupiter's atmosphere. The impacts caused tremendous explosions, some scattering debris over areas larger than the diameter of Earth.

Physical features of Jupiter

Jupiter is a giant ball of gas and liquid with little, if any, solid surface. Instead, the planet's surface is composed of dense red, brown, yellow, and white clouds. The clouds are arranged in light-colored areas called *zones* and darker regions called *belts* that circle the planet parallel to the equator.

Orbit and rotation. Jupiter travels around the sun in a slightly *elliptical* (oval-shaped) orbit. The planet completes one orbit in 4,333 Earth-days, or almost 12 Earth-years.

As Jupiter orbits the sun, the planet rotates on its *axis,* an imaginary line through its center. The axis is tilted about 3 °. Scientists measure tilt relative to a line at a right angle to the *orbital plane,* an imaginary surface touching all points of the orbit.

Jupiter rotates faster than any other planet. It takes 9 hours 55 minutes to spin around once on its axis, compared to 24 hours for Earth. Scientists cannot measure the rotation of the interior of the giant planet directly, so they have calculated the speed from indirect measurements. They first calculated the speed using an average of the speeds of the visible clouds that move with interior currents, except for a more rapid zone near the equator.

Jupiter sends out radio waves strong enough to be picked up by radio telescopes on Earth. Scientists now measure these waves to calculate Jupiter's rotational speed. The strength of the waves varies under the influence of Jupiter's magnetic field in a pattern that repeats every 9 hours 55 minutes. Because the magnetic field originates in Jupiter's core, this variation shows how fast the plant's interior spins.

Jupiter's rapid rotation makes it bulge at the equator and flatten at the poles. The planet's diameter is about 6 percent larger at the equator than at the poles.

Mass and density. Jupiter is heavier than any other planet. Its *mass* (quantity of matter) is 318 times larger than that of Earth. Although Jupiter has a large mass, it has a relatively low density. Its density averages 1.33 grams per cubic centimeter, slightly more than the density of water. The density of Jupiter is about $\frac{1}{4}$ that of

Jet Propulsion Laboratory

The layers of dense clouds around Jupiter appear in a photograph of the planet taken by the Voyager 1 space probe. The large, oval-shaped mark on the clouds is the Great Red Spot. The spot is believed to be an intense atmospheric disturbance.

Earth. Because of Jupiter's low density, astronomers believe that the planet consists primarily of hydrogen and helium, the lightest elements. Earth, on the other hand, is made up chiefly of metals and rock. Jupiter's mix of chemical elements resembles that of the sun, rather than that of Earth.

Jupiter may have a core made up of heavy elements. The core may be of about the same chemical composition as Earth, but 20 or 30 times more massive.

The force of gravity at the surface of Jupiter is up to 2.4 times stronger than on Earth. Thus, an object that weighs 100 pounds on Earth would weigh as much as 240 pounds on Jupiter.

The atmosphere of Jupiter is composed of about 86 percent hydrogen, 14 percent helium, and tiny amounts of methane, ammonia, phosphine, water, acetylene, ethane, germanium, and carbon monoxide. The percentage of hydrogen is based on the number of hydrogen molecules in the atmosphere, rather than on their total mass. Scientists have calculated these amounts from measurements taken with telescopes and other instruments on Earth and aboard spacecraft.

These chemicals have formed colorful layers of clouds at different heights. The highest white clouds in the zones are made of crystals of frozen ammonia. Darker, lower clouds of other chemicals occur in the belts. At the lowest levels that can be seen, there are blue clouds. Astronomers had expected to detect water clouds about 44 miles (70 kilometers) below the ammonia clouds. However, none have been discovered at any level.

Jupiter's most outstanding surface feature is the Great Red Spot, a swirling mass of gas resembling a hurricane. The widest diameter of the spot is about three times that of Earth. The color of the spot usually varies from brick-red to slightly brown. Rarely, the spot fades entirely. Its color may be due to small amounts of sulfur and phosphorus in the ammonia crystals.

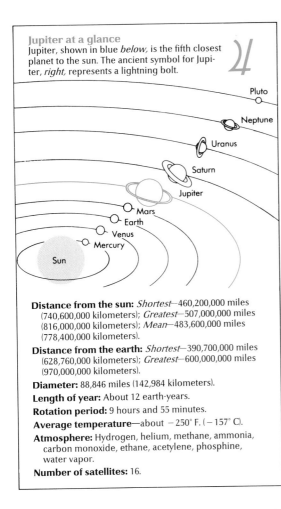

Jupiter at a glance
Jupiter, shown in blue *below,* is the fifth closest planet to the sun. The ancient symbol for Jupiter, *right,* represents a lightning bolt.

Distance from the sun: *Shortest*—460,200,000 miles (740,600,000 kilometers); *Greatest*—507,000,000 miles (816,000,000 kilometers); *Mean*—483,600,000 miles (778,400,000 kilometers).

Distance from the earth: *Shortest*—390,700,000 miles (628,760,000 kilometers); *Greatest*—600,000,000 miles (970,000,000 kilometers).

Diameter: 88,846 miles (142,984 kilometers).

Length of year: About 12 earth-years.

Rotation period: 9 hours and 55 minutes.

Average temperature—about −250° F. (−157° C).

Atmosphere: Hydrogen, helium, methane, ammonia, carbon monoxide, ethane, acetylene, phosphine, water vapor.

Number of satellites: 16.

The edge of the Great Red Spot circulates at a speed of about 225 miles (360 kilometers) per hour. The spot remains at the same distance from the equator but drifts slowly east and west.

The zones, belts, and the Great Red Spot are much more stable than similar circulation systems on Earth. Since astronomers began to use telescopes to observe these features in the late 1600's, the features have changed size and brightness but have kept the same patterns.

Temperature. The temperature at the top of Jupiter's clouds is about −220 °F (−140 °C). Measurements made by ground instruments and spacecraft show that Jupiter's temperature increases with depth below the clouds. The temperature reaches 70 °F (21 °C)—"room temperature"—at a level where the atmospheric pressure is about 10 times as great as it is on Earth. Scientists speculate that if Jupiter has any form of life, the life form would reside at this level. Such life would need to be airborne, because there is no solid surface at this location on Jupiter. Scientists have discovered no evidence for life on Jupiter.

Near the planet's center, the temperature is much higher. The core temperature may be about 43,000 °F (24,000 °C)—hotter than the surface of the sun.

Jupiter is still losing the heat produced when it became a planet. Most astronomers believe that the sun, the planets, and all the other bodies in the solar system formed from a spinning cloud of gas and dust. The gravitation of the gas and dust particles packed them together into dense clouds and solid chunks of material. By about 4.6 billion years ago, the material had squeezed together to form the various bodies in the solar system. The compression of material produced heat. So much heat was produced when Jupiter formed that the planet still radiates about twice as much heat into space as it receives from sunlight.

Magnetic field. Like Earth and many other planets, Jupiter acts like a giant magnet. The force of its magnetism extends far into space in a region surrounding the planet called its *magnetic field.* Jupiter's magnetic field is about 14 times as strong as Earth's, according to measurements made by spacecraft. Jupiter's magnetic field is the strongest in the solar system, except for fields associated with sunspots and other small regions on the sun's surface.

Scientists do not fully understand how planets produce magnetic fields. They suspect, however, that the movement of electrically charged particles in the interior of planets generates the fields. Jupiter's field would be so much stronger than Earth's because of Jupiter's greater size and faster rotation.

Jupiter's magnetic field traps electrons, protons, and other electrically charged particles in radiation belts around the planet. The particles are so powerful that they can damage instruments aboard spacecraft operating near the planet.

Within a region of space called the *magnetosphere,* Jupiter's magnetic field acts as a shield. The field protects the planet from the *solar wind,* a continuous flow of charged particles from the sun. Most of these particles are electrons and protons traveling at a speed of about 310 miles (500 kilometers) per second. The field traps the charged particles in the radiation belts. The trapped particles enter the magnetosphere near the

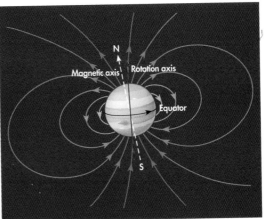

WORLD BOOK illustration by Precision Graphics

Jupiter acts like a giant magnet. The diagram above shows the planet's north (N) and south (S) magnetic poles. The curved lines indicate the direction of the *magnetic field,* the region in which the magnetism operates.

Satellites of Jupiter

Name	Mean distance from Jupiter In miles	In kilometers	Diameter of satellite In miles	In kilometers	Year of dis-covery
Metis	79,510	127,960	25	40	1979
Adrastea	80,140	128,980	12	20	1979
Amalthea	112,700	181,300	117	188	1892
Thebe	137,900	221,900	62	100	1979
Io	262,000	421,600	2,256	3,630	1610
Europa	416,900	670,900	1,950	3,138	1610
Ganymede	664,900	1,070,000	3,270	5,262	1610
Callisto	1,170,000	1,883,000	2,980	4,800	1610
Leda	6,893,000	11,094,000	10	16	1974
Himalia	7,133,000	11,480,000	116	186	1904
Lysithea	7,282,000	11,720,000	22	36	1938
Elara	7,293,000	11,737,000	47	76	1905
Ananke	13,200,000	21,200,000	19	30	1951
Carme	14,200,000	22,600,000	25	40	1938
Pasiphae	14,600,000	23,500,000	31	50	1908
Sinope	14,700,000	23,700,000	22	36	1914

poles of the magnetic field. On the side of the planet away from the sun, the magnetosphere stretches out into an enormous magnetic tail, often called a *magnetotail,* that is at least 435 million miles (700 million kilometers) long.

Radio waves given off by Jupiter reach radio telescopes on Earth in two forms—bursts of radio energy and continuous radiation. Strong bursts occur when Io, the closest of Jupiter's four large moons, passes through certain regions in the planet's magnetic field. Continuous radiation comes from Jupiter's surface and from high-energy particles in the radiation belts.

Satellites. Jupiter has 16 known satellites. The four largest, in order of their distance from Jupiter, are Io, Europa, Ganymede, and Callisto. These four moons are called the *Galilean satellites*. The Italian astronomer Galileo discovered them in 1610 with one of the earliest telescopes.

Io has many active volcanoes, which produce gases containing sulfur. The yellow-orange surface of Io probably consists largely of solid sulfur that was deposited by the eruptions. Europa ranks as the smallest of the Galilean satellites, with a diameter of 1,950 miles (3,138 kilometers). Europa has a smooth, cracked, icy surface.

The largest Galilean satellite is Ganymede, with a diameter of 3,270 miles (5,262 kilometers). Ganymede is larger than the planet Mercury. Callisto, with a diameter of 2,980 miles (4,800 kilometers), is slightly smaller than Mercury. Ganymede and Callisto appear to consist of ice and some rocky material, and they have many craters.

Jupiter's remaining 12 satellites are much smaller than the Galilean moons. Amalthea and Himalia are the largest of the 12. Potato-shaped Amalthea is about 168 miles (270 kilometers) in its long dimension. Himalia is about 116 miles (186 kilometers) in diameter. The small satellites were discovered from 1892 to 1974 by astronomers using large telescopes on Earth, and in 1979 by scientists who studied pictures taken by the Voyager spacecraft.

Rings. Jupiter has three thin rings around its equator. They are much fainter than the rings of Saturn. Jupiter's rings appear to consist mostly of fine dust particles. The main ring is about 20 miles (30 kilometers) thick and

more than 4,000 miles (6,400 kilometers) wide. It circles the planet inside the orbit of Amalthea.

The impact of Comet Shoemaker-Levy 9

In March 1993, astronomers Eugene Shoemaker, Carolyn Shoemaker, and David H. Levy discovered a comet near Jupiter. The comet, later named Shoemaker-Levy 9, probably once orbited the sun independently, but had been pulled by Jupiter's gravity into an orbit around the planet. When the comet was discovered, it had broken into 21 pieces. The comet probably had broken apart when it passed close to Jupiter.

Calculations based on the comet's location and velocity showed that the fragments would crash into Jupiter's atmosphere in July 1994. Scientists hoped to learn much about the effects of a collision between a planet and a comet.

Astronomers at all the major telescopes on Earth turned their instruments toward Jupiter at the predicted collision times. Scientists also observed Jupiter with the powerful Hubble Space Telescope, which is in orbit around Earth; and the remotely controlled space probe Galileo, which was on its way to Jupiter.

The fragments fell on the back side of Jupiter as viewed from Earth and the Hubble Space Telescope. But the rotation of Jupiter carried the impact sites around to the visible side after less than half an hour. Scientists estimate that the largest fragments were about 0.3 to 2.5 miles (0.5 to 4 kilometers) in diameter. The impacts were directly observable from Galileo, which was within about 150 million miles (240 million kilometers) from Jupiter. However, damage to certain of the probe's instruments limited its ability to record and send data. See the section *Flights to Jupiter* in this article.

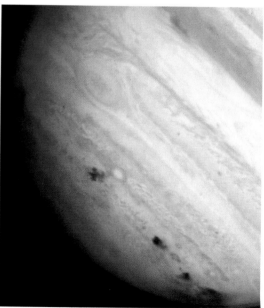

Hubble Space Telescope Comet Team and NASA

Scars from the crash of Comet Shoemaker-Levy 9 appear on Jupiter's surface as a series of maroon blotches in this photo. The comet broke into 21 pieces before it hit Jupiter in 1994.

The impacts caused large explosions, probably due to the compression, heating, and rapid expansion of atmospheric gases. The explosions scattered comet debris over large areas, some with diameters larger than that of Earth. The debris gradually spread into a dark haze of fine material that remained suspended for several months in Jupiter's upper atmosphere. If a similar comet ever collided with Earth, it might produce a haze that would cool the atmosphere and darken the planet by absorbing sunlight. If the haze lasted long enough, much of Earth's plant life could die, along with the people and animals that depend on plants.

Flights to Jupiter

The United States has sent six space probes to Jupiter: (1) Pioneer 10, (2) Pioneer-Saturn, (3) Voyager 1, (4) Voyager 2, (5) Ulysses, and (6) Galileo.

Pioneer 10 was launched in 1972 and flew within 81,000 miles (130,000 kilometers) of Jupiter on Dec. 3, 1973. The probe revealed the severe effects of Jupiter's radiation belt on spacecraft. Pioneer 10 also reported the amount of hydrogen and helium in the planet's atmosphere. In addition, the probe discovered that Jupiter has an enormous magnetosphere.

Pioneer-Saturn flew within 27,000 miles (43,000 kilometers) of Jupiter in December 1974. The craft provided close-up photographs of Jupiter's polar regions and data on the Great Red Spot, the magnetic field, and atmospheric temperatures.

Voyager 1 and Voyager 2 flew past Jupiter in March and July 1979, respectively. These craft carried more sensitive instruments than did the Pioneers, and transmitted much more information. Astronomers used photographs taken by the Voyagers to make the first detailed maps of the Galilean satellites. The Voyagers also revealed sulfur volcanoes on Io, discovered lightning in Jupiter's clouds, and mapped flow patterns in the cloud bands.

Ulysses was launched in October 1990 and passed by Jupiter in February 1992. The European Space Agency, an organization of Western European nations, had built the probe mainly to study the sun's polar regions. Scientists used the tremendous gravitational force of Jupiter to put Ulysses into an orbit that would take it over the sun's polar regions. As Ulysses passed by Jupiter, it gathered data indicating that the solar wind has a much greater effect on Jupiter's magnetosphere than earlier measurements had suggested.

Galileo began its journey to Jupiter in October 1989. The craft released an atmospheric probe in July 1995. In December 1995, the probe plunged into Jupiter's atmosphere. It penetrated deep into the cloud layers. One of Galileo's most important missions was to measure the amount of water and other chemicals in Jupiter's atmosphere.

Also in December 1995, Galileo went into orbit around Jupiter. Its first task was to record on tape the data transmitted by the probe, then relay the data to Earth. It would then monitor Jupiter's atmosphere, and map parts of its satellites. Galileo's main antenna was to transmit 50,000 pictures to Earth. In April 1991, however, engineers discovered that Galileo's main antenna was useless. That dish antenna was supposed to open like an umbrella, but it stuck. The engineers estimated that, as a result, Galileo would be able to transmit 1,500 to 4,000 pictures.   Peter J. Gierasch and Philip D. Nicholson

See also **Planet; Solar system.**

Tide is the periodic rise and fall of oceans and other waters of the earth in response to the gravitational forces of the moon and the sun. The forces that produce tides affect all objects on the earth, the atmosphere, and even the solid earth itself. The response to tidal forces is greatest in the oceans. Tides are most noticeable at shorelines where oceans and continents meet.

There are one or two *high tides* and one or two *low tides* each day. The tides occur so regularly that they can be predicted many years in advance.

The regularity of the tides has fascinated people since ancient times. Some Greek and Roman philosophers who lived between the 300's B.C. and the A.D. 300's thought that the earth was a living being whose breathing caused the tides. But other philosophers of ancient China, Greece, and Rome noticed that the times of high and low tides followed the crossing of the moon overhead. However, they did not know how the moon helps produce the tides.

Europeans began to make detailed tables of tides during the Middle Ages. These tables helped ship captains schedule arrival and departure times at ports. The oldest known tables date from 1213. They show the high tides at London Bridge.

Modern thinking about tides began in 1687, when the English scientist Isaac Newton published his discoveries of basic laws of motion and gravitation. Newton explained how objects attract one another by means of the gravitational force.

Tidal forces. The basic cause of tides is a difference in the strength of gravitational forces at various points in and on the earth. These forces involve the earth, the moon, and the sun.

The gravitational force between the earth and the moon tends to pull those two bodies together. However, their *inertia* tends to keep them apart. Inertia is a property of all matter. This property tends to make a moving object travel in a straight line at a constant speed unless a force acts upon the object. The combined effect of the gravitational force and inertia keeps the moon in orbit about the earth.

At the center of the earth, the gravitational attraction between the earth and the moon exactly balances their inertia. On the surface of the earth, however, the balance is not exact. On the side of the earth closer to the moon, the gravitational attraction is slightly stronger than in the center of the earth. On the opposite side of the earth, the attraction is slightly weaker.

The difference between the gravitational attraction and the inertia can be thought of as a *tide-generating force.* This force produces two large bulges in the waters of the earth. As the earth rotates beneath the bulges, the waters rise and fall relative to the earth.

The tide-generating force produces a bulge on the side of the earth closer to the moon, and another bulge on the opposite side of the earth. The force does not lift the water straight up, however. The force is too weak to do that. Rather, it pulls the water parallel to the earth's surface toward a point directly below the moon and a point directly opposite the first point. The water piles up around these points, forming the bulge.

WORLD BOOK photos by Kevin Shields

Tides rise and fall in a cycle that is regulated mainly by the moon's gravity. From the water's lowest point, *low tide, left,* the water rises gradually for about 6 hours until it reaches *high tide, right.* Then the water falls for about 6 hours until it reaches low tide again, and the cycle repeats itself.

The earth and the sun also produce a tide-generating force and two bulges. These bulges are smaller than those produced by the earth and the sun, and distort their shape.

The sun's tidal force is only about half as strong as that associated with the moon, even though the sun is 27 times more massive than the moon. A calculation based on Newton's discoveries shows how this can be so.

The tide-producing force associated with the sun or moon depends on the *mass* (amount of matter) of that body divided by the *cube* of the body's distance from the earth. The cube of a number is the product obtained when the number is used as a factor three times. For example, the cube of 4 is $4 \times 4 \times 4$, or 64.

The sun has 27 million times the mass of the moon but is about 390 times farther away. Thus, the sun's tide-producing force relative to that of the moon equals 27 million divided by $390 \times 390 \times 390$, or about 0.46—which is roughly one-half.

Tidal patterns. In most parts of the earth, the tide-generating forces due to the moon and the sun produce two high tides and two low tides each day. As the earth rotates beneath the bulges each day, a high tide occurs, then a low tide, then another high tide and another low tide. Because the moon's orbit is tilted, the two high tides each day usually have different heights—as do the two low tides.

The time of high and low tide at any location also changes daily because the moon revolves around the earth more rapidly than the earth rotates about its own axis. The moon revolves around the earth once in about $29\frac{1}{2}$ days in the direction in which the earth rotates. Dur-

ing the 24 hours in which the earth rotates once, the moon moves an additional 12° around the earth. So every day the earth must rotate another 12° to reach the position it had relative to the moon on the previous day. The extra turning takes about 50 minutes. Thus, each succeeding day, the tides occur 50 minutes later.

Ocean tides are affected by the inability of a single tidal bulge to move rapidly enough to stay beneath the moon. The speed of a bulge is limited by the depth of the water, and the continents get in the way of moving bulges. The oceans respond to these restrictions by generating a number of circular systems of moving bulges called *amphidromes.*

The shapes of *ocean basins* (deep, relatively flat areas of sea floors) and ocean coasts also affect the tides. The waters in basins of different shapes respond differently. For example, the east coast of the United States has mainly *semidiurnal* (twice per day) tides. Tides in the Gulf of Mexico are mostly *diurnal* (daily). The west coast has *mixed* tides—semidiurnal tides and diurnal tides occurring together.

Tidal range, the height difference between high tide and low tide, also varies widely throughout the world. Some areas have extremely large ranges. For example, in the Bay of Fundy between the Canadian provinces of New Brunswick and Nova Scotia, the range averages about 39 feet (12 meters). The range is about 33 feet (10 meters) in the Gulf of St.-Malo in France and in the Bristol Channel in the United Kingdom. By contrast, tides on the coasts of the Mediterranean and Caribbean seas and on the shores of Hawaii have ranges of only about 2 feet (0.6 meter).

Tidal cycles. Tidal patterns and ranges also vary over

Causes of ocean tides

The main cause of ocean tides is the action of tide-generating forces created by the gravitational attraction between the earth and the sun. These forces are strongest in the area directly below the moon and the area on the opposite side of the earth. As a result, water bulges out as high tides in those areas. As the earth rotates, high tide occurs twice a day.

WORLD BOOK illustrations

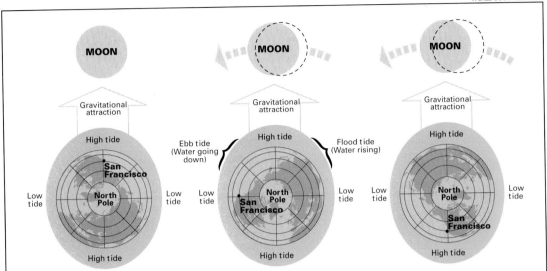

High tide occurs directly below the moon and on the opposite side of the earth. When the earth is in the position above, San Francisco has a high tide.

As the earth turns, the tides rise and fall at each place on the ocean. About 6 hours and 13 minutes after high tide, San Francisco has a low tide, *above.*

The next high tide at San Francisco occurs about 12 hours and 25 minutes after the first. The earth has turned 186° in this time. The moon has moved 6°.

Spring tides

Spring tides occur when the sun, the moon, and the earth are aligned. Spring tides have higher ranges than normal. They occur about twice a month near the times of the full and new moons. The moon then lies either between the earth and the sun, *below,* or on the side of the earth opposite the sun.

Neap tides

Neap tides occur when the sun, the earth, and the moon are at a right angle. Neap tides have lower ranges than normal tides. They occur about twice each month, when the moon is near its first and third quarters. At these times, the moon is either on the side of the earth shown *below,* or on the opposite side of the earth.

SUN

MOON

Attraction between earth and moon

Attraction between earth and sun

EARTH

Attraction between earth and sun

EARTH

Attraction between earth and moon

MOON

time. The most outstanding variations are the *spring-neap cycle* and the *tropic cycle.* These variations result from changes in the relative positions of the sun, earth, and moon.

Spring tides are semidiurnal tides with unusually high ranges twice per month when the sun, earth, and moon are in line. This alignment occurs at times of full moon and new moon. Spring tide ranges are high because the tide-generating forces associated with the sun and the moon act in a straight line. They can be especially high in the spring and autumn.

Neap tides are semidiurnal tides with unusually low ranges twice per month when an imaginary line from the sun to the earth forms a right angle with an imaginary line from the earth to the moon. This arrangement occurs when the moon is in its first and third quarters. At these times, the tide-generating forces act at a right angle to each other.

Tropic tides are diurnal tides with unusually high ranges twice per month and twice per year. These tides occur when the moon and the sun, respectively, are at the highest or lowest point in their orbits.

Reinhard E. Flick

See also **Bay of Fundy; Energy supply** (Tidal energy); **Ocean** (Tides); **Sea level; Seashore; Tsunami.**

Australopithecus, *AW struh loh PIHTH uh kuhs,* is a group of species that most anthropologists regard as one of the earliest humanlike creatures. These species lived in Africa from about 4,000,000 years ago to between 2,000,000 and 1,000,000 years ago. Members of the *genus* (group of species) known as *Australopithecus* are called *australopithecines.* Australopithecine fossils include some of the oldest known *hominid* fossils. Hominids make up the scientific family of human beings and prehistoric humanlike species.

Australopithecines stood upright and walked on two legs. They were about 4 to 5 feet (120 to 150 centimeters) tall and had a brain about one-third the size of a modern human brain.

Most anthropologists recognize five species of *Australopithecus.* They are, in the order in which they appeared, *A. anamensis, A. afarensis, A. africanus, A. boisei,* and *A. robustus. A. boisei* and *A. robustus* had much larger jaws and teeth than the first three species and are called robust australopithecines. The first three species are called *gracile* (slender) australopithecines. Most scientists believe human beings developed from the gracile species. *A africanus* and *A. robustus* lived in southern Africa, and the other three species lived in eastern Africa. The *Australopithecus* species were closely related to the earliest known hominid, *Ardipithecus ramidus,* which lived in what is now Ethiopia about 4,400,000 years ago.

Australopithecine fossils were first recognized in 1924 when South African anthropologist Raymond A. Dart identified a child's skull that had been found at Taung, near Vryburg, South Africa. Dart named the creature *Australopithecus africanus.* He believed it was a hominid, but most scientists thought it was an extinct ape. Additional fossils found during the next 35 years convinced scientists that *Australopithecus* was a hominid.

In 1974, researchers uncovered parts of the skeleton of a humanlike creature at Hadar, Ethiopia. The creature, nicknamed "Lucy," was about 3,200,000 years old. In 1978, researchers at Laetoli, Tanzania, found fossil footprints together with fossilized bones of a hominid that lived 3,600,000 years ago. These discoveries indicated that humanlike creatures had begun walking upright long before people began making stone tools about 2,500,000 years ago. Researchers have classified "Lucy" and the Laetoli fossils as *Australopithecus afarensis.*

Alan E. Mann

See also **Prehistoric people** (Prehuman ancestors; picture: The skeleton of "Lucy"); **Homo habilis; Johanson, Donald Carl; Leakey, Mary Douglas.**

Quark, *kwawrk,* is one of the three families of particles that serve as "building blocks" of matter. The other two families are the leptons and the fundamental, or gauge, bosons. Quarks are *elementary particles*—that is, they have no known smaller parts.

There are six types of quarks, each of which carries a fraction of an electric charge. Three of the quarks, called *down* (or *d*), *strange* (or *s*), and *bottom* (or *b*), have $\frac{1}{3}$ unit of negative charge. The other three—the *up* (or *u*), *charm* (or *c*), and *top* (or *t*)—have $\frac{2}{3}$ unit of positive charge.

A quark is always combined with one or two other quarks. *Composite particles* made up of quarks are known as *hadrons.* These include protons and neutrons, which form the nuclei of atoms.

There are two kinds of hadrons—(1) baryons and (2) mesons. A baryon is a three-quark combination. A proton is a baryon consisting of two *u* quarks and one *d* quark, while a neutron is a baryon made up of two *d* quarks and one *u.* A meson is made up of a quark and an *antiquark.* Antiquarks are the antimatter equivalents of quarks, opposite in electric charge and certain other properties.

Quarks have no measurable size. Physicists describe them as "pointlike." The *t* quark is the heaviest known elementary particle. Its mass is about 190 atomic mass units. This is almost as heavy as an entire atom of gold. The lightest quark, the *u,* has about 35,000 times less mass than the *t.*

The *s, c, b,* and *t* quarks are much heavier than the *u* and *d.* All the heavy quarks are unstable and they do not exist in ordinary matter. They usually break down into *u*'s, *d*'s, and other lighter particles in less than a billionth of a second. Physicists must create *s, c, b,* and *t* quarks with devices called *particle accelerators.* An accelerator causes subatomic particles to collide violently with one another to produce these quarks.

Two California Institute of Technology physicists, the American Murray Gell-Mann and Russian-born George Zweig, independently proposed the first theory of quarks in 1964. The original theory required only *u, d,* and *s* quarks to build all known hadrons. In the late 1960's and early 1970's, experiments showed that protons and neutrons contain parts much smaller than they are, and that these parts carry fractional charges. Discoveries in 1974, 1977, and 1995 proved the existence of the *c, b,* and *t,* in that order.   Robert H. March

See also **Boson; Gluon; Hadron; Lepton; Psi particle.**

How to use the index

This index covers the contents of the 1996, 1997, and 1998 editions.

Each entry gives the last two digits of the edition year, followed by a colon and the page number or numbers. For example, in this entry the information on population growth may be found on pages 144-163 of the 1998 edition, and on page 180 of the 1996 edition.

The "see" and "see also" cross-references indicates that references to a topic are listed under another entry in the index.

An entry that only begins with a capital letter indicates that there are no Science News Update articles with that title but that information on this topic may be found in the editions and on the pages listed.

When there are many references to a topic, they are grouped alphabetically by clue words under the main topic. For example, the clue words under **Proteins** group the references to that topic under the main heading and at least one subtopic.

An entry in all capital letters indicates that there is a Science News Update article with that name in at least one of the three volumes covered by this index. References to the topic in other articles may also be listed in the entry.

The indication (il.) after a page number means that the reference is to an illustration only.

An entry followed by *WBE* refers to a new or revised *World Book Encyclopedia* article in the supplement section. This entry means that there is a *World Book Encyclopedia* article on quarks on page 336 of the 1998 edition.

Index

A

Index

Index

Geller, Uri, **98:** 134-138
Gene therapy, 96: 85, 270
Genes
Alzheimer's disease, **97:** 236-238, 262-263
ataxia telangiectasia, **97:** 238
bird songs, **98:** 190
brain diseases, **98:** 105-110
cancer, **98:** 234, **97:** 238, 239, 244, **96:** 75-85, 266
DNA testing, **96:** 164
dog behavior, **98:** 41
mapping, **98:** 232, **97:** 238, **96:** 269
nurturing behavior, **98:** 260 (il.)
obesity, **97:** 244-245, 249 (il.), **96:** 282
personality traits, **98:** 259
plant development, **97:** 193-194, **96:** 232-233
premature aging, **97:** 239
risk-taking behavior, **97:** 262
see also **DNA; Drugs; Gene therapy; Genetic engineering; Genetics; Medical research**
Genetic engineering
agriculture, **98:** 166-168, 187, **97:** 165-166, **96:** 198-199
extinction problem, **96:** 182
global warming solutions, **96:** 152
Medfly control, **97:** 238-239
medical research, **96:** 276-278
see also **Cloning; Gene therapy; Genes**
Genetic medicine. See **Gene therapy; Genetic engineering**
GENETICS, 98: 230-234, **97:** 236-239, **96:** 266-270
criminal behavior, **97:** 269
Nobel Prizes, **97:** 189
see also **Genes; Human Genome Project**
Geodynamo theory, 98: 237
Geoengineering, 96: 145-157
GEOLOGY, 98: 235-240, **97:** 240-243, **96:** 270-276
books, **96:** 235
see also **Caves; Earthquakes; Fossil studies; Oceanography; Plate tectonics; Volcanoes**
Geomagnetic storms, 98: 180, 181
Geosat (satellite), **97:** 253
Gerstmann-Sträussler-Scheinker syndrome (disease), **98:** 102, 107
Getty, Jeff, 97: 246
Getty Wildlife Conservation Award, J. Paul, 97: 211
Giganotosaurus (dinosaur), **97:** 232-233
Gilman, Alfred, 96: 224
Giotto space probe, 98: 26
Glaciers, 98: 238 (il.), **97:** 114, **96:** 91 (il.)
Glass, 97: 226, **96:** 324-328
Glaucoma (disease), **98:** 232-233
Glimepiride (drug), **97:** 218
Global warming
Antarctica studies, **97:** 108-111, 113
atmospheric research, **96:** 220-221
bird migrations, **98:** 209
clouds, **98:** 187-188
disease outbreaks, **98:** 262 (il.)
ecological evidence, **96:** 251-252
fossil fuels, **98:** 152-153

geoengineering, **96:** 145-157
nitrogen, **98:** 187
ocean effects, **96:** 283-284
refrigerants, **96:** 317
scientific consensus, **97:** 185-186
tree effects, **98:** 213-215
WBE, **98:** 322-323
see also **Climate; Greenhouse effect**
Glucose, 98: 249-250, **97:** 218
Goldin, Daniel, 97: 97-98
Gondwanaland (land mass), **98:** 235 (il.), **97:** 103
Gonorrhea (disease), **98:** 262
Goodall, Jane, 96: 105-117
Gorillas, Mountain, 97: 210-211
Graham, Matthew David, 97: 192
Grand Canyon National Park, 97: 213
Grand Staircase-Escalante National Monument, 98: 206
Gravitation
antimatter research, **97:** 259
Earth's inner rotation, **98:** 237
expansion of universe, **98:** 75, 82-86, **97:** 41
lenses, **97:** 40, 179
space research, **98:** 271
underwater, **98:** 122
Graviton (particle), **98:** 83
Gravity. See **Gravitation**
Great Lakes, 97: 72, 75 (il.)
Great Lakes Water Quality Guidance Regulations (1995), **97:** 83-84
Green ash trees, 98: 192
Greenhouse effect, 98: 187
Antarctica studies, **97:** 108
geoengineering, **96:** 145-146
methane extraction, **98:** 127
population growth, **98:** 152-153
predictions, **97:** 185, **96:** 220
refrigerants, **96:** 317
Venus, **98:** 17-18
WBE, **98:** 322-323
see also **Global warming**
Greenpeace, 96: 188 (il.)
Grissom, Virgil I. (Gus), 97: 92
Growth factors (cancer), **96:** 78-79
Guano, 96: 100, 102
Guide dogs, 98: 37-38
Guns. See **Firearms**
Gypsy moths, 98: 192

H

H2-blockers (drugs), **98:** 285, 287, 288
Habitat (construction), **98:** 223
Habitats, 98: 150-151, 158-159, **97:** 211-213, 220-221, **96:** 191
see also **Ecology**
Hadrons, 96: 286
Hair, 97: 289-293
Hair cells, 97: 277, 278 (il.), 280
Haise, Fred W., Jr., 97: 87, 90, 91
Hale-Bopp, Comet, 98: 177-178, **97:** 177-178
Half-life (physics), **98:** 79, 80 (il.)
Halley's Comet, 98: 26, **96:** 14-16
Halo (space object), **97:** 179
Handwriting recognition (computers), **98:** 204 (il.), **97:** 151 (il.)
Hantavirus, 98: 159
Hares, 97: 219-220
Hawaii, 98: 251 (il.), **96:** 174

Headphones, 97: 279, 280
Health, Public. See **Public health**
Hearing, 98: 33, 38, **97:** 276-280
Hearing-ear dogs, 98: 35 (il.), 38-40
Heart disease, 98: 212, 243, 290, **97:** 245-248, 250-252, **96:** 270
Heart failure, Congestive, 98: 245, **97:** 228-229
Heart transplants, 97: 247, **96:** 278-279
Heartburn, 98: 285, 286, 288
Heavy metals, 98: 283
Helictites (formations), **96:** 96
Helium, 98: 23, 246-248
Helsingius, Johan, 96: 295
Hemochromatosis, 98: 233-234
Hemoglobin, 98: 233, 290, **97:** 250, **96:** 236
Hepatitis, 98: 261
Heredity, *WBE,* **96:** 341-350
see also **Genes; Genetics**
Herman, Robert, 98: 210
Higgs boson (particle), **98:** 257, **96:** 288
High blood pressure. See **Hypertension**
Hipparcos (satellite), **98:** 186
Histamine (chemical), **98:** 288
Histamine H2-receptor antagonists. See **H2-blockers**
Histamine-2 receptors (proteins), **98:** 288
HIV. See **AIDS**
Homeopathy, 98: 138-139
Homicides, 98: 261
Hominids. See **Prehistoric people**
Homo erectus (hominid), **98:** 168, **96:** 201
Homo fossil, **98:** 169-170
Homo habilis (hominid), **96:** 201-202, 208
Homo sapiens, **98:** 146
Homocysteine (amino acid), **97:** 250
Horites (people), **97:** 172-174
Hormones, 98: 279
Horses, 97: 166, 195 (il.), **96:** 279-281
Hot spot (geology), **98:** 61
Housing, 98: 148-149, **97:** 161, 224
Hubble, Edwin P., 98: 74, 76 (il.)
Hubble constant, 97: 30-31, 34, **96:** 216-217
Hubble relation, 97: 30-31, 36, 40-41
Hubble Space Telescope, 98: 270-271, 272 (il.), **97:** 116-127
solar system studies, **96:** 211, 214-215, 302
universe studies, **98:** 183-185, **97:** 28-29, 36-38, 40, 179-184, **96:** 217, 219
see also **Galaxies**
Huggins, Charles B., 98: 210
Human Genome Project, 98: 232, **96:** 269
Human immunodeficiency virus. See **AIDS**
Human sacrifice, 97: 169-170
Humboldt Current. See **Peru Current**
Hunger, and population, 98: 147
Hunting, 97: 24-25, 174-175, **96:** 185
Hurrian civilization, 97: 172-174
Hurricanes, 98: 187 (il.), **97:** 186, **96:** 28-43
Hyakutake, Comet, 97: 177-178
Hybrids, 97: 165, 166

Index

Index

16 (il.)
Penguins, 98: 189-190, **97:** 110 (il.), 112, 115
WBE, **98:** 322-323
Pentium (microprocessor), **98:** 204-205, **97:** 147-149, **96:** 239-240
Periphyton (microbes), **96:** 37
Perl, Martin L., 97: 188-189, 189 (il.)
Permian Period, 97: 243, **96:** 265
Personal computers. See **Computers and Electronics**
Personal digital assistants, 96: 241
Personality, and genetics, 98: 259
Peru, 96: 211
Peru Current, 98: 63
Pesticides, 98: 226, 283, **97:** 79, 81, 228, 285-288, **96:** 261
Petroglyphs (rock carvings), **98:** 171, 174 (il.)
Petroleum, 98: 127, 156, **96:** 46
see also **Gasoline; Internal-combustion engines; Oil pipelines; Oil spills**
Pheomelanin (pigment), **97:** 290
Pheromones, 97: 288
Phosphatase (enzyme), **98:** 234
Phosphorus, 97: 77 (il.), 78, 81-84
Photonic wire (molecule), **96:** 238
Photons, 97: 261
Photosynthesis
algae, **97:** 79, 230
cycle of nature, **96:** 182
global warming, **98:** 215, **96:** 145, 148 (il.)
plant regulator gene, **96:** 268-269
soil erosion, **98:** 151
Photovoltaic cells, 97: 223
PHYSICS, 98: 253-257, **97:** 256-261, **96:** 286-291
laws of, **98:** 86
Nobel Prizes, **98:** 246-248, **97:** 188-189, **96:** 223-224
see also **Subatomic particles**
Physiology or medicine, Nobel Prize for, 98: 248, **97:** 189, 190 (il.), **96:** 224
Phytoplankton, 97: 85, 223, 253-255, **96:** 146, 149
Piezoelectric effect, 96: 255
Pigeons, 97: 61, 63-64, 65 (il.)
Pigs, 97: 246-247
Pinatubo, Mount, 96: 154, 220, 222
Pine trees, 96: 228-229
Pineal gland, 98: 279, 280 (il.)
Pioneer Seamount, 98: 252
Pioneer space probes, 98: 17, 20
Pioneer species (plants), **96:** 31, 42
Pipelining (computing), **97:** 148-149
Pixels (film), **98:** 48-49
Placental cord blood, 98: 242
Plague, 96: 293
Planck (space probe), **98:** 87
Planets, Extrasolar, 98: 182, **97:** 182-183
Planets, Solar-system. See **Solar system** and individual planets
Plankton (marine animals), **98:** 127
Plants
Antarctica, **96:** 251
biodiversity benefits, **96:** 182
biological clock gene, **96:** 268-269
cave, **96:** 97-100
drought, **98:** 214-215
flowering, **97:** 193-194

fossils, **98:** 94 (il.), 97 (il.)
Galapagos, **98:** 60-71
global warming, **96:** 149-151
oil spill cleanups, **97:** 229
see also **Agriculture; Biology; Conservation; Ecosystems; Endangered species; Forests; Wetlands**
Plasmin (substance), **98:** 212
Plastics, 97: 224, **96:** 58, 198-199, 237
Plate tectonics, 98: 18, 20, 61, 117-118
PlayStation (machine), **97:** 209
Pluto, 98: 26-27
Plutonium, 98: 264
Police dogs, 98: 37
Pollination, 97: 164-165
Pollution. See **Air pollution; Environmental pollution; Water pollution**
Polychlorinated biphenyls, 98: 224-225, **97:** 79, 81, 84, 296
Polycyclic aromatics, 97: 296
Polyhydroxybutyrate (plastic), **96:** 198-199
Polymerase chain reaction, 96: 161, 164-166
Polymers (molecules), **98:** 196, **97:** 200-201
Polynias (ocean), **97:** 113
Polypropylene (plastic), **96:** 237
Polystyrene (plastic), **98:** 199
Poplars, 97: 166
Population growth, 98: 144-163, **96:** 180
Pornography, 97: 268
Positron emission tomography, 98: 258 (il.)
Positrons, 97: 258, 259
Power plants, 98: 217
PowerPro (battery), **97:** 150
Prairies, 98: 207
Pregnancy, 98: 280, 286, **97:** 250, **96:** 294
Prehistoric animals, 97: 174-175
see also **Dinosaurs; Fossil studies; Pterodactyls**
Prehistoric people, 98: 168-171, **97:** 166-169, **96:** 200-202
cave art, **97:** 13-27, **96:** 204, 206-207
see also **Anthropology; Archaeology; Fossil studies; Native Americans**
Premature birth, 96: 294-295
Prickly pear cactus, 98: 63
Primordial fireball, 98: 74, 76
Primordial soup, 98: 257, **97:** 48 (il.), 51-55
Prions (proteins), **98:** 100-113, 246, **97:** 164
Project FAMOUS (study), **98:** 123
Prokinetic agents (drugs), **98:** 287, 288
Propane. See **Liquefied petroleum gas**
Propetamphos (pesticide), **97:** 287
Proplyds (space objects), **97:** 121 (il.)
Propoxur (pesticide), **97:** 286
Prosalirus bitis (frog), **97:** 235-236
Prostate cancer, 98: 234, **96:** 83
Protarchaeopteryx robusta (dinosaur), **98:** 226-228
Protease inhibitors (drugs), **98:** 244-

245, **97:** 216
Proteins
bacterial, **97:** 197
cancer genes, **96:** 77-83
HIV, **97:** 243-244
origin of life, **97:** 47, 50, 52-53, 57
prions, **98:** 100-113
Proton-pump inhibitors (drugs), **98:** 287, 288
Protons, 96: 120, 124, 125, 128, 135
PSYCHOLOGY, 98: 258-260, **97:** 262-264, **96:** 291-293
book, **98:** 195
see also **Brain**
Psychotherapy, 97: 263-264
Pteranodon (animal), **96:** 65 (il.), 66 (il.), 72, 73
Pterodactyls, 96: 60-73
PUBLIC HEALTH, 98: 261-262, **97:** 265-267, **96:** 293-295
ionizing radiation, **96:** 133-143
mad cow disease, **98:** 280-281, **97:** 164, 265-266
mobile clinics, **98:** 147 (il.)
Pueblos (housing), **96:** 209-210
Puerto Rico Trench, 98: 118
Pumas. See **Cougars**
Pylons (aviation), **97:** 134 (il.), 140
Pyrethroids (pesticides), **97:** 285, 286

Q

Quality-control genes, 96: 81-83
Quantum CEP (waste processing), **98:** 218
Quantum computing, 97: 159-161, 260-261
Quantum mechanics, 98: 83-87, 248, 253, **97:** 256
Quarks, 96: 119-131
WBE, **98:** 336
Quasars (astronomy), **98:** 184, **97:** 125 (il.)
Quetzalcoatlus (animal), **96:** 63-64

R

Rabbit calicivirus disease, 97: 209-210
Raccoons, 97: 63 (il.), 64-66
Racetrack (lake bed), **97:** 241-242
Radar, 98: 14, 18, 122
Radiation
experiments on humans, **98:** 263-264, **97:** 269, **96:** 133-134
ionizing, and health, **96:** 133-143
WBE, **97:** 318-325
window efficiency, **96:** 325
see also **Radioactivity; X rays**
Radiation sickness, 96: 139
Radiation therapy, 96: 81
Radio computer networks, 97: 157 (il.), 158
Radio occultation, 98: 14-16
Radioactive decay, 96: 135
Radioactivity, 96: 134-135
see also **Radiation**
Radiocarbon dating, 98: 172, **97:** 22
Radiometers, 98: 14
Radium, 96: 134-139
Radon, 98: 226, **96:** 139
Rain. See **Acid rain; Drought**
Rain forests, 98: 150-151, 155, 161-162, 213, **96:** 181 (il.), 183 (il.), 188

Index

Index

ACKNOWLEDGMENTS

The publishers gratefully acknowledge the courtesy of the following artists, photographers, publishers, institutions, agencies, and corporations for the illustrations in this volume. Credits are listed from top to bottom, and left to right, on their respective pages. All entries marked with an asterisk (*) denote illustrations created exclusively for this yearbook. All maps, charts, and diagrams were staff-prepared unless otherwise noted.

2	© Tony Hallas; © Kenneth Garrett, National Geographic Society Image Collection
3	© Corre-Ribeiro, Gamma/Liaison;
4	© Norbert Wu; © Fridman, Sygma
5	© John Russell, Columbia University; Safety 1st
10	Jacklyn Beckett © American Museum of Natural History; NASA
11	© 1995 Universal City Studios, Inc. Courtesy of Universal Studios Publishing Rights. All Rights Reserved.
12	NASA
15	Jet Propulsion Laboratory; NASA
17-18	Jet Propulsion Laboratory
19	NASA
21-22	Jet Propulsion Laboratory
24	Jet Propulsion Laboratory; NASA
26	NASA
27	NASA artwork by Pat Rawlings/SAIC
28	© David Falconer
32	WORLD BOOK photos
35	© David Falconer; Canine Companions
36	© Charles Krebs; U.S. Dept. of Agriculture
39	© Lana Tyree, Gamma/Liasion; © David Falconer
40	© Elaine Ostrander; Dave Barry © *Discover* Magazine
42	© 1995 Universal City Studios, Inc. Universal Studios Publishing Rights. All Rights Reserved.
45	Movie Still Archives; Kobal Collection
47	© Erica Salzman, Pacific Data Images
49	© 1985 Universal Studios, Inc. Universal Studios Publishing Rights. All Rights Reserved. © Lucasfilms from Industrial Light & Magic
52	© 1993 Universal Studios, Inc. Universal Studios Publishing Rights. All Rights Reserved.; © 1996 Universal Studios, Inc. Universal Studios Publishing Rights. All Rights Reserved. © 1996 Universal Studios, Inc. Universal Studios Publishing Rights. All Rights Reserved.
55	Kleiser-Walczak Contruction Company/Digital Visual Effects
56	™ © DC Comics/Warner Bros., Warner Digital and Pacific Data Images
58	© Jack Stein Grove
62	Granger Collection
64	© Tui De Roy, Bruce Coleman, Inc.; © Jack Stein Grove
65	© Jack Stein Grove
68	© Joe McDonald, Animals Animals © Stephen Frink, Waterhouse
70	© Tui De Roy, Bruce Coleman, Inc.
72	© David Nunk/SPL from Photo Researchers
76-81	Roberta Polfus*.
84	Rob Wood*; Roberta Polfus.
85	Roberta Polfus*
88-90	Jacklyn Beckett © American Museum of Natural History
91	David Grimaldi © American Museum of Natural History; Jacklyn Beckett © American Museum of Natural History
92-94	Jacklyn Beckett © American Museum of Natural History
96	P. Nash © American Museum of Natural History
97	David Grimaldi © American Museum of Natural History; Jacklyn Beckett © American Museum of Natural History
98	Ed Bridges © American Museum of Natural History; David Grimaldi © American Museum of Natural History
99	Jacklyn Beckett © American Musuem of Natural History
100	© Hubert Raguet/Eurlios/SPL from Photo Researchers
103	© CVL/Eurlios/SPL from Photo Researchers
100	Bill Nation, Sygma
104	© CNRI/SPL from Photo Researchers; © Biophoto Associates from Photo Researchers; © EM unit/CVL/Weybridge/SPL from Photo Researchers
108	Barbara Cousins*
111	© J. Fraser/NUI/Eurlios/SPL from Photo Researchers; © J. Fraser/NUI/Eurlios/SPL from Photo Researchers; © Ralph Eagle Jr., Photo Researchers
112	© Hubert Raguet/Eurlios/SPL from Photo Researchers
115	© Norbert Wu
117	© Hammond Incorporated
120	Barbara Cousins*; © Kenneth L. Smith; © Norbert Wu; Rod Catanack, Woods Hole Oceanographic Institution; U.S. Naval Historical Center
121	Jamstec; Jamstec; Woods Hole Oceanographic Institution; © Norbert Wu; © Kenneth L. Smith/Norbert Wu
125	T. Kleindinst, Woods Hole Oceanographic Institution; © Chuck Davis; Lamont Doherty Earth Observatory
128	© R. R. Hessler; © W. Jack Jones
130	AP/Wide World
132	Terry Renna*
133	Robert Duyos*; Terry Renna*
134	AP/Wide World
135	Collection of James Randi
137-138	Terry Renna*
139	Robert Duyos*
141-142	Terry Renna*
144-145	© Dilip Mehta, Contact Press Images
147	© Jeremy Hartley, Panos Pictures; © Greg Girard; Contact Press Images
149	© Dilip Mehta, Contact Press Images
150	© Daniel O'Leary, Panos Pictures
152	© Louis Da Almeida, Sygma
155	© Tom Pich, Sygma
158	© Liz Gilbert, Sygma
160	© Fridman, Sygma
162	© Dilip Mehta, Contact Press Images
164	© Jan Chochorowski; Archive Photos
165	Jet Propulsion Laboratory; © M. Lammertink
166	Donald Peterson, U.S. Department of Agriculture/ARS
167	U.S. Department of Agriculture/ARS
169	Kenneth Garrett © National Geographic Image Collection
170	Reprinted by permission from *Nature*, Vol. 385, 1997
173	Bonnie Blackwell, Queens College, NY
174	© *Sydney Morning Herald* from Rex Features
175	John Russell, Columbia University
176	© Jan Chochorowski
178	© Tony Hallas
180	AP/Wide World
182-185	Jet Propulsion Laboratory
187	NASA
191	Paul M. Brakefield, University of Leiden, the Netherlands
192	© M. Lammertink
193	J. Emmett Duffy, Virginia Institute of Marine Science
196	Prasad, et al from SUNY at Buffalo, NY
197	Larry Arnold, Bechtel Corporation; Charles Carrigan, Lawrence Livermore National Laboratory
198	NASA/Lewis Research Center
201	Nokia
203	Princeton Video Image
204	U.S. Postal Service

World Book Encyclopedia, Inc., provides high-quality educational and reference products for the family and school. They include THE WORLD BOOK MEDICAL ENCYCLOPEDIA, a 1,040-page fully illustrated family health reference; THE WORLD BOOK OF MATH POWER, a two-volume set that helps students and adults build math skills; THE WORLD BOOK OF WORD POWER, a two-volume set that is designed to help your entire family write and speak more successfully; and the HOW TO STUDY video, a video presentation of key study skills with information students need to succeed in school. For further information, write WORLD BOOK ENCYCLOPEDIA, INC., 525 W. Monroe St., Chicago IL, 60661.